GW00645709

Kahlil Gibran
Masterpieces

ISBN: 1 86476 351 5

Copyright © Axiom Publishing, 2005.
Unit 2, 1 Union Street, Stepney, South Australia 5069

This book is copyright. Apart from any fair dealing for the purpose of private study, research, criticism or review, as permitted under the Copyright Act, no part may be reproduced by any process without written permission.
Enquiries should be made to the publisher.

AXIOM
AUSTRALIA

www.axiompublishers.com.au

Printed in Malaysia

Kahlil Gibran
Masterpieces

Contents

The Prophet 7

The Madman 63

Jesus, The Son of Man 90

The Forerunner 228

The Wanderer 253

The Broken Wings 293

The Tear and a Smile 349

The Life of Love 380

The Prophet

The Coming Of The Ship

ALMUSTAFA, the chosen and the beloved, who was a dawn unto his own day, had waited twelve years in the city of Orphalese for his ship that was to return and bear him back to the isle of his birth.

And in the twelfth year, on the seventh day of Ielool, the month of reaping, he climbed the hill without the city walls and looked seaward; and he beheld his ship coming with the mist.

Then the gates of his heart were flung open, and his joy flew far over the sea. And he closed his eyes and prayed in the silences of his soul.

But as he descended the hill, a sadness came upon him, and he thought in his heart:

How shall I go in peace and without sorrow? Nay, not without a wound in the spirit shall I leave this city.

Long were the days of pain I have spent within its walls, and long were the nights of aloneness; and who can depart from his pain and his aloneness without regret?

Too many fragments of the spirit have I scattered in these streets, and too many are the children of my longing that walk naked among these hills, and I cannot withdraw from them without a burden and an ache.

It is not a garment I cast off this day, but a skin that I tear with my hands.

Nor is it a thought I leave behind me, but a heart made sweet with hunger and with thirst.

Yet I cannot tarry longer.

The sea that calls all things unto her calls me, and I must embark.

For to stay, though the hours burn in the night, is to freeze and crystallise and be bound in a mould.

Fain would I take with me all that is here. But how shall I?

A voice cannot carry the tongue and the lips that gave it wings. Alone must it seek the ether.

And alone and without his nest shall the eagle fly across the sun.

Now when he reached the foot of the hill, he again turned towards the sea, and he saw his ship approaching the harbour, and upon her prow the mariners, the men of his own land.

And his soul cried out to them, and he said:

Sons of my ancient mother, you riders of the tides,

How often have you sailed in my dreams. And now you come in my awakening, which is my deeper dream.

Ready am I to go, and my eagerness with sails full set awaits the wind.

Only another breath will I breathe in this still air, only another loving look cast backward,

And then I shall stand among you, a seafarer among seafarers.

And you, vast sea, sleeping mother,

Who alone are peace and freedom to the river and the stream,

Only another winding will this stream make, only another murmur in this glade,

And then I shall come to you, a boundless drop to a boundless ocean.

And as he walked he saw from afar men and women leaving their fields and their vineyards and hastening towards the city gates.

And he heard their voices calling his name, and shouting from field to field telling one another of the coming of his ship.

And he said to himself:

Shall the day of parting be the day of gathering?

And shall it be said that my eve was in truth my dawn?

And what shall I give unto him who has left his plough in midfurrow, or to him who has stopped the wheel of his winepress?

Shall my heart become a tree heavy-laden with fruit that I may gather and give unto them?

And shall my desires flow like a fountain that I may fill their cups?

Am I a harp that the hand of the mighty may touch me, or a flute that his breath may pass through me?

A seeker of silences am I, and what treasure have I found in silences that I may dispense with confidence?

If this is my day of harvest, in what fields have I sowed the seed, and in what unremembered seasons?

If this indeed be the hour in which I lift up my lantern, it is not my flame that shall burn therein.

Empty and dark shall I raise my lantern.

And the guardian of the night shall fill it with oil and he shall light it also.

These things he said in words. But much in his heart remained unsaid. For he himself could not speak his deeper secret.

And when he entered into the city all the people came to meet him, and they were crying out to him as with one voice.

And the elders of the city stood forth and said:

Go not yet away from us.

A noontide have you been in our twilight, and your youth has given us dreams to dream.

No stranger are you among us, nor a guest, but our son and our dearly beloved.

Suffer not yet our eyes to hunger for your face.

And the priests and the priestesses said unto him:

Let not the waves of the sea separate us now, and the years you have spent in our midst become a memory.

You have walked among us a spirit, and your shadow has been a light upon our faces.

Much have we loved you. But speechless was our love, and with veils has it been veiled.

Yet now it cries aloud unto you, and would stand revealed before you.

And ever has it been that love knows not its own depth until the hour of separation.

And others came also and entreated him. But he answered them not. He only bent his head; and those who stood near saw his tears falling upon his breast.

And he and the people proceeded towards the great square before the temple.

And there came out of the sanctuary a woman whose name was Almitra. And she was a seeress.

And he looked upon her with exceeding tenderness, for it was she who had first sought and believed in him when he had been but a day in their city.

And she hailed him, saying:

Prophet of God, in quest of the uttermost, long have you searched the distances for your ship.

And now your ship has come, and you must needs go.

Deep is your longing for the land of your memories and the dwelling-place of your greater desires; and our love would not bind you nor our needs hold you.

Yet this we ask ere you leave us, that you speak to us and give us of your truth.

And we will give it unto our children, and they unto their children, and it shall not perish.

In your aloneness you have watched with our days, and in your wakefulness you have listened to the weeping and the laughter of our sleep.

Now therefore disclose us to ourselves, and tell us all that has been shown you of that which is between birth and death.

And he answered:

People of Orphalese, of what can I speak save of that which is even now moving within your souls?

On Love

THEN said Almitra, "Speak to us of Love."

And he raised his head and looked upon the people, and there fell a stillness upon them. And with a great voice he said:

When love beckons to you, follow him,

Though his ways are hard and steep.

And when his wings enfold you yield to him,

Though the sword hidden among his pinions may wound you.

And when he speaks to you believe in him,

Though his voice may shatter your dreams as the north wind lays waste the garden.

For even as love crowns you so shall he crucify you.

Even as he is for your growth so is he for your pruning.

Even as he ascends to your height and caresses your tenderest branches that quiver in the sun,

So shall he descend to your roots and shake them in their clinging to the earth.

Like sheaves of corn he gathers you unto himself.

He threshes you to make you naked.

He sifts you to free you from your husks.

He grinds you to whiteness.

He kneads you until you are pliant;

And then he assigns you to his sacred fire, that you may become sacred bread for God's sacred feast.

All these things shall love do unto you that you may know the secrets of your heart, and in that knowledge become a fragment of Life's heart.

But if in your fear you would seek only love's peace and love's pleasure,

Then it is better for you that you cover your nakedness and pass out of love's threshing-floor,

Into the seasonless world where you shall laugh, but not all of your laughter, and weep, but not all of your tears.

Love gives naught but itself and takes naught but from itself.

Love possesses not nor would it be possessed;

For love is sufficient unto love.

When you love you should not say, "God is in my heart," but rather,"I am in the heart of God."

And think not you can direct the course of love, for love,if it finds you worthy, directs your course.

Love has no other desire but to fulfil itself.

But if you love and must needs have desires, let these be your desires:

To melt and be like a running brook that sings its melody to the night.

To know the pain of too much tenderness.

To be wounded by your own understanding of love;

And to bleed willingly and joyfully.

To wake at dawn with a winged heart and give thanks for another day of loving;

To rest at the noon hour and meditate love's ecstasy;

To return home at eventide with gratitude;

And then to sleep with a prayer for the beloved in your heart and a song of praise upon your lips.

On Marriage

THEN Almitra spoke again and said, "And what of Marriage, master?"

And he answered saying:

You were born together, and together you shall be for evermore.

You shall be together when the white wings of death scatter your days.

Aye, you shall be together even in the silent memory of God.

But let there be spaces in your togetherness.

And let the winds of the heavens dance between you.

Love one another, but make not a bond of love:

Let it rather be a moving sea between the shores of your souls.

Fill each other's cup but drink not from one cup.

Give one another of your bread but eat not from the same loaf.

Sing and dance together and be joyous, but let each one of you be alone,

Even as the strings of a lute are alone though they quiver with the same music.

Give your hearts, but not into each other's keeping.

For only the hand of Life can contain your hearts.

And stand together yet not too near together:

For the pillars of the temple stand apart,

And the oak tree and the cypress grow not in each other's shadow.

On Children

AND a woman who held a babe against her bosom said, "Speak to us of Children."

And he said:

Your children are not your children.

They are the sons and daughters of Life's longing for itself.

They come through you but not from you,

And though they are with you yet they belong not to you.

You may give them your love but not your thoughts,

For they have their own thoughts.

You may house their bodies but not their souls,

For their souls dwell in the house of tomorrow, which you cannot visit, not even in your dreams.

You may strive to be like them, but seek not to make them like you.

For life goes not backward nor tarries with yesterday.

You are the bows from which your children as living arrows are sent forth.

The archer sees the mark upon the path of the infinite, and He bends you with His might that His arrows may go swift and far.

Let your bending in the Archer's hand be for gladness;

For even as He loves the arrow that flies, so He loves also the bow that is stable.

On Giving

THEN said a rich man, "Speak to us of Giving."

And he answered:

You give but little when you give of your possessions.

It is when you give of yourself that you truly give.

For what are your possessions but things you keep and guard for fear you may need them tomorrow?

And tomorrow, what shall tomorrow bring to the over-prudent dog burying bones in the trackless sand as he follows the pilgrims to the holy city?

And what is fear of need but need itself?

Is not dread of thirst when your well is full, the thirst that is unquenchable?

There are those who give little of the much which they have—and they give it for recognition and their hidden desire makes their gifts unwholesome.

And there are those who have little and give it all.

These are the believers in life and the bounty of life, and their coffer is never empty.

There are those who give with joy, and that joy is their reward.

And there are those who give with pain, and that pain is their baptism.

And there are those who give and know not pain in giving, nor do they seek joy, nor give with mindfulness of virtue;

They give as in yonder valley the myrtle breathes its fragrance into space.

Through the hands of such as these God speaks, and from behind their eyes He smiles upon the earth.

It is well to give when asked, but it is better to give unasked, through understanding;

And to the open-handed the search for one who shall receive is joy greater than giving.

And is there aught you would withhold?

All you have shall some day be given;

Therefore give now, that the season of giving may be yours and not your inheritors'.

You often say, "I would give, but only to the deserving."

The trees in your orchard say not so, nor the flocks in your pasture.

They give that they may live, for to withhold is to perish.

Surely he who is worthy to receive his days and his nights is worthy of all else from you.

And he who has deserved to drink from the ocean of life deserves to fill his cup from your little stream.

And what desert greater shall there be, than that which lies in the courage and the confidence, nay the charity, of receiving?

And who are you that men should rend their bosom and unveil their pride, that you may see their worth naked and their pride unabashed?

See first that you yourself deserve to be a giver, and an instrument of giving.

For in truth it is life that gives unto life—while you, who deem yourself a giver, are but a witness.

And you receivers—and you are all receivers—assume no weight of gratitude, lest you lay a yoke upon yourself and upon him who gives.

Rather rise together with the giver on his gifts as on wings;

For to be overmindful of your debt is to doubt his generosity who has the free-hearted earth for mother, and God for father.

On Eating And Drinking

THEN an old man, a keeper of an inn, said, "Speak to us of Eating and Drinking."

And he said:

Would that you could live on the fragrance of the earth, and like an air plant be sustained by the light.

But since you must kill to eat, and rob the newly born of its mother's milk to quench your thirst, let it then be an act of worship,

And let your board stand an altar on which the pure and the innocent of forest and plain are sacrificed for that which is purer and still more innocent in man.

When you kill a beast say to him in your heart:

"By the same power that slays you, I too am slain; and I too shall be consumed.

For the law that delivered you into my hand shall deliver me into a mightier hand.

Your blood and my blood is naught but the sap that feeds the tree of heaven."

And when you crush an apple with your teeth, say to it in your heart:

"Your seeds shall live in my body,

And the buds of your tomorrow shall blossom in my heart,

And your fragrance shall be my breath,

And together we shall rejoice through all the seasons."

And in the autumn, when you gather the grapes of your vineyards for the winepress, say in your heart:

"I too am a vineyard, and my fruit shall be gathered for the winepress,

And like new wine I shall be kept in eternal vessels."

And in winter, when you draw the wine, let there be in your heart a song for each cup;

And let there be in the song a remembrance for the autumn days, and for the vineyard, and for the winepress.

On Work

THEN a ploughman said, "Speak to us of Work."

And he answered, saying:

You work that you may keep pace with the earth and the soul of the earth.

For to be idle is to become a stranger unto the seasons, and to step out of life's procession that marches in majesty and proud submission towards the infinite.

When you work you are a flute through whose heart the whispering of the hours turns to music.

Which of you would be a reed, dumb and silent, when all else sings together in unison?

Always you have been told that work is a curse and labour a misfortune.

But I say to you that when you work you fulfil a part of earth's furthest dream, assigned to you when that dream was born,

And in keeping yourself with labour you are in truth loving life,

And to love life through labour is to be intimate with life's inmost secret.

But if you in your pain call birth an affliction and the support of the flesh a curse written upon your brow, then I answer that naught but the sweat of your brow shall wash away that which is written.

You have been told also that life is darkness, and in your weariness you echo what was said by the weary.

And I say that life is indeed darkness save when there is urge, And all urge is blind save when there is know ledge.

And all knowledge is vain save when there is work,

And all work is empty save when there is love;

And when you work with love you bind your self to yourself, and to one another, and to God.

And what is it to work with love?

It is to weave the cloth with threads drawn from your heart, even as if your beloved were to wear that cloth.

It is to build a house with affection, even as if your beloved were to dwell in that house.

It is to sow seeds with tenderness and reap the harvest with joy, even as if your beloved were to eat the fruit.

It is to charge all things your fashion with a breath of your own spirit,

And to know that all the blessed dead are standing about you and watching.

Often have I heard you say, as if speaking in sleep, "He who works in marble, and finds the shape of his own soul in the stone, is nobler than he who ploughs the soil.

And he who seizes the rainbow to lay it on a cloth in the likeness of man, is more than he who makes the sandals for our feet."

But I say, not in sleep, but in the overwakefulness of noontide, that the wind speaks not more sweetly to the giant oaks than to the least of all the blades of grass;

And he alone is great who turns the voice of the wind into a song made sweeter by his own loving.

Work is love made visible. And if you cannot work with love but only with distaste, it is better that you should leave your work and sit at the gate of the temple and take alms of those who work with joy.

For if you bake bread with indifference, you bake a bitter bread that feeds but half man's hunger.

And if you grudge the crushing of the grapes, your grudge distills a poison in the wine.

And if you sing though as angels, and love not the singing, you muffle man's ears to the voices of the day and the voices of the night.

On Joy And Sorrow

THEN a woman said, "Speak to us of Joy and Sorrow."

And he answered:

Your joy is your sorrow unmasked.

And the selfsame well from which your laughter rises was oftentimes filled with your tears.

And how else can it be?

The deeper that sorrow carves into your being, the more joy you can contain.

Is not the cup that holds your wine the very cup that was burned in the potter's oven?

And is not the lute that soothes your spirit the very wood that was hollowed with knives?

When you are joyous, look deep into your heart and you shall find it is only that which has given you sorrow that is giving you joy.

When you are sorrowful, look again in your heart, and you shall see that in truth you are weeping for that which has been your delight.

Some of you say, "Joy is greater than sorrow," and others say, "Nay, sorrow is the greater."

But I say unto you, they are inseparable.

Together they come, and when one sits alone with you at your board, remember that the other is asleep upon your bed.

Verily you are suspended like scales between your sorrow and your joy.

Only when you are empty are you at standstill and balanced.

When the treasure-keeper lifts you to weigh his gold and his silver, needs must your joy or your sorrow rise or fall.

On Houses

THEN a mason came forth and said, "Speak to us of Houses."

And he answered and said:

Build of your imaginings a bower in the wilderness ere you build a house within the city walls.

For even as you have home-comings in your twilight, so has the wanderer in you, the ever distant and alone.

Your house is your larger body.

It grows in the sun and sleeps in the stillness of the night; and it is not dreamless.

Does not your house dream? and dreaming, leave the city for grove or hilltop?

Would that I could gather your houses into my hand, and like a sower scatter them in forest and meadow.

Would the valleys were your streets, and the green paths your alleys, that you might seek one another through vineyards, and come with the fragrance of the earth in your garments.

But these things are not yet to be.

In their fear your forefathers gathered you too near together.

And that fear shall endure a little longer.

A little longer shall your city walls separate your hearths from your fields.

And tell me, people of Orphalese, what have you in these houses?

And what is it you guard with fastened doors?

Have you peace, the quiet urge that reveals your power?

Have you remembrances, the glimmering arches that span the summits of the mind?

Have you beauty, that leads the heart from things fashioned of wood and stone to the holy mountain?

Tell me, have you these in your houses?

Or have you only comfort, and the lust for comfort, that stealthy thing that enters the house a guest, and then becomes a host, and then a master?

Aye, and it becomes a tamer, and with hook and scourge makes puppets of your larger desires.

Though its hands are silken, its heart is of iron.

It lulls you to sleep only to stand by your bed and jeer at the dignity of the flesh.

It makes mock of your sound senses, and lays them in thistledown like fragile vessels.

Verily the lust for comfort murders the passion of the soul, and then walks grinning in the funeral.

But you, children of space, you restless in rest, you shall not be trapped nor tamed.

Your house shall be not an anchor but a mast.

It shall not be a glistening film that covers a wound, but an eyelid that guards the eye.

You shall not fold your wings that you may pass through doors, nor bend your heads that they strike not against a ceiling, nor fear to breathe lest walls should crack and fall down.

You shall not dwell in tombs made by the dead for the living.

And though of magnificence and splendour, your house shall not hold your secret nor shelter your longing.

For that which is boundless in you abides in the mansion of the sky, whose door is the morning mist, and whose windows are the songs and the silences of night.

On Clothes

AND the weaver said, "Speak to us of Clothes."

And he answered:

Your clothes conceal much of your beauty, yet they hide not the unbeautiful.

And though you seek in garments the freedom of privacy you may find in them a harness and a chain.

Would that you could meet the sun and the wind with more of your skin and less of your raiment.

For the breath of life is in the sunlight and the hand of life is in the wind.

Some of you say, "It is the north wind who has woven the clothes we wear."

And I say, Aye, it was the north wind,

But shame was his loom, and the softening of the sinews was his thread.

And when his work was done he laughed in the forest.

Forget not that modesty is for a shield against the eye of the unclean.

And when the unclean shall be no more, what were modesty but a fetter and a fouling of the mind?

And forget not that the earth delights to feel your bare feet and the winds long to play with your hair.

On Buying And Selling

AND a merchant said, "Speak to us of Buying and Selling."

And he answered and said:

To you the earth yields her fruit, and you shall not want if you but know how to fill your hands.

It is in exchanging the gifts of the earth that you shall find abundance and be satisfied.

Yet unless the exchange be in love and kindly justice it will but lead some to greed and others to hunger.

When in the market-place you toilers of the sea and fields and vineyards meet the weavers and the potters and the gatherers of spices,

Invoke then the master spirit of the earth, to come into your midst and sanctify the scales and the reckoning that weighs value against value.

And suffer not the barren-handed to take part in your transactions, who would sell their words for your labour.

To such men you should say:

"Come with us to the field, or go with our brothers to the sea and cast your net;

For the land and the sea shall be bountiful to you even as to us."

And if there come the singers and the dancers and the flute players,— buy of their gifts also.

For they too are gatherers of fruit and frankincense, and that which they bring, though fashioned of dreams, is raiment and food for your soul.

And before you leave the market-place, see that no one has gone his way with empty hands.

For the master spirit of the earth shall not sleep peacefully upon the wind till the needs of the least of you are satisfied.

On Crime And Punishment

THEN one of the judges of the city stood forth and said, "Speak to us of Crime and Punishment."

And he answered, saying:

It is when your spirit goes wandering upon the wind,

That you, alone and unguarded, commit a wrong unto others and therefore unto yourself.

And for that wrong committed must you knock and wait a while unheeded at the gate of the blessed.

Like the ocean is your god-self;

It remains for ever undefiled.

And like the ether it lifts but the winged.

Even like the sun is your god-self;

It knows not the ways of the mole nor seeks it the holes of the serpent.

But your god-self dwells not alone in your being.

Much in you is still man, and much in you is not yet man,

But a shapeless pigmy that walks asleep in the mist searching for its own awakening.

And of the man in you would I now speak.

For it is he and not your god-self nor the pigmy in the mist that knows crime and the punishment of crime.

Oftentimes have I heard you speak of one who commits a wrong as though he were not one of you, but a stranger unto you and an intruder upon your world.

But I say that even as the holy and the righteous cannot rise beyond the highest which is in each one of you,

So the wicked and the weak cannot fall lower than the lowest which is in you also.

And as a single leaf turns not yellow but with the silent knowledge of the whole tree,

So the wrong-doer cannot do wrong without the hidden will of you all.

Like a procession you walk together towards your god-self.

You are the way and the wayfarers.

And when one of you falls down he falls for those behind him, a caution against the stumbling stone.

Aye, and he falls for those ahead of him, who, though faster and surer of foot, yet removed not the stumbling stone.

And this also, though the word lie heavy upon your hearts:

The murdered is not unaccountable for his own murder,

And the robbed is not blameless in being robbed.

The righteous is not innocent of the deeds of the wicked,

And the white-handed is not clean in the doings of the felon.

Yea, the guilty is oftentimes the victim of the injured,

And still more often the condemned is the burden bearer for the guiltless and unblamed.

You cannot separate the just from the unjust and the good from the wicked;

For they stand together before the face of the sun even as the black thread and the white are woven together.

And when the black thread breaks, the weaver shall look into the whole cloth, and he shall examine the loom also.

If any of you would bring to judgment the unfaithful wife,

Let him also weigh the heart of her husband in scales, and measure his soul with measurements.

And let him who would lash the offender look unto the spirit of the offended.

And if any of you would punish in the name of righteousness and lay the axe unto the evil tree, let him see to its roots;

And verily he will find the roots of the good and the bad, the fruitful and the fruitless, all entwined together in the silent heart of the earth.

And you judges who would be just.

What judgment pronounce you upon him who though honest in the flesh yet is a thief in spirit?

What penalty lay you upon him who slays in the flesh yet is himself slain in the spirit?

And how prosecute you him who in action is a deceiver and an oppressor,

Yet who also is aggrieved and outraged?

And how shall you punish those whose remorse is already greater than their misdeeds?

Is not remorse the justice which is administered by that very law which you would fain serve?

Yet you cannot lay remorse upon the innocent nor lift it from the heart of the guilty.

Unbidden shall it call in the night, that men may wake and gaze upon themselves.

And you who would understand justice, how shall you unless you look upon all deeds in the fullness of light?

Only then shall you know that the erect and the fallen are but one man standing in twilight between the night of his pigmy-self and the day of his god-self,

And that the corner-stone of the temple is not higher than the lowest stone in its foundation.

On Laws

THEN a lawyer said, "But what of our Laws, master?"

And he answered:

You delight in laying down laws,

Yet you delight more in breaking them.

Like children playing by the ocean who build sand-towers with constancy and then destroy them with laughter.

But while you build your sand-towers the ocean brings more sand to the shore,

And when you destroy them the ocean laughs with you.

Verily the ocean laughs always with the innocent.

But what of those to whom life is not an ocean, and man-made laws are not sand-towers,

But to whom life is a rock, and the law a chisel with which they would carve it in their own likeness?

What of the cripple who hates dancers?

What of the ox who loves his yoke and deems the elk and deer of the forest stray and vagrant things?

What of the old serpent who cannot shed his skin, and calls all others naked and shameless?

And of him who comes early to the wedding feast, and when over-fed and tired goes his way saying that all feasts are violation and all feasters law-breakers?

What shall I say of these save that they too stand in the sunlight, but with their backs to the sun?

They see only their shadows, and their shadows are their laws.

And what is the sun to them but a caster of shadows?

And what is it to acknowledge the laws but to stoop down and trace their shadows upon the earth?

But you who walk facing the sun, what images drawn on the earth can hold you?

You who travel with the wind, what weather vane shall direct your course?

What man's law shall bind you if you break your yoke but upon no man's prison door?

What laws shall you fear if you dance but stumble against no man's iron chains?

And who is he that shall bring you to judgment if you tear off your garment yet leave it in no man's path?

People of Orphalese, you can muffle the drum, and you can loosen the strings of the lyre, but who shall command the skylark not to sing?

On Freedom

AND an orator said, "Speak to us of Freedom."

And he answered:

At the city gate and by your fireside I have seen you prostrate yourself and worship your own freedom,

Even as slaves humble themselves before a tyrant and praise him though he slays them.

Aye, in the grove of the temple and in the shadow of the citadel I have seen the freest among you wear their freedom as a yoke and a handcuff.

And my heart bled within me; for you can only be free when even the desire of seeking freedom becomes a harness to you, and when you cease to speak of freedom as a goal and a fulfilment.

You shall be free indeed when your days are not without a care nor your nights without a want and a grief,

But rather when these things girdle your life and yet you rise above them naked and unbound.

And how shall you rise beyond your days and nights unless you break the chains which you at the dawn of your understanding have fastened around your noon hour?

In truth that which you call freedom is the strongest of these chains, though its links glitter in the sun and dazzle your eyes.

And what is it but fragments of your own self you would discard that you may become free?

If it is an unjust law you would abolish, that law was written with your own hand upon your own forehead.

You cannot erase it by burning your law books nor by washing the foreheads of your judges, though you pour the sea upon them.

And if it is a despot you would dethrone, see first that his throne erected within you is destroyed.

For how can a tyrant rule the free and the proud, but for a tyranny in their own freedom and a shame in their own pride?

And if it is a care you would cast off, that care has been chosen by you rather than imposed upon you.

And if it is a fear you would dispel, the seat of that fear is in your heart and not in the hand of the feared.

Verily all things move within your being in constant half embrace, the desired and the dreaded, the repugnant and the cherished, the pursued and that which you would escape.

These things move within you as lights and shadows in pairs that cling.

And when the shadow fades and is no more, the light that lingers becomes a shadow to another light.

And thus your freedom when it loses its fetters becomes itself the fetter of a greater freedom.

On Reason And Passion

AND the priestess spoke again and said: "Speak to us of Reason and Passion."

And he answered, saying:

Your soul is oftentimes a battlefield, upon which your reason and your judgment wage war against your passion and your appetite.

Would that I could be the peacemaker in your soul, that I might turn the discord and the rivalry of your elements into oneness and melody.

But how shall I, unless you yourselves be also the peacemakers, nay, the lovers of all your elements?

Your reason and your passion are the rudder and the sails of your seafaring soul.

If either your sails or your rudder be broken, you can but toss and drift, or else be held at a standstill in mid-seas.

For reason, ruling alone, is a force confining; and passion, unattended, is a flame that burns to its own destruction.

Therefore let your soul exalt your reason to the height of passion, that it may sing;

And let it direct your passion with reason, that your passion may livethrough its own daily resurrection, and like the phoenix rise above its own ashes.

I would have you consider your judgment and your appetite even as you would two loved guests in your house.

Surely you would not honour one guest above the other; for he who is more mindful of one loses the love and the faith of both.

Among the hills, when you sit in the cool shade of the white poplars, sharing the peace and serenity of distant fields and meadows—then let your heart say in silence, "God rests in reason."

And when the storm comes, and the mighty wind shakes the forest, and thunder and lightning proclaim the majesty of the sky,--then let your heart say in awe, "God moves in passion."

And since you are a breath in God's sphere, and a leaf in God's forest, you too should rest in reason and move in passion.

On Pain

AND a woman spoke, saying, "Tell us of Pain."

And he said:

Your pain is the breaking of the shell that encloses your understanding.

Even as the stone of the fruit must break, that its heart may stand in the sun, so must you know pain.

And could you keep your heart in wonder at the daily miracles of your life, your pain would not seem less wondrous than your joy;

And you would accept the seasons of your heart, even as you have always accepted the seasons that pass over your fields.

And you would watch with serenity through the winters of your grief.

Much of your pain is self-chosen.

It is the bitter potion by which the physician within you heals your sick self.

Therefore trust the physician, and drink his remedy in silence and tranquillity:

For his hand, though heavy and hard, is guided by the tender hand of the Unseen,

And the cup he brings, though it burn your lips, has been fashioned of the clay which the Potter has moistened with His own sacred tears.

Self-Knowledge

AND a man said, "Speak to us of Self-Knowledge."

And he answered, saying:

Your hearts know in silence the secrets of the days and the nights.

But your ears thirst for the sound of your heart's knowledge.

You would know in words that which you have always known in thought.

You would touch with your fingers the naked body of your dreams.

And it is well you should.

The hidden well-spring of your soul must needs rise and run murmuring to the sea;

And the treasure of your infinite depths would be revealed to your eyes.

But let there be no scales to weigh your unknown treasure;

And seek not the depths of your knowledge with staff or sounding line.

For self is a sea boundless and measureless.

Say not, "I have found the truth," but rather, "I have found a truth."

Say not, "I have found the path of the soul." Say rather, "I have met the soul walking upon my path."

For the soul walks upon all paths.

The soul walks not upon a line, neither does it grow like a reed.

The soul unfolds itself, like a lotus of countless petals.

On Teaching

THEN said a teacher, "Speak to us of Teaching."

And he said:

No man can reveal to you aught but that which already lies half asleep in the dawning of your knowledge.

The teacher who walks in the shadow of the temple, among his followers, gives not of his wisdom but rather of his faith and his lovingness.

If he is indeed wise he does not bid you enter the house of his wisdom, but rather leads you to the threshold of your own mind.

The astronomer may speak to you of his understanding of space, but he cannot give you his understanding.

The musician may sing to you of the rhythm which is in all space, but he cannot give you the ear which arrests the rhythm, nor the voice that echoes it.

And he who is versed in the science of numbers can tell of the regions of weight and measure, but he cannot conduct you thither.

For the vision of one man lends not its wings to another man.

And even as each one of you stands alone in God's knowledge, so must each one of you be alone in his knowledge of God and in his understanding of the earth.

On Friendship

AND a youth said, "Speak to us of Friendship."

And he answered, saying:

Your friend is your needs answered.

He is your field which you sow with love and reap with thanksgiving.

And he is your board and your fireside.

For you come to him with your hunger, and you seek him for peace.

When your friend speaks his mind you fear not the "nay" in your own mind, nor do you with hold the "aye."

And when he is silent your heart ceases not to listen to his heart;

For without words, in friendship, all thoughts, all desires, all expectations are born and shared, with joy that is unclaimed.

When you part from your friend, you grieve not;

For that which you love most in him may be clearer in his absence, as the mountain to the climber is clearer from the plain.

And let there be no purpose in friendship save the deepening of the spirit.

For love that seeks aught but the disclosure of its own mystery is not love but a net cast forth: and only the unprofitable is caught.

And let your best be for your friend.

If he must know the ebb of your tide, let him know its flood also.

For what is your friend that you should seek him with hours to kill?

Seek him always with hours to live.

For it is his to fill your need, but not your emptiness.

And in the sweetness of friendship let there be laughter, and sharing of pleasures.

For in the dew of little things the heart finds its morning and is refreshed.

On Talking

AND then a scholar said, "Speak of Talking."

And he answered, saying:

You talk when you cease to be at peace with your thoughts;

And when you can no longer dwell in the solitude of your heart you live in your lips, and sound is a diversion and a pastime.

And in much of your talking, thinking is half murdered. For thought is a bird of space, that in a cage of words may indeed unfold its wings but cannot fly.

There are those among you who seek the talkative through fear of being alone.

The silence of aloneness reveals to their eyes their naked selves and they would escape.

And there are those who talk, and without knowledge or forethought reveal a truth which they themselves do not understand.

And there are those who have the truth within them, but they tell it not in words.

In the bosom of such as these the spirit dwells in rhythmic silence.

When you meet your friend on the roadside or in the market-place, let the spirit in you move your lips and direct your tongue.

Let the voice within your voice speak to the ear of his ear;

For his soul will keep the truth of your heart as the taste of the wine is remembered.

When the colour is forgotten and the vessel is no more.

On Time

AND an astronomer said, "Master, what of Time?"

And he answered:

You would measure time the measureless and the immeasurable.

You would adjust your conduct and even direct the course of your spirit according to hours and seasons.

Of time you would make a stream upon whose bank you would sit and watch its flowing.

Yet the timeless in you is aware of life's timelessness,

And knows that yesterday is but today's memory and tomorrow is today's dream.

And that which sings and contemplates in you is still dwelling within the bounds of that first moment which scattered the stars into space.

Who among you does not feel that his power to love is boundless?

And yet who does not feel that very love, though boundless, encompassed within the centre of his being, and moving not from love thought to love thought, nor from love deeds to other love deeds?

And is not time even as love is, undivided and paceless?

But if in your thought you must measure time into seasons, let each season encircle all the other seasons,

And let today embrace the past with remembrance and the future with longing.

On Good And Evil

AND one of the elders of the city said, "Speak to us of Good and Evil."

And he answered:

Of the good in you I can speak, but not of the evil.

For what is evil but good tortured by its own hunger and thirst?

Verily when good is hungry it seeks food even in dark caves, and when it thirsts it drinks even of dead waters.

You are good when you are one with yourself.

Yet when you are not one with yourself you are not evil.

For a divided house is not a den of thieves; it is only a divided house.

And a ship without rudder may wander aimlessly among perilous isles yet sink not to the bottom.

You are good when you strive to give of yourself.

Yet you are not evil when you seek gain for yourself.

For when you strive for gain you are but a root that clings to the earth and sucks at her breast.

Surely the fruit cannot say to the root, "Be like me, ripe and full and ever giving of your abundance."

For to the fruit giving is a need, as receiving is a need to the root.

You are good when you are fully awake in your speech.

Yet you are not evil when you sleep while your tongue staggers without purpose.

And even stumbling speech may strengthen a weak tongue.

You are good when you walk to your goal firmly and with bold steps.

Yet you are not evil when you go thither limping.

Even those who limp go not backward.

But you who are strong and swift, see that you do not limp before the lame, deeming it kindness.

You are good in countless ways, and you are not evil when you are not good,

You are only loitering and sluggard.

Pity that the stags cannot teach swiftness to the turtles.

In your longing for your giant self lies your goodness: and that longing is in all of you.

But in some of you that longing is a torrent rushing with might to the sea, carrying the secrets of the hillsides and the songs of the forest.

And in others it is a flat stream that loses itself in angles and bends and lingers before it reaches the shore.

But let not him who longs much say to him who longs little, "Wherefore are you slow and halting?"

For the truly good ask not the naked, "Where is your garment?" nor the houseless, "What has befallen your house?"

On Prayer

THEN a priestess said, "Speak to us of Prayer."

And he answered, saying:

You pray in your distress and in your need; would that you might pray also in the fullness of your joy and in your days of abundance.

For what is prayer but the expansion of your self into the living ether?

And if it is for your comfort to pour your darkness into space, it is also for your delight to pour forth the dawning of your heart.

And if you cannot but weep when your soul summons you to prayer, she should spur you again and yet again, though weeping, until you shall come laughing.

When you pray you rise to meet in the air those who are praying at that very hour, and whom save in prayer you may not meet.

Therefore let your visit to that temple invisible be for naught but ecstasy and sweet communion.

For if you should enter the temple for no other purpose than asking you shall not receive:

And if you should enter into it to humble yourself you shall not be lifted:

Or even if you should enter into it to beg for the good of others you shall not be heard.

It is enough that you enter the temple invisible.

I cannot teach you how to pray in words.

God listens not to your words save when He Himself utters them through your lips.

And I cannot teach you the prayer of the seas and the forests and the mountains.

But you who are born of the mountains and the forests and the seas can find their prayer in your heart,

And if you but listen in the stillness of the night you shall hear them saying in silence:

"Our God, who art our winged self, it is thy will in us that willeth.

"It is thy desire in us that desireth.

"It is thy urge in us that would turn our nights, which are thine, into days, which are thine also.

"We cannot ask thee for aught, for thou knowest our needs before they are born in us:

"Thou art our need; and in giving us more of thyself thou givest us all."

On Pleasure

THEN a hermit, who visited the city once a year, came forth and said, "Speak to us of Pleasure."

And he answered, saying:

Pleasure is a freedom-song,

But it is not freedom.

It is the blossoming of your desires,

But it is not their fruit.

It is a depth calling unto a height,

But it is not the deep nor the high.

It is the caged taking wing,

But it is not space encompassed.

Aye, in very truth, pleasure is a freedom-song.

And I fain would have you sing it with fullness of heart; yet I would not have you lose your hearts in the singing.

Some of your youth seek pleasure as if it were all, and they are judged and rebuked.

I would not judge nor rebuke them. I would have them seek.

For they shall find pleasure, but not her alone;

Seven are her sisters, and the least of them is more beautiful than pleasure.

Have you not heard of the man who was digging in the earth for roots and found a treasure?

And some of your elders remember pleasures with regret like wrongs committed in drunkenness.

But regret is the beclouding of the mind and not its chastisement.

They should remember their pleasures with gratitude, as they would the harvest of a summer.

Yet if it comforts them to regret, let them be comforted.

And there are among you those who are neither young to seek nor old to remember;

And in their fear of seeking and remembering they shun all pleasures, lest they neglect the spirit or offend against it.

But even in their foregoing is their pleasure.

And thus they too find a treasure though they dig for roots with quivering hands.

But tell me, who is he that can offend the spirit?

Shall the nightingale offend the stillness of the night, or the firefly the stars?

And shall your flame or your smoke burden the wind?

Think you the spirit is a still pool which you can trouble with a staff?

Oftentimes in denying yourself pleasure you do but store the desire in the recesses of your being.

Who knows but that which seems omitted to day, waits for tomorrow?

Even your body knows its heritage and its rightful need and will not be deceived.

And your body is the harp of your soul,

And it is yours to bring forth sweet music from it or confused sounds.

And now you ask in your heart, "How shall we distinguish that which is good in pleasure from that which is not good?"

Go to your fields and your gardens, and you shall learn that it is the pleasure of the bee to gather honey of the flower,

But it is also the pleasure of the flower to yield its honey to the bee.

For to the bee a flower is a fountain of life,

And to the flower a bee is a messenger of love,

And to both, bee and flower, the giving and the receiving of pleasure is a need and an ecstasy.

People of Orphalese, be in your pleasures like the flowers and the bees.

On Beauty

AND a poet said, "Speak to us of Beauty."

And he answered:

Where shall you seek beauty, and how shall you find her unless she herself be your way and your guide?

And how shall you speak of her except she be the weaver of your speech?

The aggrieved and the injured say, "Beauty is kind and gentle.

"Like a young mother half-shy of her own glory she walks among us."

And the passionate say, "Nay, beauty is a thing of might and dread.

"Like the tempest she shakes the earth beneath us and the sky above us."

The tired and the weary say, "Beauty is of soft whisperings.

"She speaks in our spirit.

"Her voice yields to our silences like a faint light that quivers in fear of the shadow."

But the restless say, "We have heard her shouting among the mountains,

"And with her cries came the sound of hoofs, and the beating of wings and the roaring of lions."

At night the watchmen of the city say, "Beauty shall rise with the dawn from the east."

And at noontide the toilers and the wayfarers say, "We have seen her leaning over the earth from the windows of the sunset."

In winter say the snow-bound, "She shall come with the spring leaping upon the hills."

And in the summer heat the reapers say, "We have seen her dancing with the autumn leaves, and we saw a drift of snow in her hair."

All these things have you said of beauty,

Yet in truth you spoke not of her but of needs unsatisfied,

And beauty is not a need but an ecstasy.

It is not a mouth thirsting nor an empty hand stretched forth,

But rather a heart inflamed and a soul enchanted.

It is not the image you would see nor the song you would hear,

But rather an image you see though you close your eyes and a song you hear though you shut your ears.

It is not the sap within the furrowed bark, nor a wing attached to a claw,

But rather a garden for ever in bloom and a flock of angels for ever in flight.

People of Orphalese, beauty is life when life unveils her holy face.

But you are life and you are the veil.

Beauty is eternity gazing at itself in a mirror.

But you are eternity and you are the mirror.

On Religion

AND an old priest said, "Speak to us of Religion."

And he said:

Have I spoken this day of aught else?

Is not religion all deeds and all reflection,

And that which is neither deed nor reflection, but a wonder and a surprise ever springing in the soul, even while the hands hew the stone or tend the loom?

Who can separate his faith from his actions, or his belief from his occupations?

Who can spread his hours before him, saying,

"This for God and this for myself;

"This for my soul and this other for my body"?

All your hours are wings that beat through space from self to self.

He who wears his morality but as his best garment were better naked.

The wind and the sun will tear no holes in his skin.

And he who defines his conduct by ethics imprisons his song-bird in a cage.

The freest song comes not through bars and wires.

And he to whom worshipping is a window, to open but also to shut, has not yet visited the house of his soul whose windows are from dawn to dawn.

Your daily life is your temple and your religion.

Whenever you enter into it take with you your all.

Take the slough and the forge and the mallet and the lute,

The things you have fashioned in necessity or for delight.

For in reverie you cannot rise above your achievements nor fall lower than your failures.

And take with you all men:

For in adoration you cannot fly higher than their hopes nor humble yourself lower than their despair.

And if you would know God, be not therefore a solver of riddles.

Rather look about you and you shall see Him playing with your children.

And look into space; you shall see Him walking in the cloud, outstretching His arms in the lightning and descending in rain.

You shall see Him smiling in flowers, then rising and waving His hands in trees.

On Death

THEN Almitra spoke, saying, "We would ask now of Death."

And he said:

You would know the secret of death.

But how shall you find it unless you seek it in the heart of life?

The owl whose night-bound eyes are blind unto the day cannot unveil the mystery of light.

If you would indeed behold the spirit of death, open your heart wide unto the body of life.

For life and death are one, even as the river and the sea are one.

In the depth of your hopes and desires lies your silent knowledge of the beyond;

And like seeds dreaming beneath the snow your heart dreams of spring.

Trust the dreams, for in them is hidden the gate to eternity.

Your fear of death is but the trembling of the shepherd when he stands before the king whose hand is to be laid upon him in honour.

Is the shepherd not joyful beneath his trembling, that he shall wear the mark of the king?

Yet is he not more mindful of his trembling?

For what is it to die but to stand naked in the wind and to melt into the sun?

And what is it to cease breathing but to free the breath from its restless tides, that it may rise and expand and seek God unencumbered?

Only when you drink from the river of silence shall you indeed sing.

And when you have reached the mountain top, then you shall begin to climb.

And when the earth shall claim your limbs, then shall you truly dance.

The Farewell

AND now it was evening.

And Almitra the seeress said, "Blessed be this day and this place and your spirit that has spoken."

And he answered,

Was it I who spoke?

Was I not also a listener?

Then he descended the steps of the Temple and all the people followed him.

And he reached his ship and stood upon the deck.

And facing the people again, he raised his voice and said:

People of Orphalese, the wind bids me leave you.

Less hasty am I than the wind, yet I must go.

We wanderers, ever seeking the lonelier way, begin no day where we have ended another day; and no sunrise finds us where sunset left us.

Even while the earth sleeps we travel.

We are the seeds of the tenacious plant, and it is in our ripeness and our fullness of heart that we are given to the wind and are scattered.

Brief were my days among you, and briefer still the words I have spoken.

But should my voice fade in your ears, and my love vanish in your memory, then I will come again,

And with a richer heart and lips more yielding to the spirit will I speak.

Yea, I shall return with the tide,

And though death may hide me, and the greater silence enfold me, yet again will I seek your under standing.

And not in vain will I seek.

If aught I have said is truth, that truth shall reveal itself in a clearer voice, and in words more kin to your thoughts.

I go with the wind, people of Orphalese, but not down into emptiness;

And if this day is not a fulfilment of your needs and my love, then let it be a promise till another day.

Man's needs change, but not his love, nor his desire that his love should satisfy his needs.

Know, therefore, that from the greater silence I shall return.

The mist that drifts away at dawn, leaving but dew in the fields, shall rise and gather into a cloud and then fall down in rain.

And not unlike the mist have I been.

In the stillness of the night I have walked in your streets, and my spirit has entered your houses,

And your heart-beats were in my heart, and your breath was upon my face, and I knew you all.

Aye, I knew your joy and your pain, and in your sleep your dreams were my dreams.

And oftentimes I was among you a lake among the mountains.

I mirrored the summits in you and the bending slopes, and even the passing flocks of your thoughts and your desires.

And to my silence came the laughter of your children in streams, and the longing of your youths in rivers.

And when they reached my depth the streams and the rivers ceased not yet to sing.

But sweeter still than laughter and greater than longing came to me.

It was the boundless in you;

The vast man in whom you are all but cells and sinews;

He in whose chant all your singing is but a soundless throbbing.

It is in the vast man that you are vast,

And in beholding him that I beheld you and loved you.

For what distances can love reach that are not in that vast sphere?

What visions, what expectations and what presumptions can outsoar that flight?

Like a giant oak tree covered with apple blossoms is the vast man in you.

His might binds you to the earth, his fragrance lifts you into space, and in his durability you are deathless.

You have been told that, even like a chain, you are as weak as your weakest link.

This is but half the truth.

You are also as strong as your strongest link.

To measure you by your smallest deed is to reckon the power of ocean by the frailty of its foam.

To judge you by your failures is to cast blame upon the seasons for their inconstancy.

Aye, you are like an ocean,

And though heavy-grounded ships await the tide upon your shores, yet, even like an ocean, you cannot hasten your tides.

And like the seasons you are also,

And though in your winter you deny your spring,

Yet spring, reposing within you, smiles in her drowsiness and is not offended.

Think not I say these things in order that you may say the one to the other,

"He praised us well.

"He saw but the good in us."

I only speak to you in words of that which you yourselves know in thought.

And what is word knowledge but a shadow of wordless knowledge?

Your thoughts and my words are waves from a sealed memory that keeps records of our yesterdays,

And of the ancient days when the earth knew not us nor herself,

And of nights when earth was upwrought with confusion.

Wise men have come to you to give you of their wisdom.

I came to take of your wisdom:

And behold I have found that which is greater than wisdom.

It is a flame spirit in you ever gathering more of itself,

While you, heedless of its expansion, bewail the withering of your days.

It is life in quest of life in bodies that fear the grave.

There are no graves here.

These mountains and plains are a cradle and a stepping-stone.

Whenever you pass by the field where you have laid your ancestors look well thereupon, and you shall see yourselves and your children dancing hand in hand.

Verily you often make merry without knowing.

Others have come to you to whom for golden promises made unto you faith you have given but riches and power and glory.

Less than a promise have I given, and yet more generous have you been to me.

You have given me my deeper thirsting after life.

Surely there is no greater gift to a man than that which turns all his aims into parching lips and all life into a fountain.

And in this lies my honour and my reward,

That whenever I come to the fountain to drink I find the living water itself thirsty;

And it drinks me while I drink it.

Some of you have deemed me proud and over shy to receive gifts.

Too proud indeed am I to receive wages, but not gifts.

And though I have eaten berries among the hills when you would have had me sit at your board,

And slept in the portico of the temple when you would gladly have sheltered me,

Yet it was not your loving mindfulness of my days and my nights that made food sweet to my mouth and girdled my sleep with visions?

For this I bless you most:

You give much and know not that you give at all.

Verily the kindness that gazes upon itself in a mirror turns to stone,

And a good deed that calls itself by tender names becomes the parent to a curse.

And some of you have called me aloof, and drunk with my own aloneness,

And you have said,

"He holds council with the trees of the forest, but not with men.

"He sits alone on hill-tops and looks down upon our city."

True it is that I have climbed the hills and walked in remote places.

How could I have seen you save from a great height or a great distance?

How can one be indeed near unless he be far?

And others among you called unto me, not in words, and they said:

"Stranger, stranger, lover of unreachable heights, why dwell you among the summits where eagles build their nests?

"Why seek you the unattainable?

"What storms would you trap in your net,

"And what vaporous birds do you hunt in the sky?

"Come and be one of us.

"Descend and appease your hunger with our bread and quench your thirst with our wine."

In the solitude of their souls they said these things;

But were their solitude deeper they would have known that I sought but the secret of your joy and your pain,

And I hunted only your larger selves that walk the sky.

But the hunter was also the hunted;

For many of my arrows left my bow only to seek my own breast.

And the flier was also the creeper;

For when my wings were spread in the sun their shadow upon the earth was a turtle.

And I the believer was also the doubter;

For often have I put my finger in my own wound that I might have the greater belief in you and the greater knowledge of you.

And it is with this belief and this knowledge that I say,

You are not enclosed within your bodies, nor confined to houses or fields.

That which is you dwells above the mountain and roves with the wind.

It is not a thing that crawls into the sun for warmth or digs holes into darkness for safety,

But a thing free, a spirit that envelops the earth and moves in the ether.

If these be vague words, then seek not to clear them.

Vague and nebulous is the beginning of all things, but not their end,

And I fain would have you remember me as a beginning.

Life, and all that lives, is conceived in the mist and not in the crystal.

And who knows but a crystal is mist in decay?

This would I have you remember in remembering me:

That which seems most feeble and bewildered in you is the strongest and most determined.

Is it not your breath that has erected and hardened the structure of your bones?

And is it not a dream which none of you remember having dreamt, that built your city and fashioned all there is in it?

Could you but see the tides of that breath you would cease to see all else,

And if you could hear the whispering of the dream you would hear no other sound.

But you do not see, nor do you hear, and it is well.

The veil that clouds your eyes shall be lifted by the hands that wove it,

And the clay that fills your ears shall be pierced by those fingers that kneaded it.

And you shall see.

And you shall hear.

Yet you shall not deplore having known blindness, nor regret having been deaf.

For in that day you shall know the hidden purposes in all things,

And you shall bless darkness as you would bless light.

After saying these things he looked about him, and he saw the pilot of his ship standing by the helm and gazing now at the full sails and now at the distance.

And he said:

Patient, over patient, is the captain of my ship.

The wind blows, and restless are the sails;

Even the rudder begs direction;

Yet quietly my captain awaits my silence.

And these my mariners, who have heard the choir of the greater sea, they too have heard me patiently.

Now they shall wait no longer.

I am ready.

The stream has reached the sea, and once more the great mother holds her son against her breast.

Fare you well, people of Orphalese.

This day has ended.

It is closing upon us even as the water-lily upon its own tomorrow.

What was given us here we shall keep,

And if it suffices not, then again must we come together and together stretch our hands unto the giver.

Forget not that I shall come back to you.

A little while, and my longing shall gather dust and foam for another body.

A little while, a moment of rest upon the wind, and another woman shall bear me.

Farwell to you and the youth I have spent with you.

It was but yesterday we met in a dream.

You have sung to me in my aloneness, and I of your longings have built a tower in the sky.

But now our sleep has fled and our dream is over, and it is no longer dawn.

The noontide is upon us and our half waking has turned to fuller day, and we must part.

If in the twilight of memory we should meet once more, we shall speak again together and you shall sing to me a deeper song.

And if our hands should meet in another dream we shall build another tower in the sky.

So saying he made a signal to the seamen, and straightaway they weighed anchor and cast the ship loose from its moorings, and they moved eastward.

And a cry came from the people as from a single heart, and it rose into the dusk and was carried out over the sea like a great trumpeting.

Only Almitra was silent, gazing after the ship until it had vanished into the mist.

And when all the people were dispersed she still stood alone upon the sea-wall, remembering in her heart his saying:

"A little while, a moment of rest upon the wind, and another woman shall bear."

The Madman

His Parables and Poems

You ask me how I became a madman. It happened thus: One day, long before many gods were born, I woke from a deep sleep and found all my masks were stolen,—the seven masks I have fashioned an worn in seven lives,—I ran maskless through the crowded streets shouting, "Thieves, thieves, the cursed thieves."

Men and women laughed at me and some ran to their houses in fear of me.

And when I reached the market place, a youth standing on a house-top cried, "He is a madman." I looked up to behold him; the sun kissed my own naked face for the first time. For the first time the sun kissed my own naked face and my soul was inflamed with love for the sun, and I wanted my masks no more. And as if in a trance I cried, "Blessed, blessed are the thieves who stole my masks."

Thus I became a madman.

And I have found both freedom and safety in my madness; the freedom of loneliness and the safety from being understood, for those who understand us enslave something in us.

But let me not be too proud of my safety. Even a Thief in a jail is safe from another thief.

God

In the ancient days, when the first quiver of speech came to my lips, I ascended the holy mountain and spoke unto God, saying, "Master, I am thy slave. Thy hidden will is my law and I shall obey thee for ever more."

But God made no answer, and like a mighty tempest passed away.

And after a thousand years I ascended the holy mountain and again spoke unto God, saying, "Creator, I am thy creation. Out of clay hast thou fashioned me and to thee I owe mine all."

And God made no answer, but like a thousand swift wings passed away.

And after a thousand years I climbed the holy mountain and spoke unto God again, saying, "Father, I am thy son. In pity and love thou hast given me birth, and through love and worship I shall inherit thy kingdom."

And God made no answer, and like the mist that veils the distant hills he passed away.

And after a thousand years I climbed the sacred mountain and gain spoke unto God, saying, "My God, my aim and my fulfilment; I am thy yesterday and thou are my tomorrow. I am thy root in the earth and thou art my flower in the sky, and together we grow before the face of the sun."

Then God leaned over me, and in my ears whispered words of sweetness, and even as the sea that enfoldeth a brook that runneth down to her, he enfolded me.

And when I descended to the valleys and the plains God was there also.

My Friend

My friend, I am not what I seem. Seeming is but a garment I wear—a care-woven garment that protects me from thy questionings and thee from my negligence.

The "I" in me, my friend, dwells in the house of silence, and therein it shall remain for ever more, unperceived, unapproachable.

I would not have thee believe in what I say nor trust in what I do—for my words are naught but thy own thoughts in sound and my deeds thy own hopes in action.

When thou sayest, "The wind bloweth eastward," I say, "Aye it doth blow eastward"; for I would not have thee know that my mind doth not dwell upon the wind but upon the sea.

Thou canst not understand my seafaring thoughts, nor would I have thee understand. I would be at sea alone.

When it is day with thee, my friend, it is night with me; yet even then I speak of the noontide that dances upon the hills and of the purple shadow that steals its way across the valley; for thou canst not hear the songs of my darkness nor see my wings beating against the stars—and I fain would not have thee hear or see. I would be with night alone.

When thou ascendest to thy Heaven I descend to my Hell—even then thou callest to me across the unbridgeable gulf, "My companion, my comrade," and I call back to thee, "My comrade, my companion"—for I would not have thee see my Hell. The flame would burn thy eyesight and the smoke would crowd thy nostrils. And I love my Hell too well to have thee visit it. I would be in Hell alone.

Thou lovest Truth and Beauty and Righteousness; and I for thy sake say it is well and seemly to love these things. But in my heart I laugh at thy love. Yet I would not have thee see my laughter. I would laugh alone.

My friend, thou art good and cautious and wise; nay, thou art perfect—and I, too, speak with thee wisely and cautiously. And yet I am mad. But I mask my madness. I would be mad alone.

My friend, thou art not my friend, but how shall I make thee understand? My path is not thy path, yet together we walk, hand in hand.

The Scarecrow

Once I said to a scarecrow, "You must be tired of standing in this lonely field."

And he said, "The joy of scaring is a deep and lasting one, and I never tire of it."

Said I, after a minute of thought, "It is true; for I too have known that joy."

Said he, "Only those who are stuffed with straw can know it."

Then I left him, not knowing whether he had complimented or belittled me.

A year passed, during which the scarecrow turned philosopher.

And when I passed by him again I saw two crows building a nest under his hat.

The Sleep-Walker

In the town where I was born lived a woman and her daughter, who walked in their sleep.

One night, while silence enfolded the world, the woman and her daughter, walking, yet asleep, met in their mist-veiled garden.

And the mother spoke, and she said: "At last, at last, my enemy! You by whom my youth was destroyed—who have built up your life upon the ruins of mine! Would I could kill you!"

And the daughter spoke, and she said: "O hateful woman, selfish and old! Who stand between my freer self and me! Who would have my life an echo of your own faded life! Would you were dead!"

At that moment a cock crew, and both women awoke. The mother said gently, "Is that you, darling?" And the daughter answered gently, "Yes, dear."

The Wise Dog

One day there passed by a company of cats a wise dog.

And as he came near and saw that they were very intent and heeded him not, he stopped.

Then there arose in the midst of the company a large, grave cat and looked upon them and said, "Brethren, pray ye; and when ye have prayed again and yet again, nothing doubting, verily then it shall rain mice."

And when the dog heard this he laughed in his heart and turned from them saying, "O blind and foolish cats, has it not been written and have I not known and my fathers before me, that that which raineth for prayer and faith and supplication is not mice but bones."

The Two Hermits

Upon a lonely mountain, there lived two hermits who worshipped God and loved one another.

Now these two hermits had one earthen bowl, and this was their only possession.

One day an evil spirit entered into the heart of the older hermit and he came to the younger and said, "It is long that we have lived together. The time has come for us to part. Let us divide our possessions."

Then the younger hermit was saddened and he said, "It grieves me, Brother, that thou shouldst leave me. But if thou must needs go, so be it," and he brought the earthen bowl and gave it to him saying, "We cannot divide it, Brother, let it be thine."

Then the older hermit said, "Charity I will not accept. I will take nothing but mine own. It must be divided."

And the younger one said, "If the bowl be broken, of what use would it be to thee or to me? If it be thy pleasure let us rather cast a lot."

But the older hermit said again, "I will have but justice and mine own, and I will not trust justice and mine own to vain chance. The bowl must be divided."

Then the younger hermit could reason no further and he said, "If it be indeed thy will, and if even so thou wouldst have it let us now break the bowl."

But the face of the older hermit grew exceedingly dark, and he cried, "O thou cursed coward, thou wouldst not fight."

The Giving And Taking

Once there lived a man who had a valleyful of needles. And one day the mother of Jesus came to him and said: "Friend, my son's garment is torn and I must needs mend it before he goeth to the temple. Wouldst thou not give me a needle?"

And he gave her not a needle, but he gave her a learned discourse on Giving and Taking to carry to her son before he should go to the temple.

The Seven Selves

In the stillest hour of the night, as I lay half asleep, my seven selves sat together and thus conversed in whisper:

First Self: Here, in this madman, I have dwelt all these years, with naught to do but renew his pain by day and recreate his sorrow by night. I can bear my fate no longer, and now I rebel.

Second Self: Yours is a better lot than mine, brother, for it is given to me to be this madman's joyous self. I laugh his laughter and sing his happy hours, and with thrice winged feet I dance his brighter thoughts. It is I that would rebel against my weary existence.

Third Self: And what of me, the love-ridden self, the flaming brand of wild passion and fantastic desires? It is I the love-sick self who would rebel against this madman.

Fourth Self: I, amongst you all, am the most miserable, for naught was given me but odious hatred and destructive loathing. It is I, the tempest-like self, the one born in the black caves of Hell, who would protest against serving this madman.

Fifth Self: Nay, it is I, the thinking self, the fanciful self, the self of hunger and thirst, the one doomed to wander without rest in search of unknown things and things not yet created; it is I, not you, who would rebel.

Sixth Self: And I, the working self, the pitiful labourer, who, with patient hands, and longing eyes, fashion the days into images and give the formless elements new and eternal forms—it is I, the solitary one, who would rebel against this restless madman.

Seventh Self: How strange that you all would rebel against this man, because each and every one of you has a preordained fate to fulfil. Ah! could I but be like one of you, a self with a determined lot! But I have none, I am the do-nothing self, the one who sits in the dumb, empty nowhere and nowhen, while you are busy re-creating life. Is it you or I, neighbours, who should rebel?

When the seventh self thus spake the other six selves looked with pity upon him but said nothing more; and as the night grew deeper one after the other went to sleep enfolded with a new and happy submission.

But the seventh self remained watching and gazing at nothingness, which is behind all things.

War

One night a feat was held in the palace, and there came a man and prostrated himself before the prince, and all the feasters looked upon him; and they saw that one of his eyes was out and that the empty socket bled. And the prince inquired of him, "What has befallen you?" And the man replied, "O prince, I am by profession a thief, and this night, because there was no moon, I went to rob the money-changer's shop, and as I climbed in through the window I made a mistake and entered the weaver's shop, and in the dark I ran into the weaver's loom and my eye was plucked out. And now, O prince, I ask for justice upon the weaver."

Then the prince sent for the weaver and he came, and it was decreed that one of his eyes should be plucked out.

"O prince," said the weaver, "the decree is just. It is right that one of my eyes be taken. And yet, alas! both are necessary to me in order that I may see the two sides of the cloth that I weave. But I have a neighbour, a cobbler, who has also two eyes, and in his trade both eyes are not necessary." Then the prince sent for the cobbler. And he came. And they took out one of the cobbler's two eyes. And justice was satisfied.

The Fox

A fox looked at his shadow at sunrise and said, "I will have a camel for lunch today." And all morning he went about looking for camels. But at noon he saw his shadow again—and he said, "A mouse will do."

The Wise King

Once there ruled in the distant city of Wirani a king who was both mighty and wise. And he was feared for his might and loved for his wisdom.

Now, in the heart of that city was a well, whose water was cool and crystalline, from which all the inhabitants drank, even the king and his courtiers; for there was no other well.

One night when all were asleep, a witch entered the city, and poured seven drops of strange liquid into the well, and said, "From this hour he who drinks this water shall become mad."

Next morning all the inhabitants, save the king and his lord chamberlain, drank from the well and became mad, even as the witch had foretold.

And during that day the people in the narrow streets and in the market places did naught but whisper to one another, "The king is mad. Our king and his lord chamberlain have lost their reason. Surely we cannot be ruled by a mad king.

We must dethrone him." That evening the king ordered a golden goblet to be filled from the well. And when it was brought to him he drank deeply, and gave it to his lord chamberlain to drink.

And there was great rejoicing in that distant city of Wirani, because its king and its lord chamberlain had regained their reason.

Ambitions

Three men met at a tavern table. One was a weaver, another a carpenter and the third a ploughman.

Said the weaver, "I sold a fine linen shroud today for two pieces of gold. Let us have all the wine we want."

"And I," said the carpenter, "I sold my best coffin. We will have a great roast with the wine."

"I only dug a grave," said the ploughman, "but my patron paid me double. Let us have honey cakes too."

And all that evening the tavern was busy, for they called often for wine and meat and cakes. And they were merry. And the host rubbed his hands and smiled at his wife; for his guests were spending freely.

When they left the moon was high, and they walked along the road singing and shouting together.

The host and his wife stood in the tavern door and looked after them.

"Ah!" said the wife, "these gentlemen! So freehanded and so gay! If only they could bring us such luck every day! Then our son need not be a tavern-keeper and work so hard. We could educate him, and he could become a priest."

The New Pleasure

Last night I invented a new pleasure, and as I was giving it the first trial an angel and a devil came rushing toward my house. They met at my door and fought with each other over my newly created pleasure; the one crying, "It is a sin!"—the other, "It is a virtue!"

The Other Language

Three days after I was born, as I lay in my silken cradle, gazing with astonished dismay on the new world round about me, my mother spoke to the wet-nurse, saying, "How does my child?"

And the wet-nurse answered, "He does well, Madame, I have fed him three times; and never before have I seen a babe so young yet so gay."

And I was indignant; and I cried, "It is not true, mother; for my bed is hard, and the milk I have sucked is bitter to my mouth, and the odour of the breast is foul in my nostrils, and I am most miserable."

But my mother did not understand, nor did the nurse; for the language I spoke was that of the world from which I came.

And on the twenty-first day of my life, as I was being christened, the priest said to my mother, "You should indeed by happy, Madame, that your son was born a Christian."

And I was surprised,—and I said to the priest, "Then your mother in Heaven should be unhappy, for you were not born a Christian."

But the priest too did not understand my language.

And after seven moons, one day a soothsayer looked at me, and he said to my mother, "Your son will be a statesman and a great leader of men."

But I cried out,—"That is a false prophecy; for I shall be a musician, and naught but a musician shall I be."

But even at that age my language was not understood—and great was my astonishment.

And after three and thirty years, during which my mother, and the nurse, and the priest have all died, (the shadow of God be upon their spirits) the soothsayer still lives. And yesterday I met him near the gates of the temple; and while we were talking together he said, "I have always known you would become a great musician. Even in your infancy I prophesied and foretold your future."

And I believed him—for now I too have forgotten the language of that other world.

The Pomegranate

Once when I was living in the heart of a pomegranate, I heard a seed saying, "Someday I shall become a tree, and the wind will sing in my branches, and the sun will dance on my leaves, and I shall be strong and beautiful through all the seasons."

Then another seed spoke and said, "When I was as young as you, I too held such views; but now that I can weigh and measure things, I see that my hopes were vain."

And a third seed spoke also, "I see in us nothing that promises so great a future."

And a fourth said, "But what a mockery our life would be, without a greater future!"

Said a fifth, "Why dispute what we shall be, when we know not even what we are."

But a sixth replied, "Whatever we are, that we shall continue to be."

And a seventh said, "I have such a clear idea how everything will be, but I cannot put it into words."

Then an eight spoke—and a ninth—and a tenth—and then many—until all were speaking, and I could distinguish nothing for the many voices.

And so I moved that very day into the heart of a quince, where the seeds are few and almost silent.

The Two Cages

In my father's garden there are two cages. In one is a lion, which my father's slaves brought from the desert of Ninavah; in the other is a songless sparrow.

Every day at dawn the sparrow calls to the lion, "Good morrow to thee, brother prisoner."

The Three Ants

Three ants met on the nose of a man who was asleep in the sun. And after they had saluted one another, each according to the custom of his tribe, they stood there conversing.

The first ant said, "These hills and plains are the most barren I have known. I have searched all day for a grain of some sort, and there is none to be found."

Said the second ant, "I too have found nothing, though I have visited every nook and glade. This is, I believe, what my people call the soft, moving land where nothing grows."

Then the third ant raised his head and said, "My friends, we are standing now on the nose of the Supreme Ant, the mighty and infinite Ant, whose body is so great that we cannot see it, whose shadow is so vast that we cannot trace it, whose voice is so loud that we cannot hear it; and He is omnipresent."

When the third ant spoke thus the other ants looked at each other and laughed.

At that moment the man moved and in his sleep raised his hand and scratched his nose, and the three ants were crushed.

The Grave Digger

Once, as I was burying one of my dead selves, the grave-digger came by and said to me, "Of all those who come here to bury, you alone I like."

Said I, "You please me exceedingly, but why do you like me?"

"Because," said he, "They come weeping and go weeping—you only come laughing and go laughing."

On The Steps Of The Temple

Yestereve, on the marble steps of the Temple, I saw a woman sitting between two men. One side of her face was pale, the other was blushing.

The Blessed City

In my youth I was told that in a certain city every one lived according to the Scriptures.

And I said, "I will seek that city and the blessedness thereof." And it was far. And I made great provision for my journey. And after forty days I beheld the city and on the forty-first day I entered into it.

And lo! the whole company of the inhabitants had each but a single eye and but one hand. And I was astonished and said to myself, "Shall they of this so holy city have but one eye and one hand?"

Then I saw that they too were astonished, for they were marvelling greatly at my two hands and my two eyes. And as they were speaking together I inquired of them saying, "Is this indeed the Blessed City, where each man lives according to the Scriptures?" And they said, "Yes, this is that city."

"And what," said I, "hath befallen you, and where are your right eyes and your right hands?"

And all the people were moved. And they said, "Come thou and see."

And they took me to the temple in the midst of the city. And in the temple I saw a heap of hands and eyes. All withered. Then said I, "Alas! what conqueror hath committed this cruelty upon you?"

And there went a murmur amongst them. And one of their elders stood forth and said, "This doing is of ourselves. God hath made us conquerors over the evil that was in us."

And he led me to a high altar, and all the people followed. And he showed me above the altar an inscription graven, and I read:

"If thy right eye offend thee, pluck it out and cast it from thee; for it is profitable for thee that one of thy members should perish, and not that the whole body should be cast into hell. And if thy right hand offend thee, cut it off and cast it from thee; for it is profitable for thee that one of thy members should perish, and not that thy whole body should be cast into hell."

Then I understood. And I turned about to all the people and cried, "Hath no man or woman among you two eyes or two hands?"

And they answered me saying, "No, not one. There is none whole save such as are yet too young to read the Scripture and to understand its commandment."

And when we had come out of the temple, I straightway left that Blessed City; for I was not too young, and I could read the scripture.

The Good God and the Evil God

The Good God and the Evil God met on the mountain top.

The Good God said, "Good day to you, brother."

The Evil God did not answer.

And the Good God said, "You are in a bad humour today."

"Yes," said the Evil God, "for of late I have been often mistaken for you, called by your name, and treated as if I were you, and it ill-pleases me."

And the Good God said, "But I too have been mistaken for you and called by your name."

The Evil God walked away curing the stupidity of man.

Defeat

Defeat, my Defeat, my solitude and my aloofness;
You are dearer to me than a thousand triumphs,
And sweeter to my heart than all world-glory.

Defeat, my Defeat, my self-knowledge and my defiance,
Through you I know that I am yet young and swift of foot
And not to be trapped by withering laurels.
And in you I have found aloneness
And the joy of being shunned and scorned.

Defeat, my Defeat, my shining sword and shield,
In your eyes I have read
That to be enthroned is to be enslaved,
and to be understood is to be leveled down,
And to be grasped is but to reach one's fullness
And like a ripe fruit to fall and be consumed.

Defeat, my Defeat, my bold companion,
You shall hear my songs and my cries an my silences,
And none but you shall speak to me of the beating of wings,
And urging of seas,
And of mountains that burn in the night,
And you alone shall climb my steep and rocky soul.

Defeat, my Defeat, my deathless courage,
You and I shall laugh together with the storm,
And together we shall dig graves for all that die in us,
And we shall stand in the sun with a will,
And we shall be dangerous.

Night and the Madman

"I am like thee, O, Night, dark and naked; I walk on the flaming path which is above my day-dreams, and whenever my foot touches earth a giant oak tree comes forth."

"Nay, thou art not like me, O, Madman, for thou still lookest backward to see how large a foot-print thou leavest on the sand."

"I am like thee, O, Night, silent and deep; and in the heart of my loneliness lies a Goddess in child-bed; and in him who is being born Heaven touches Hell."

"Nay, thou art not like me, O, Madman, for thou shudderest yet before pain, and the song of the abyss terrifies thee."

"I am like thee, O, Night, wild and terrible; for my ears are crowded with cries of conquered nations and sighs for forgotten lands."

"Nay, thou art not like me, O, Madman, for thou still takest thy little-self for a comrade, and with thy monster-self thou canst not be friend."

"I am like thee, O, Night, cruel and awful; for my bosom is lit by burning ships at sea, and my lips are wet with blood of slain warriors."

"Nay, thou art not like me, O, Madman; for the desire for a sister-spirit is yet upon thee, and thou has not become a law unto thyself."

"I am like thee, O, Night, joyous and glad; for he who dwells in my shadow is now drunk with virgin wine, and she who follows me is sinning mirthfully."

"Nay, thou art not like me, O, Madman, for thy soul is wrapped in the veil of seven folds and thou holdest not they heart in thine hand."

"I am like thee, O, Night, patient and passionate; for in my breast a thousand dead lovers are buried in shrouds of withered kisses."

"Yea, Madman, art thou like me? Art thou like me? And canst thou ride the tempest as a steed, and grasp the lightning as a sword?"

"Like thee, O, Night, like thee, mighty and high, and my throne is built upon heaps of fallen Gods; and before me too pass the days to kiss the hem of my garment but never to gaze at my face."

"Art thou like me, child of my darkest heart? And dost thou think my untamed thoughts and speak my vast language?"

"Yea, we are twin brothers, O, Night; for thou revealest space and I reveal my soul."

Faces

I have seen a face with a thousand countenances, and a face that was but a single countenance as if held in a mould.

I have seen a face whose sheen I could look through to the ugliness beneath, and a face whose sheen I had to lift to see how beautiful it was.

I have seen an old face much lined with nothing, and a smooth face in which all things were graven.

I know faces, because I look through the fabric my own eye weaves, and behold the reality beneath.

The Greater Sea

My soul and I went to the great sea to bathe. And when we reached the shore, we went about looking for a hidden and lonely place.

But as we walked, we saw a man sitting on a grey rock taking pinches of salt from a bag and throwing them into the sea.

"This is the pessimist," said my soul, "Let us leave this place. We cannot bathe here."

We walked on until we reached an inlet. There we saw, standing on a white rock, a man holding a bejeweled box, from which he took sugar and threw it into the sea.

"And this is the optimist," said my soul, "And he too must not see our naked bodies.

Further on we walked. And on a beach we saw a man picking up dead fish and tenderly putting them back into the water.

"And we cannot bathe before him," said my soul. "He is the humane philanthropist."

And we passed on.

Then we came where we saw a man tracing his shadow on the sand. Great waves came and erased it. But he went on tracing it again and again.

"He is the mystic," said my soul, "Let us leave him."

And we walked on, till in a quiet cove we saw a man scooping up the foam and putting it into an alabaster bowl.

"He is the idealist," said my soul, "Surely he must not see our nudity."

And on we walked. Suddenly we heard a voice crying, "This is the sea. This is the deep sea. This is the vast and mighty sea." And when we reached the voice it was a man whose back was turned to the sea, and at his ear he held a shell, listening to its murmur.

And my soul said, "Let us pass on. He is the realist, who turns his back on the whole he cannot grasp, and busies himself with a fragment."

So we passed on. And in a weedy place among the rocks was a man with his head buried in the sand. And I said to my soul, "We can bath here, for he cannot see us."

"Nay," said my soul, "For he is the most deadly of them all. He is the puritan."

Then a great sadness came over the face of my soul, and into her voice.

"Let us go hence," she said, "For there is no lonely, hidden place where we can bathe. I would not have this wind lift my golden hair, or bare my white bosom in this air, or let the light disclose my sacred nakedness."

Then we left that sea to seek the Greater Sea.

Crucified

I cried to men, "I would be crucified!"

And they said, "Why should your blood be upon our heads?"

And I answered, "How else shall you be exalted except by crucifying madmen?"

And they heeded and I was crucified. And the crucifixion appeased me.

And when I was hanged between earth and heaven they lifted up their heads to see me. And they were exalted, for their heads had never before been lifted.

But as they stood looking up at me one called out, "For what art thou seeking to atone?"

And another cried, "In what cause dost thou sacrifice thyself?"

And a third said, "Thinkest thou with this price to buy world glory?"

Then said a fourth, "Behold, how he smiles! Can such pain be forgiven?"

And I answered them all, and said:

"Remember only that I smiled. I do not atone—nor sacrifice—nor wish for glory; and I have nothing to forgive. I thirsted—and I besought you to give me my blood to drink. For what is there can quench a madman's thirst but his own blood? I was dumb—and I asked wounds of you for mouths. I was imprisoned in your days and nights—and I sought a door into larger days and nights.

And now I go—as others already crucified have gone. And think not we are weary of crucifixion. For we must be crucified by larger and yet larger men, between greater earths and greater heavens."

The Astronomer

In the shadow of the temple my friend and I saw a blind man sitting alone. And my friend said, "Behold the wisest man of our land."

Then I left my friend and approached the blind man and greeted him. And we conversed.

After a while I said, "Forgive my question; but since when has thou been blind?"

"From my birth," he answered.

Said I, "And what path of wisdom followest thou?"

Said he, "I am an astronomer."

Then he placed his hand upon his breast saying, "I watch all these suns and moons and stars."

The Great Longing

Here I sit between my brother the mountain and my sister the sea.

We three are one in loneliness, and the love that binds us together is deep and strong and strange. Nay, it is deeper than my sister's depth and stronger than my brother's strength, and stranger than the strangeness of my madness.

Aeons upon aeons have passed since the first grey dawn made us visible to one another; and though we have seen the birth and the fullness and the death of many worlds, we are still eager and young.

We are young and eager and yet we are mateless and unvisited, and though we lie in unbroken half embrace, we are uncomforted. And what comfort is there for controlled desire and unspent passion? Whence shall come the flaming god to warm my sister's bed? And what she-torrent shall quench my brother's fire? And who is the woman that shall command my heart?

In the stillness of the night my sister murmurs in her sleep the fire-god's unknown name, and my brother calls afar upon the cool and distant goddess. But upon whom I call in my sleep I know not.

* * *

Here I sit between my brother the mountain and my sister the sea. We three are one in loneliness, and the love that binds us together is deep and strong and strange.

Said a Blade of Grass

Said a blade of grass to an autumn leaf, "You make such a noise falling! You scatter all my winter dreams."

Said the leaf indignant, "Low-born and low-dwelling! Songless, peevish thing! You live not in the upper air and you cannot tell the sound of singing."

Then the autumn leaf lay down upon the earth and slept. And when spring came she waked again—and she was a blade of grass.

And when it was autumn and her winter sleep was upon her, and above her through all the air the leaves were falling, she muttered to herself, "O these autumn leaves! They make such noise! They scatter all my winter dreams."

The Eye

Said the Eye one day, "I see beyond these valleys a mountain veiled with blue mist. Is it not beautiful?"

The Ear listened, and after listening intently awhile, said, "But where is any mountain? I do not hear it."

Then the Hand spoke and said, "I am trying in vain to feel it or touch it, and I can find no mountain."

And the Nose said, "There is no mountain, I cannot smell it."

Then the Eye turned the other way, and they all began to talk together about the Eye's strange delusion. And they said, "Something must be the matter with the Eye."

The Two Learned Men

Once there lived in the ancient city of Afkar two learned men who hated and belittled each other's learning. For one of them denied the existence of the gods and the other was a believer.

One day the two met in the marketplace, and amidst their followers they began to dispute and to argue about the existence or the non-existence of the gods. And after hours of contention they parted.

That evening the unbeliever went to the temple and prostrated himself before the altar and prayed the gods to forgive his wayward past.

And the same hour the other learned man, he who had upheld the gods, burned his sacred books. For he had become an unbeliever.

When My Sorrow Was Born

When my Sorrow was born I nursed it with care, and watched over it with loving tenderness.

And my Sorrow grew like all living things, strong and beautiful and full of wondrous delights.

And we loved one another, my Sorrow and I, and we loved the world about us; for Sorrow had a kindly heart and mine was kindly with Sorrow.

And when we conversed, my Sorrow and I, our days were winged and our nights were girdled with dreams; for Sorrow had an eloquent tongue, and mine was eloquent with Sorrow.

And when we sang together, my Sorrow and I, our neighbours sat at their windows and listened; for our songs were deep as the sea and our melodies were full of strange memories. And when we walked together, my Sorrow and I, people gazed at us with gentle eyes and whispered in words of exceeding sweetness. And there were those who looked with envy upon us, for Sorrow was a noble thing and I was proud with Sorrow.

But my Sorrow died, like all living things, and alone I am left to muse and ponder.

And now when I speak my words fall heavily upon my ears.

And when I sing my songs my neighbours come not to listen.

And when I walk the streets no one looks at me. Only in my sleep I hear voices saying in pity, "See, there lies the man whose Sorrow is dead."

And When my Joy was Born

And when my Joy was born, I held it in my arms and stood on the house-top shouting, "Come ye, my neighbours, come and see, for Joy this day is born unto me. Come and behold this gladsome thing that laugheth in the sun."

But none of my neighbours came to look upon my Joy, and great was my astonishment.

And every day for seven moons I proclaimed my Joy from the house-top—and yet no one heeded me. And my Joy and I were alone, unsought and unvisited.

Then my Joy grew pale and weary because no other heart but mine held its loveliness and no other lips kissed its lips.

Then my Joy died of isolation.

And now I only remember my dead Joy in remembering my dead Sorrow. But memory is an autumn leaf that murmurs a while in the wind and then is heard no more.

The Perfect World

God of lost souls, thou who are lost amongst the gods, hear me:

Gentle Destiny that watchest over us, mad, wandering spirits, hear me:

I dwell in the midst of a perfect race, I the most imperfect.

I, a human chaos, a nebula of confused elements, I move amongst finished worlds—peoples of complete laws and pure order, whose thoughts are assorted, whose dreams are arranged, and whose visions are enrolled and registered.

Their virtues, O God, are measured, their sins are weighed, and even the countless things that pass in the dim twilight of neither sin nor virtue are recorded and catalogued.

Here days and night are divided into seasons of conduct and governed by rules of blameless accuracy.

To eat, to drink, to sleep, to cover one's nudity, and then to be weary in due time.

To work, to play, to sing, to dance, and then to lie still when the clock strikes the hour.

To think thus, to feel thus much, and then to cease thinking and feeling when a certain star rises above yonder horizon. To rob a neighbour with a smile, to bestow gifts with a graceful wave of the hand, to praise prudently, to blame cautiously, to destroy a sound with a word, to burn a body with a breath, and then to wash the hands when the day's work is done.

To love according to an established order, to entertain one's best self in a preconceived manner, to worship the gods becomingly, to intrigue the devils artfully—and then to forget all as though memory were dead. To fancy with a motive, to contemplate with consideration, to be happy sweetly, to suffer nobly—and then to empty the cup so that tomorrow may fill it again.

All these things, O God, are conceived with forethought, born with determination, nursed with exactness, governed by rules, directed by reason, and then slain and buried after a prescribed method. And even their silent graves that lie within the human soul are marked and numbered.

It is a perfect world, a world of consummate excellence, a world of supreme wonders, the ripest fruit in God's garden, the master-thought of the universe.

But why should I be here, O God, I a green seed of unfulfilled passion, a mad tempest that seeketh neither east nor west, a bewildered fragment from a burnt planet?

Why am I here, O God of lost souls, thou who art lost amongst the gods?

Jesus, The Son of Man

James The Son Of Jebedee:
On the Kingdom of the World

UPON a day in the spring of the year Jesus stood in the market-place of Jerusalem and He spoke to the multitudes of the kingdom of heaven.

And He accused the scribes and the Pharisees of setting snares and digging pitfalls in the path of those who long after the kingdom; and He denounced them.

Now amongst the crowd was a company of men who defended the Pharisees and the scribes, and they sought to lay hands upon Jesus and upon us also.

But He avoided them and turned aside from them, and walked towards the north gate of the city.

And He said to us, "My hour has not yet come. Many are the things I have still to say unto you, and many are the deeds I shall yet perform ere I deliver myself up to the world."

Then He said, and there was joy and laughter in His voice, "Let us go into the North Country and meet the spring. Come with me to the hills, for winter is past and the snows of Lebanon are descending to the valleys to sing with the brooks.

"The fields and the vineyards have banished sleep and are awake to greet the sun with their green figs and tender grapes."

And He walked before us and we followed Him, that day and the next.

And upon the afternoon of the third day we reached the summit of Mount Hermon, and there He stood looking down upon the cities of the plains.

And His face shone like molten gold, and He outstretched His arms and He said to us, "Behold the earth in her green raiment, and see how the streams have hemmed the edges of her garments with silver.

"In truth the earth is fair and all that is upon her is fair.

"But there is a kingdom beyond all that you behold, and therein I shall rule. And if it is your choice, and if it is indeed

your desire, you too shall come and rule with me.

"But there is a kingdom beyond all that you behold, and therein I shall rule. And if it is your choice, and if it is indeed your desire, you too shall come and rule with me.

"My face and your faces shall not be masked; our hand shall hold neither sword nor sceptre, and our subjects shall love us in peace and shall not be in fear of us."

Thus spoke Jesus, and unto all the kingdoms of the earth I was blinded, and unto all the cities of walls and towers; and it was in my heart to follow the Master to His kingdom.

Then just at that moment Judas of Iscariot stepped forth. And he walked up to Jesus, and spoke and said, "Behold, the kingdoms of the world are vast, and behold the cities of David and Solomon shall prevail against the Romans. If you will be the king of the Jews we shall stand beside you with sword and shield and we shall overcome the alien."

But when Jesus heard this He turned upon Judas, and His face was filled with wrath. And He spoke in a voice terrible as the thunder of the sky and He said, "Get you behind me, Satan. Think you that I came down the years to rule an ant-hill for a day?

"My throne is a throne beyond your vision. Shall he whose wings encircle the earth seek shelter in a nest abandoned and forgotten?

"Shall the living be honoured and exalted by the wearer of shrouds?"

"My kingdom is not of this earth, and my seat is not builded upon the skulls of your ancestors.

"If you seek aught save the kingdom of the spirit then it were better for you to leave me here, and go down to the caves of your dead, where the crowned heads of yore hold court in their tombs and may still be bestowing honours upon the bones of your forefathers.

"Dare you tempt me with a crown of dross, when my forehead seeks the Pleiades, or else your thorns?

"Were it not for a dream dreamed by a forgotten race I would not suffer your sun to rise upon my patience, nor your moon to throw my shadow across your path.

"Were it not for a mother's desire I would have stripped me of the swaddling-clothes and escaped back to space.

"And were it not for sorrow in all of you I would not have stayed to weep.

"Who are you and what are you, Judas Iscariot? And why do you tempt me?

"Have you in truth weighed me in the scale and found me one to lead legions of pygmies, and to direct chariots of the shapeless against an enemy that encamps only in your hatred and marches nowhere but in your fear?

"Too many are the worms that crawl about me feet, and I will give them no battle. I am weary of the jest, and weary of pitying the creepers who deem me coward because I will not move among their guarded walls and towers.

"Pity it is that I must needs pity to the very end. Would that I could turn my steps towards a larger world where larger men dwell. But how shall I?

"Your priest and your emperor would have my blood. They shall be satisfied ere I go hence. I would not change the course of the law. And I would not govern folly.

"Let ignorance reproduce itself until it is weary of its own offspring.

"Let the blind lead the blind to the pitfall.

"And let the dead bury the dead till the earth be choked with its own bitter fruit.

"My kingdom is not of the earth. My kingdom shall be where two or three of you shall meet in love, and in wonder at the loveliness of life, and in good cheer, and in remembrance of me."

Then of a sudden He turned to Judas, and He said, "Get you behind me, man. Your kingdoms shall never be in my kingdom."

And now it was twilight, and He turned to us and said, "Let us go down. The night is upon us. Let us walk in light while the light is with us."

Then He went down from the hills and we followed Him. And Judas followed afar off.

And when we reached the lowland it was night.

And Thomas, the son of Diophanes, said unto Him, "Master, it is dark now, and we can no longer see the way. If it is in your will, lead us to the lights of yonder village where we may find meat and shelter."

And Jesus answered Thomas, and He said, "I have led you to the heights when you were hungry, and I have brought you down to the plains with a greater hunger. But I cannot stay with you this night. I would be alone."

Then Simon Peter stepped forth, and said: Master, suffer us not to go alone in the dark. Grant that we may stay with you even here on this byway. The night and the shadows of the night will not linger, and the morning shall soon find us if you will but stay with us."

And Jesus answered, "This night the foxes shall have their holes, and the birds of the air their nests, but the Son of Man has not where on earth to lay His head. And indeed I would now be alone. Should you desire me you will find me again by the lake where I found you."

Then we walked away from Him with heavy hearts, for it was not in our will to leave Him.

Many times did we stop and turn our faces towards Him, and we saw him in lonely majesty, moving westward.

The only man among us who did not turn to behold Him in His aloneness was Judas Iscariot.

And from that day Judas became sullen and distant. And methought there was danger in the sockets of his eyes.

Anna, The Mother Of Mary:
On The Birth of Jesus

JESUS, the son of my daughter, was born here in Nazareth in the month of January. And the night that Jesus was born we were visited by men from the East. They were Persians who came to Esdraelon with the caravans of the Midianites on their way to Egypt. And because they did not find rooms at the inn they sought shelter in our house. And I welcomed them and I said, "My daughter has given birth to a son this night. Surely you will forgive me if I do not serve you as it behooves a hostess."

Then they thanked me for giving them shelter. And after they had supped they said to me, "We would see the new-born."

Now the Son of Mary was beautiful to behold, and she too was comely.

And when the Persians beheld Mary and her babe, they took gold and silver from their bags, and myrrh and frankincense, and laid them all at the feet of the child.

Then they fell down and prayed in a strange tongue which we did not understand.

And when I led them to the bedchamber prepared for them they walked as if they were in awe at what they had seen.

When morning was come they left us and followed the road to Egypt.

But at parting they spoke to me and said, "The child is not but a day old, yet we have seen the light of our God in His eyes and the smile of our God upon His mouth.

"We bid you protect Him that He may protect you all."

And so saying, they mounted their camels and we saw them no more.

Now Mary seemed not so much joyous in her first-born, as full of wonder and surprise.

She would look upon her babe, and then turn her face to the window and gaze far away into the sky as if she saw visions.

And there were valleys between her heart and mine.

And the child grew in body and in spirit, and He was different from other children. He was aloof and hard to govern, and I could not lay my hand upon Him.

But He was beloved by everyone in Nazareth, and in my heart I knew why.

Oftentimes He would take away our food to give to the passerby. And He would give other children the sweetmeat I had given Him, before He had tasted it with His own mouth.

He would climb the trees of my orchard to get the fruits, but never to eat them Himself.

And He would race with other boys, and sometimes, because He was swifter of foot, He would delay so that they might pass the stake ere He should reach it.

And sometimes when I led Him to His bed He would say, "Tell my mother and the others that only my body will sleep. My mind will be with them till their mind come to my morning."

And many other wondrous words He said when He was a boy, but I am too old to remember.

Now they tell me I shall see Him no more. But how shall I believe what they say?

I still hear His laughter, and the sound of His running about my house. And whenever I kiss the cheek of my daughter His fragrance returns to my heart, and His body seems to fill my arms.

But is it not passing strange that my daughter does not speak of her first-born to me?

Sometimes it seems that my longing for Him is greater than hers. She stands as firm before the day as if she were a bronzen image, while my heart melts and runs into streams.

Perhaps she knows what I do not know. Would that she might tell me also.

Asaph, Called The Operator Of Typer:
On The Speech of Jesus

WHAT shall I say of His speech? Perhaps something about His person lent power to His words and swayed those who heard Him. For He was comely, and the sheen of the day was upon His countenance. Men and women gazed at Him more than they listened to His argument. But at times He spoke with the power of a spirit, and that spirit had authority over those who heard Him.

In my youth I had heard the orators of Rome and Athens and Alexandria. The young Nazarene was unlike them all.

They assembled their words with an art to enthral the ear, but when you heard Him your heart would leave you and go wandering into regions not yet visited.

He would tell a story or relate a parable, and the like of His stories and parables had never been heard in Syria. He seemed to spin them out of the seasons, even as time spins the years and the generations.

He would begin a story thus: "The ploughman went forth to the field to sow his seeds."

Or, "Once there was a rich man who had many vineyards."

Or, "A shepherd counted his sheep at eventide and found that one sheep was missing."

And such words would carry His listeners into their simpler selves, and into the ancient of their days.

At heart we are all ploughmen, and we all love the vineyard. And in the pastures of our memory there is a shepherd and a flock and the lost sheep.

And there is the plough-share and the winepress and the threshing-floor.

He knew the source of our older self, and the persistent thread of which we are woven.

The Greek and the Roman orators spoke to their listeners of life as it seemed to the mind. The Nazarene spoke of a longing that lodged in the heart.

They saw life with eyes only a little clearer than yours and mine. He saw life in the light of God.

I often think that He spoke to the crowd as a mountain would speak to the plain.

And in His speech there was a power that was not commanded by the orators of Athens or of Rome.

Mary Magdalen:
On Meeting Jesus for the First Time

IT was in the month of June when I saw Him for the first time. He was walking in the wheatfield when I passed by with my handmaidens, and He was alone. The rhythm of His steps was different from other men's, and the movement of His body was like naught I had seen before.

Men do not pace the earth in that manner. And even now I do not know whether He walked fast or slow.

My handmaidens pointed their fingers at Him and spoke in shy whispers to one another. And I stayed my steps for a moment, and raised my hand to hail Him. But He did not turn His face, and He did not look at me. And I hated Him. I was swept back into myself, and I was as cold as if I had been in a snow-drift. And I shivered.

That night I beheld Him in my dreaming; and they told me afterward that I screamed in my sleep and was restless upon my bed.

It was in the month of August that I saw Him again, through my window. He was sitting in the shadow of the cypress tree across my garden, and He was still as if He had been carved out of stone, like the statues in Antioch and other cities of the North Country.

And my slave, the Egyptian, came to me and said, "That man is here again. He is sitting there across your garden."

And I gazed at Him, and my soul quivered within me, for He was beautiful.

His body was single and each part seemed to love every other part.

Then I clothed myself with raiment of Damascus, and I left my house and walked towards Him.

Was it my aloneness, or was it His fragrance, that drew me to Him? Was it a hunger in my eyes that desired comeliness, or was it His beauty that sought the light of my eyes?

Even now I do not know.

I walked to Him with my scented garments and my golden sandals, the sandals the Roman captain had given me, even these sandals. And when I reached Him, I said, "Good-morrow to you."

And He said, "Good-morrow to you, Miriam."

And He looked at me, and His night-eyes saw me as no man had seen me. And suddenly I was as if naked, and I was shy.

Yet He had only said, "Good-morrow to you."

And then I said to Him, "Will you not come to my house?"

And He said, "Am I not already in your house?"

I did not know what He meant then, but I know now.

And I said, "Will you not have wine and bread with me?"

And He said, "Yes, Miriam, but not now."

Not now, not now, He said. And the voice of the sea was in those two words, and the voice of the wind and the trees. And when He said them unto me, life spoke to death.

For mind you, my friend, I was dead. I was a woman who had divorced her soul. I was living apart from this self which you now see. I belonged to all men, and to none. They called me harlot, and a woman possessed of seven devils. I was cursed, and I was envied.

But when His dawn-eyes looked into my eyes all the stars of my night faded away, and I became Miriam, only Miriam, a woman lost to the earth she had known, and finding herself in new places.

And now again I said to Him, "Come into my house and share bread and wine with me."

And He said, "Why do you bid me to be your guest?"

And I said, "I beg you to come into my house." And it was all that was sod in me, and all that was sky in me calling unto Him.

Then He looked at me, and the noontide of His eyes was upon me, and He said, "You have many lovers, and yet I alone love you. Other men love themselves in your nearness. I love you in your self. Other men see a beauty in you that shall fade away sooner than their own years. But I see in you a beauty that shall not fade away, and in the autumn of your days that beauty shall not be afraid to gaze at itself in the mirror, and it shall not be offended."

"I alone love the unseen in you."

Then He said in a low voice, "Go away now. If this cypress tree is yours and you would not have me sit in its shadow, I will walk my way."

And I cried to Him and I said, "Master, come to my house. I have incense to burn for you, and a silver basin for your feet. You are a stranger and yet not a stranger. I entreat you, come to my house."

Then He stood up and looked at me even as the seasons might look down upon the field, and He smiled. And He said again:

"All men love you for themselves. I love you for yourself."

And then He walked away.

But no other man ever walked the way He walked. Was it a breath born in my garden that moved to the east? Or was it a storm that would shake all things to their foundations?

I knew not, but on that day the sunset of His eyes slew the dragon in me, and I became a woman, I became Miriam, Miriam of Mijdel.

Philemon A Greek Apothecary:
On Jesus The Master Physician

THE Nazarene was the Master Physician of His people. No other man knew so much of our bodies and of their elements and properties. He made whole those who were afflicted with diseases unknown to the Greeks and the Egyptians. They say He even called back the dead to life. And whether this be true or not true, it declares His power; for only to him who has wrought great things is the greatest ever attributed.

They say also that Jesus visited India and the Country between the Two Rivers, and that there the priests revealed to Him the knowledge of all that is hidden in the recesses of our flesh.

Yet that knowledge may have been given to Him direct by the gods, and not through the priests. For that which has remained unknown to all men for an eon may be disclosed to one man in but a moment. And Apollo may lay his hand on the heart of the obscure and make it wise.

Many doors were open to the Tyrians and the Thebans, and to this man also certain sealed doors were opened. He entered the temple of the soul, which is the body; and He beheld the evil spirits that conspire against our sinews, and also the good spirits that spin the threads thereof.

Methinks it was by the power of opposition and resistance that He healed the sick, but in a manner unknown to our philosophers. He astonished fever with His snowlike touch and it retreated; and He surprised the hardened limbs with His own calm and they yielded to Him and were at peace.

He knew the ebbing sap within the furrowed bark – but how He reached the sap with His fingers I do not know. He knew the sound steel underneath the rust – but how He freed the sword and made it shine no man can tell.

Sometimes it seems to me that He heard the murmuring pain of all things that grow in the sun, and that then He lifted them up and supported them, not only by His own knowledge, but also by disclosing to them their own power to rise and become whole.

Yet He was not much concerned with Himself as a physician. He was rather preoccupied with the religion and the politics of this land. And this I regret, for first of all things we must be sound of body.

But these Syrians, when they are visited by an illness, seek an argument rather than medicine.

And pity it is that the greatest of all their physicians chose rather to be but a maker of speeches in the market-place.

Simon, Who Was Called Peter:
When He and His Brother Were Called

I WAS on the shore of the Lake of Galilee when I first beheld Jesus my Lord and my Master. My brother Andrew was with me and we were casting out net into the waters.

The waves were rough and high and we caught but few fish. And our hearts were heavy.

Suddenly Jesus stood near us, as if He had taken form that very moment, for we had not seen Him aproaching.

He called us by our names, and He said, "If you will follow me I will lead you to an inlet where the fishes are swarming."

And as I looked at His face the net fell from my hands, for a flame kindled within me and I recognised Him.

And my brother Andrew spoke and said, "We know all the inlets upon these shores, and we know also that on a windy day like this the fish seek a depth beyond our nets."

And Jesus answered, "Follow me to the shores of a greater sea.

I shall make you fishers of men. And your net shall never be empty."

And we abandoned our boat and our net and followed Him.

I myself was drawn by a power, viewless, that walked beside His person.

I walked near Him, breathless and full of wonder, and my brother Andrew was behind us, bewildered and amazed.

And as we walked on the sand I made bold and said unto Him,

"Sir, I and my brother will follow your footsteps, and where you go we too will go. But if it please you to come to our house this night, we shall be graced by your visit. Our house is not large and our ceiling not high, and you will sit at but a frugal meal. Yet if you will abide in our hovel it will be to us a palace. And would you break bread with us, we in your presence were to be envied by the princes of the land."

And He said, "Yea, I will be your guest this night."

And I rejoiced in my heart. And we walked behind Him in silence until we reached our house.

And as we stood at the threshold Jesus said, "Peace be to this house, and to those who dwell in it."

Then He entered and we followed Him.

My wife and my wife's mother and my daughter stood before Him and they worshipped Him; then they knelt before Him and kissed the hem of His sleeve.

They were astonished that He, the chosen and the well beloved, had come to be our guest; for they had already seen Him by the River Jordan when John the Baptist had proclaimed Him before the people.

And straightaway my wife and my wife's mother began to prepare the supper.

My brother Andrew was a shy man, but his faith in Jesus was deeper than my faith.

And my daughter, who was then but twelve year old, stood by Him and held His garment as if she were in fear He would leave us and go out again into the night. She clung to Him like a lost sheep that has found its shepherd.

Then we sat at the board, and He broke the bread and poured the wine; and He turned to us saying, "My friends, grace me now in sharing this food with me, even as the Father has graced us in giving it unto us."

These words He said ere He touched a morsel, for He wished to follow an ancient custom that the honoured guest becomes the host.

And as we sat with Him around the board we felt as if we were sitting at the feast of the great King.

My daughter Petronelah, who was young and unknowing, gazed at His face and followed the movements of His hands. And I saw a veil of tears in her eyes.

When He left the board we followed Him and sat about Him in the vine-arbor.

And He spoke to us and we listened, and our hearts fluttered within us like birds.

He spoke of the second birth of man, and of the opening of the gates of the heavens; and of angels descending and bringing peace and good cheer to all men, and of angels ascending to the throne bearing the longings of men to the Lord God.

Then He looked into my eyes and gazed into the depths of my heart. And He said, "I have chosen you and your brother, and you must come with me. You have laboured and you have been heavy-laden. Now I shall give you rest. Take up my yoke and learn of me, for in my heart is peace, and your soul shall find abundance and a home-coming."

When He spoke thus I and my brother stood up before Him, and I said to Him, "Master, we will follow you to the ends of the earth. And if our burden were as heavy as the mountain we would bear it with you in gladness. And should we fall by the wayside we shall know that we have fallen on the way to heaven, and we shall be satisfied."

And my brother Andrew spoke and said, "Master, we would be threads between your hands and your loom. Weave us into the cloth if you will, for we would be in the raiment of the Most High."

And my wife raised her face, and the tears were upon her cheeks and she spoke with joy, and she said, "Blessed are you who come in the name of the Lord. Blessed is the womb that carried you, and the breast that gave you milk."

And my daughter, who was but twelve years old, sat at His feet and she nestled close to Him.

And the mother of my wife, who sat at the threshold, said no word. She only wept in silence and her shawl was wet with her tears.

Then Jesus walked over to her and He raised her face to His face and He said to her, "You are the mother of all these. You weep for joy, and I will keep your tears in my memory."

And now the old moon rose above the horizon. And Jesus gazed upon it for a moment, and then He turned to us and said, "It is late. Seek your beds, and may God visit your repose. I will be here in this arbor until dawn. I have cast my net this day and I have caught two men; I am satisfied, and now I bid you good-night."

Then my wife's mother said, "But we have laid your bed in the house, I pray you enter and rest."

And He answered her saying, "I would indeed rest, but not under a roof. Suffer me to lie this night under the canopy of the grapes and the stars."

And she made haste and brought out the mattress and the pillows and the coverings. And He smiled at her and He said, "Behold, I shall lie down upon a bed twice made."

Then we left Him and entered into the house, and my daughter was the last one to enter. And her eyes were upon Him until I had closed the door.

Thus for the first time I knew my Lord and Master.

And though it was many years ago, it still seems but of today.

Caiaphas The High Priest

IN speaking of that man Jesus and of His death let us consider two salient facts: the Torah must needs be held in safety by us, and this kingdom must needs be protected by Rome. Now that man was defiant to us and to Rome. He poisoned the mind of the simple people, and He led them as if by magic against us and against Caesar.

My own slaves, both men and women, after hearing him speak in the market-place, turned sullen and rebellious. Some of them left my house and escaped to the desert whence they came. Forget not that the Torah is our foundation and our tower of strength. No man shall undermine us while we have this power to restrain his hand, and no man shall overthrow Jerusalem so long as its walls stand upon the ancient stone that David laid.

If the seed of Abraham is indeed to live and thrive this soil must remain undefiled.

And that man Jesus was a defiler and a corrupter. We slew Him with a conscience both deliberate and clean. And we shall slay all those who would debase the laws of Moses or seek to befoul our sacred heritage.

We and Pontius Pilatus knew the danger in that man, and that it was wise to bring Him to an end.

I shall see that His followers come to the same end, and the echo of His words to the same silence.

If Judea is to live all men who oppose her must be brought down to the dust. And ere Judea shall die I will cover my gray head with ashes even as did Samuel the prophet, and I will tear off this garment of Aaron and clothe me in sackcloth until I go hence for ever.

Joanna, The Wife Of Herod's Steward:
On Children

JESUS was never married but He was a friend of women, and He knew them as they would be known in sweet comradeship. And He loved children as they would be loved in faith and understanding.

In the light of His eyes there was a father and a brother and a son.

He would hold a child upon His knees and say, "Of such is your might and your freedom; and of such is the kingdom of the spirit."

They say that Jesus heeded not the law of Moses, and that He was over-forgiving to the prostitutes of Jerusalem and the country side.

I myself at that time was deemed a prostitute, for I loved a man who was not my husband, and he was a Sadducee.

And on a day the Sadducees came upon me in my house when my lover was with me, and they seized me and held me, and my lover walked away and left me.

Then they led me to the market-place where Jesus was teaching.

It was their desire to hold me up before Him as a test and a trap for Him.

But Jesus judged me not. He laid shame upon those who would have had me shamed, and He reproached them.

And He bade me go my way.

And after that all the tasteless fruit of life turned sweet to my mouth, and the scentless blossoms breathed fragrance into my nostrils. I became a woman without a tainted memory, and I was free, and my head was no longer bowed down.

Rafca, The Bride Of Cana

THIS happened before he was known to the people.

I was in my mother's garden tending the rose-bushes, when He stopped at our gate.

And He said, "I am thirsty. Will you give me water from your well?"

And I ran and brought the silver cup, and filled it with water; and I poured into it a few drops from the jasmin vial.

And He drank deep and was pleased.

Then He looked into my eyes and said, "My blessing shall be upon you."

When He said that I felt as it were a gust of wind rushing through my body. And I was no longer shy; and I said, "Sir, I am betrothed to a man of Cana in Galilee. And I shall be married on the fourth day of the coming week. Will you not come to my wedding and grace my marriage with your presence?"

And He answered, "I will come, my child."

Mind you, He said, "My child," yet He was but a youth, and I was nearly twenty.

Then He walked on down the road.

And I stood at the gate of our garden until my mother called me into the house.

On the fourth day of the following week I was taken to the house of my bridegroom and given in marriage.

And Jesus came, and with Him His mother and His brother James.

And they sat around the wedding-board with our guests whilst my maiden comrades sang the wedding-songs of Solomon the King. And Jesus ate our food and drank our wine and smiled upon me and upon the others.

And He heeded all the songs of the lover bringing his beloved into his tent; and of the young vineyard-keeper who loved the daughter of the lord of the vineyard and led her to his mother's house; and of the prince who met the beggar maiden and bore her to his realm and crowned her with the crown of his fathers.

And it seemed as if He were listening to yet other songs also, which I could not hear.

At sundown the father of my bridegroom came to the mother of Jesus and whispered saying, "We have no more wine for our guests. And the day is not yet over."

And Jesus heard the whispering, and He said, "The cup bearer knows that there is still more wine."

And so it was indeed – and as long as the guests remained there was fine wine for all who would drink. Presently Jesus began to speak with us. He spoke of the wonders of earth and heaven; of sky flowers that bloom when night is upon the earth, and of earth flowers that blossom when the day hides the stars.

And He told us stories and parables, and His voice enchanted us so that we gazed upon Him as if seeing visions, and we forgot the cup and the plate.

And as I listened to Him it seemed as if I were in a land distant and unknown.

After a while one of the guests said to the father of my bridegroom, "You have kept the best wine till the end of the feast. Other hosts do not so."

And all believed that Jesus had wrought a miracle, that they should have more wine and better at the end of the wedding-feast than at the beginning.

I too thought that Jesus had poured the wine, but I was not astonished; for in His voice I had already listened to miracles.

And afterwards indeed, His voice remained close to my heart, even until I had been delivered of my first-born child.

And now even to this day in our village and in the villages near by, the word of our guest is still remembered. And they say, "The spirit of Jesus of Nazareth is the best and the oldest wine."

A Persian Philosopher In Damascus:
Of Ancient Gods and New

I CANNOT tell the fate of this man, nor can I say what shall befall His disciples. A seed hidden in the heart of an apple is an orchard invisible. Yet should that seed fall upon a rock, it will come to naught.

But this I say: The ancient God of Israel is harsh and relentless. Israel should have another God; one who is gentle and forgiving, who would look down upon them with pity; one who would descend with the rays of the sun and walk on the path of their limitations, rather than sit for ever in the judgment seat to weigh their faults and measure their wrong-doings.

Israel should bring forth a God whose heart is not a jealous heart, and whose memory of their shortcomings is brief; one who would not avenge Himself upon them even to the third and the fourth generation.

Man here in Syria is like man in all lands. He would look into the mirror of his own understanding and therein find his deity. He would fashion the gods after his own likeness, and worship that which reflects his own image.

In truth man prays to his deeper longing, that it may rise and fulfil the sum of his desires.

There is no depth beyond the soul of man, and the soul is the deep that calls unto itself; for there is no other voice to speak and there are no other ears to hear.

Even we in Persia would see our faces in the disc of the sun and our bodies dancing in the fire that we kindle upon the altars.

Now the God of Jesus, whom He called Father, would not be a stranger unto the people of Jesus, and He would fulfil their desires.

The gods of Egypt have cast off their burden of stones and fled to the Nubian desert, to be free among those who are still free from knowing.

The gods of Greece and Rome are vanishing into their own sunset. They were too much like men to live in the ecstasy of men. The groves in which their magic was born have been cut down by the axes of the Athenians and the Alexandrians.

And in this land also the high places are made low by the lawyers of Beirut and the young hermits of Antioch.

Only the old women and the weary men seek the temples of their forefathers; only the exhausted at the end of the road seek its beginning.

But this man Jesus, this Nazarene, He has spoken of a God too vast to be unlike the soul of any man, too knowing to punish, too loving to remember the sins of His creatures. And this God of the Nazarene shall pass over the threshold of the children of the earth, and He shall sit at their hearth, and He shall be a blessing within their walls and a light upon their path.

But my God is the God of Zoroaster, the God who is the sun in the sky and fire upon the earth and light in the bosom of man. And I am content. I need no other God.

David, One Of His Followers:
Jesus the Practical

I DID not know the meaning of His discourses or His parables until He was no longer among us. Nay, I did not understand until His words took living forms before my eyes and fashioned themselves into bodies that walk in the procession of my own day. Let me tell you this: On a night as I sat in my house pondering, and remembering His words and His deeds that I might inscribe them in a book, three thieves entered my house. And though I knew they came to rob me of my goods, I was too mindful of what I was doing to meet them with the sword, or even to say, "What do you here?"

But I continued writing my remembrances of the Master.

And when the thieves had gone then I remembered His saying, "He who would take your cloak, let him take your other cloak also."

And I understood.

As I sat recording His words no man could have stopped me even were he to have carried away all my possessions.

For though I would guard my possessions and also my person, I know there lies the greater treasure.

Luke:
On Hypocrities

JESUS despised and scorned the hypocrites, and His wrath was like a tempest that scourged them. His voice was thunder in their ears and He cowed them. In their fear of Him they sought His death; and like moles in the dark earth they worked to undermine His footsteps. But He fell not into their snares.

He laughed at them, for well He knew that the spirit shall not be mocked, nor shall it be taken in the pitfall.

He held a mirror in His hand and therein He saw the sluggard and the limping and those who stagger and fall by the roadside on the way to the summit.

And He pitied them all. He would even have raised them to His stature and He would have carried their burden. Nay, He would have bid their weakness lean on His strength.

He did not utterly condemn the liar or the thief or the murderer, but He did utterly condemn the hypocrite whose face is masked and whose hand is gloved.

Often I have pondered on the heart that shelters all who come from the wasteland to its sanctuary, yet against the hypocrite is closed and sealed.

On a day as we rested with Him in the Garden of Pomegranates, I said to Him, "Master, you forgive and console the sinner and all the weak and the infirm save only the hypocrite alone."

And He said, "You have chosen your words well when you called the sinners weak and infirm. I do forgive them their weakness of body and their infirmity of spirit

"For their failings have been laid upon them by their forefathers, or by the greed of their neighbours."

"But I tolerate not the hypocrite, because he himself lays a yoke upon the guileless and the yielding.

"Weaklings, whom you call sinners, are like the featherless young that fall from the nest. The hypocrite is the vulture waiting upon a rock for the death of the prey.

"Weaklings are men lost in a desert. But the hypocrite is not lost. He knows the way yet he laughs between the sand and the wind.

"For this cause I do not receive him."

Thus our Master spoke, and I did not understand. But I understand now.

Then the hypocrites of the land laid hands upon Him and they judged Him; and in so doing they deemed themselves justified. For they cited the law of Moses in the Sanhedrim in witness and evidence against Him.

And they who break the law at the rise of every dawn and break it again at sunset, brought about His death.

Matthew:
The Sermon on the Mount

ONE harvest day Jesus called us and His other friends to the hills. The earth was fragrant, and like the daughter of a king at her wedding-feast, she wore all her jewels. And the sky was her bridegroom. When we reached the heights Jesus stood still in the grove of the laurels, and He said, "Rest here, quiet your mind and tune your heart, for I have much to tell you."

Then we reclined on the grass, and the summer flowers were all about us, and Jesus sat in our midst.

And Jesus said:

"Blessed are the serene in spirit.

"Blessed are they who are not held by possessions, for they shall be free.

"Blessed are they who remember their pain, and in their pain await their joy.

"Blessed are they who hunger after truth and beauty, for their hunger shall bring bread, and their thirst cool water.

"Blessed are the kindly, for they shall be consoled by their own kindliness.

"Blessed are the pure in heart, for they shall be one with God.

"Blessed are the merciful, for mercy shall be in their portion.

"Blessed are the peacemakers, for their spirit shall dwell above the battle, and they shall turn the potter's field into a garden.

"Blessed are they who are hunted, for they shall be swift of foot and they shall be winged.

"Rejoice and be joyful, for you have found the kingdom of heaven within you. The singers of old were persecuted when they sang of that kingdom. You too shall be persecuted, and therein lies your honour, therein your reward.

"You are the salt of the earth; should the salt lose its savour wherewith shall the food of man's heart be salted?

"You are the light of the world. Put not that light under a bushel. Let it shine rather from the summit, to those who seek the City of God.

"Think not I came to destroy the laws of the scribes and the Pharisees; for my days among you are numbered and my words are counted, and I have but hours in which to fulfil another law and reveal a new covenant.

"You have been told that you shall not kill, but I say unto you, you shall not be angry without a cause.

"You have been charged by the ancients to bring your calf and your lamb and your dove to the temple, and to slay them upon the altar, that the nostrils of God may feed upon the odour of their fat, and that you may be forgiven your failings.

"But I say unto you, would you give God that which was His own from the beginning; and would you appease Him whose throne is above the silent deep and whose arms encircle space?

"Rather, seek out your brother and be reconciled unto him ere you seek the temple; and be a loving giver unto your neighbour. For in the soul of these God has builded a temple that shall not be destroyed, and in their heart He has raised an altar that shall never perish.

"You have been told, an eye for an eye and a tooth for a tooth. But I say unto you: Resist not evil, for resistance is food unto evil and makes it strong. And only the weak would revenge themselves. The strong of soul forgive, and it is honour in the injured to forgive.

"Only the fruitful tree is shaken or stoned for food.

"Be not heedful of the morrow, but rather gaze upon today, for sufficient for today is the miracle thereof.

"Be not over-mindful of yourself when you give but be mindful of the necessity. For every giver himself receives from the Father, and that much more abundantly.

"And give to each according to his need; for the Father gives not salt to the thirsty, nor a stone to the hungry, nor milk to the weaned.

"And give not that which is holy to dogs; nor cast your pearls before swine. For with such gifts you mock them; and they also shall mock your gift, and in their hate would fain destroy you.

"Lay not up for yourselves treasures that corrupt or that thieves may steal away. Lay up rather treasure which shall not corrupt or be stolen, and whose loveliness increases when many eyes behold it. For where your treasure is, your heart is also.

"You have been told that the murderer shall be put to the sword, that the thief shall be crucified, and the harlot stoned. But I say unto you that you are not free from wrongdoing of the murderer and the thief and the harlot, and when they are punished in the body your own spirit is darkened.

"Verily no crime is committed by one man or one woman. All crimes are committed by all. And he who pays the penalty may be breaking a link in the chain that hangs upon your own ankles. Perhaps he is paying with his sorrow the price for your passing joy."

Thus spoke Jesus, and it was in my desire to kneel down and worship Him, yet in my shyness I could not move nor speak a word.

But at last I spoke; and I said, "I would pray this moment, yet my tongue is heavy. Teach me to pray."

And Jesus said, "When you would pray, let your longing pronounce the words. It is in my longing now to pray thus:

"Our Father in earth and heaven, sacred is Thy name.

Thy will be done with us, even as in space.

Give us of Thy bread sufficient for the day.

In Thy compassion forgive us and enlarge us to forgive one another.

Guide us towards Thee and stretch down Thy hand to us in darkness.

For Thine is the kingdom, and in Thee is our power and our fulfilment."

And it was now evening, and Jesus walked down from the hills, and all of us followed Him. And as I followed I was repeating His prayer, and remembering all that He had said; for I knew that the words that had fallen like flakes that day must set and grow firm like crystals, and that wings that had fluttered above our heads were to beat the earth like iron hoofs.

John, The Son Of Zebedee:
On the Various Appellations of Jesus

YOU have remarked that some of us call Jesus *the Christ*, and some *the Word*, and others call Him the *Nazarene*, and still others the *Son of Man*. I will try to make these names clear in the light that is given me.

The Christ, He who was in the ancient of days, is the flame of God that dwells in the spirit of man. He is the breath of life that visits us, and takes unto Himself a body like our bodies.

He is the will of the Lord.

He is the first Word, which would speak with our voice and live in our ear that we may heed and understand.

And the Word of the Lord our God builded a house of flesh and bones, and was man like unto you and myself.

For we could not hear the song of the bodiless wind nor see our greater self walking in the mist.

Many times the Christ has come to the world, and He has walked many lands. And always He has been deemed a stranger and a madman.

Yet the sound of His voice descended never to emptiness, for the memory of man keeps that which his mind takes no care to keep.

This is the Christ, the innermost and the height, who walks with man towards eternity.

Have you not heard of Him at the cross-roads of India?

And in the land of the Magi, and upon the sands of Egypt.

And here in your North Country your bards of old sang of Prometheus, the fire-bringer, he who was the desire of man fulfiled, the caged hope made free; and Orpheus, who came with a voice and a lyre to quicken the spirit in beast and man.

And know you not of Mithra the king, and of Zoroaster the prophet of the Persians, who woke from man's ancient sleep and stood at the bed of our dreaming?

We ourselves become man anointed when we meet in the Temple Invisible, once every thousand years. Then comes one forth, embodied and at His coming our silence turns to singing.

Yet our ears turn not always to listening nor our eyes to seeing.

Jesus the Nazarene was born and reared like ourselves; His mother and father were like our parents, and He was a man.

But the Christ, the Word, who was in the beginning, the Spirit who would have us live our fuller life, came unto Jesus and was with Him.

And the Spirit was the versed hand of the Lord, and Jesus was the harp.

The Spirit was the psalm, and Jesus was the turn thereof.

And Jesus, the Man of Nazareth, was the host and the mouthpiece of the Christ, who walked with us in the sun and who called us His friends.

In those days the hills of Galilee and her valleys heard but His voice. And I was a youth then, and trod in His path and pursued His footprints.

I pursued His footprints and trod in His path, to hear the words of the Christ from the lips of Jesus of Galilee.

Now you would know why some of us call Him the Son of Man.

He Himself desired to be called by that name, for He knew the hunger and the thirst of man, and He beheld man seeking after His greater self.

The Son of Man was Christ the Gracious, who would be with us all.

He was Jesus the Nazarene who would lead His brothers to the Anointed One, even to the Word which was in the beginning with God.

In my heart dwells Jesus of Galilee, the Man above men, the Poet who makes poets of us all, the Spirit who knocks at our door that we may wake and rise and walk out to meet truth naked and unencumbered

A Young Priest Of Capernaum:
Of Jesus the Magician

HE was a magician, warp and woof, and a sorcerer, a man who bewildered the simple by charms and incantations. And He juggled with the words of our prophets and with the sanctities of our forefathers. Aye, He even bade the dead be His witnesses, and the voiceless graves His forerunners and authority.

He sought the women of Jerusalem and the women of the countryside with the cunning of the spider that seeks the fly; and they were caught in His web.

For women are weak and empty-headed, and they follow the man who would comfort their unspent passion with soft and tender words. Were it not for these women, infirm and possessed by His evil spirit, His name would have been erased from the memory of man.

And who were the men who followed Him?

They were of the horde that are yoked and trodden down. In their ignorance and fear they would never have rebelled against their rightful masters. But when He promised them high stations in His kingdom of mirage, they yielded to His fantasy as clay to the potter.

Know you not, the slave in his dreaming would always be master; and the weakling would be a lion?

The Galilean was a conjuror and a deceiver, a man who forgave the sins of all sinners that He might hear Hail and Hosanna from their unclean mouths; and who fed the faint heart of the hopeless and the wretched that He might have ears for His voice and a retinue at His command.

He broke the sabbath with those who break that He might gain the support of the lawless; and He spoke ill of our high priests that He might win attention in Sanhedrim, and by opposition increase His fame.

I have said often that I hated that man. Aye, I hate Him more than I hate the Romans who govern our country. Even His

coming was from Nazareth, a town cursed by our prophets, a dunghill of the Gentiles, from which no good shall ever proceed.

A Rich Levite In The Neighbourhood Of Nazareth
Jesus the Good Carpenter

HE was a good carpenter. The doors He fashioned were never unlocked by thieves, and the windows he made were always ready to open to the east wind and to the west.

And He made chests of cedar wood, polished and enduring, and ploughs and pitchforks strong and yielding to the hand.

And He carved lecterns for our synagogues. He carved them out of the golden mulberry; and on both sides of the support, where the sacred book lies, He chiselled wings outspreading; and under the support, heads of bulls and doves, and large-eyed deer.

All this He wrought in the manner of the Chaldeans and the Greeks. But there was that in His skill which was neither Chaldean nor Greek.

Now this my house was builded by many hands thirty years ago. I sought builders and carpenters in all the towns of Galilee. They had each the skill and the art of building, and I was pleased and satisfied with all that they did.

But come now, and behold two doors and a window that were fashioned by Jesus of Nazareth. They in their stability mock at all else in my house.

See you not that these two doors are different from all other doors? And this window opening to the east, is it not different from other windows?

All my doors and windows are yielding to the years save these which He made. They alone stand strong against the elements.

And see those cross-beams, how he placed them; and these nails, how they are driven from one side of the board, and then caught and fastened so firmly upon the other side.

And what is passing strange is that that labourer who was worthy the wages of two men received but the wage of one man; and that same labourer now is deemed a prophet in Israel.

Had I known then that this youth with saw and plane was a prophet, I would have begged Him to speak rather than work, and then I would have overpaid Him for his words.

And now I still have many men working in my house and fields. How shall I know the man whose own hand is upon his tool, from the man upon whose hand God lays His hand?

Yea, how shall I know God's hand?

A Shepherd In South Lebanon:
A Parable

IT was late summer when He and three other men first walked upon that road yonder. It was evening, and He stopped and stood there at the end of the pasture. I was playing upon my flute, and my flock was grazing all around me. When He stopped I rose and walked over and stood before Him.

And He asked me, "Where is the grave of Elijah? Is it not somewhere near this place?"

And I answered Him, "It is there, Sir, underneath that great heap of stones. Even unto this day every passerby brings a stone and places it upon the heap."

And He thanked me and walked away, and His friends walked behind Him.

And after three days Ganaliel who was also a shepherd, said to me that the man who had passed by was a prophet in Judea; but I did not believe him. Yet I thought of that man for many a moon.

When spring came Jesus passed once more by this pasture, and this time He was alone.

I was not playing on my flute that day for I had lost a sheep and I was bereaved, and my heart was downcast within me.

And I walked towards Him and stood still before Him, for I desired to be comforted.

And He looked at me and said, "You do not play upon your flute this day. Whence is the sorrow in your eyes?"

And I answered, "A sheep from among my sheep is lost. I have sought her everywhere but I find her not. And I know not what to do."

And He was silent for a moment. Then He smiled upon me and said, "Wait here awhile and I will find your sheep." And He walked away and disappeared among the hills.

After an hour He returned, and my sheep was close behind Him. And as He stood before me, the sheep looked up into His face even as I was looking. Then I embraced her in gladness.

And He put His hand upon my shoulder and said, "From this day you shall love this sheep more than any other in your flock, for she was lost and now she is found."

And again I embraced my sheep in gladness, and she came close to me, and I was silent.

But when I raised my head to thank Jesus, He was already walking afar off, and I had not the courage to follow Him.

John the Baptist:
He Speaks in Prison to His Disciples

I AM not silent in this foul hole while the voice of Jesus is heard on the battlefield. I am not to be held nor confined while He is free. They tell me the vipers are coiling round His loins, but I answer: The vipers shall awaken His strength, and He shall crush them with His heel.

I am only the thunder of His lightning. Though I spoke first, His was the word and the purpose.

They caught me unwarned. Perhaps they will lay hands on Him also. Yet not before He has pronounced His word in full. And He shall overcome them.

His chariot shall pass over them, and the hoofs of His horses shall trample them, and He shall be triumphant.

They shall go forth with lance and sword, but He shall meet them with the power of the Spirit.

His blood shall run upon the earth, but they themselves shall know the wounds and the pain thereof, and they shall be baptised in their tears until they are cleansed of their sins.

Their legions shall march towards His cities with rams of iron, but on their way they shall be drowned in the River Jordan.

And His walls and His towers shall rise higher, and the shields of His warriors shall shine brighter in the sun.

They say I am in league with Him, and that our design is to urge the people to rise and revolt against the kingdom of Judea.

I answer, and would that I had flames for words: if they deem this pit of iniquity a kingdom, let it fall into destruction and be no more. Let it go the way Sodom and Gomorrah, and let this race be forgotten by God, and this land be turned to ashes.

Aye, behind these prison walls I am indeed an ally to Jesus of Nazareth, and He shall lead my armies, horse and foot. And I myself, though a captain, am not worthy to loose the strings of His sandals.

Go to Him and repeat my words, and then in my name beg Him for comfort and blessing.

I shall not be here long. At night, 'twixt waking and waking I feel slow feet with measured steps treading above this body. And when I hearken, I hear the rain falling upon my grave.

Go to Jesus, and say that John of Kedron, whose soul is filled with shadows and then emptied again, prays for Him, while the grave-digger stands close by, and the swordman outstretches his hand for his wages.

Joseph of Arimathea:
On the Primal Aims of Jesus

YOU would know the primal aim of Jesus, and I would fain tell you. But none can touch with fingers the life of the blessed wine, nor see the sap that feeds the branches. And though I have eaten of the grapes and have tasted the new vintage at the winepress, I cannot tell you all.

I can only relate what I know of Him.

Our Master and our Beloved lived but three prophet's seasons. They were the spring of His song, the summer of His ecstasy, and the autumn of His passion; and each season was a thousand years.

The spring of His song was spent in Galilee. It was there that He gathered His lovers about Him, and it was on the shores of the blue lake that He first spoke of the Father, and of our release and our freedom.

By the Lake of Galilee we lost ourselves to find our way to the Father; and oh, the little loss that turned to such gain.

It was there the angels sang in our ears and bade us leave the arid land for the garden of heart's desire.

He spoke of fields and green pastures; of the slopes of Lebanon where the white lilies are heedless of the caravans passing in the dust of the valley.

He spoke of the wild brier that smiles in the sun and yields its incense to the passing breeze.

And He would say, "The lilies and the brier live but a day, yet that day is eternity spent in freedom."

And one evening as we sat beside the stream He said, "Behold the brook and listen to its music. Forever shall it seek the sea, and though it is for ever seeking, it sings its mystery from noon to noon.

"Would that you seek the Father as the brook seeks the sea."

Then came the summer of His ecstasy, and the June of His love was upon us. He spoke of naught then but the other man – the neighbour, the road-fellow, the stranger, and our childhood's playmates.

He spoke of the traveller journeying from the east to Egypt, of the ploughman coming home with his oxen at eventide, of the chance guest led by dusk to our door.

And He would say, "Your neighbour is your unknown self made visible. His face shall be reflected in your still waters, and if you gaze therein you shall behold your own countenance.

"Should you listen in the night, you shall hear him speak, and his words shall be the throbbing of your own heart.

"Be unto him that which you would have him be unto you.

"This is my law, and I shall say it unto you, and unto your children, and they unto their children until time is spent and generations are no more."

And on another day He said, "You shall not be yourself alone. You are in the deeds of other men, and they, though unknowing, are with you all your days.

"They shall not commit a crime and your hand not be with their hand.

"They shall not fall down but that you shall also fall down; and they shall not rise but that you shall rise with them.

"Their road to the sanctuary is your road, and when they seek the wasteland you too seek with them.

"You and your neighbour are two seeds sown in the field. Together you grow and together you shall sway in the wind. And neither of you shall claim the field. For a seed on its way to growth claims not even its own ecstasy.

"Today I am with you. tomorrow I go westward; but ere I go, I say unto you that your neighbour is your unknown self made visible. Seek him in love that you may know yourself, for only in that knowledge shall you become my brothers."

Then came the autumn of His passion.

And He spoke to us of freedom, even as He had spoken in Galilee in the spring of His song; but now His words sought our deeper understanding.

He spoke of leaves that sing only when blown upon the wind; and of man as a cup filled by the ministering angel of the day to quench the thirst of another angel. Yet whether that cup is full or empty it shall stand crystalline upon the board of the Most High.

He said, "You are the cup and you are the wine. Drink yourselves to the dregs; or else remember me and you shall be quenched."

And on our way to the southward He said, "Jerusalem, which stands in pride upon the height, shall descend to the depth of Jahannum the dark valley, and in the midst of her desolation I shall stand alone.

"The temple shall fall to dust, and around the portico you shall hear the cry of widows and orphans; and men in their haste to escape shall not know the faces of their brothers, for fear shall be upon them all.

"But even there, if two of you shall meet and utter my name and look to the west, you shall see me, and these my words shall again visit your ears."

And when we reached the hill of Bethany, He said, "Let us go to Jerusalem. The city awaits us. I will enter the gate riding upon a colt, and I will speak to the multitude.

"Many are there who would chain me, and many who would put out my flame, but in my death you shall find life and you shall be free.

"They shall seek the breath that hovers betwixt heart and mind as the swallow hovers between the field and his nest. But my breath has already escaped them, and they shall not overcome me.

"The walls that my Father has built around me shall not fall down, and the acre He has made holy shall not be profaned.

"When the dawn shall come, the sun will crown my head and I shall be with you to face the day. And that day shall be long, and the world shall not see its eventide.

"The scribes and the Pharisees say the earth is thirsty for my blood. I would quench the thirst of the earth with my blood. But the drops shall rise oak trees and maple, and the east shall carry the acorns to other lands."

And then He said, "Judea would have a king, and she would march against the legions of Rome.

"I shall not be her king. The diadems of Zion were fashioned for lesser brows. And the ring of Solomon is small for this finger.

"Behold my hand. See you not that it is over-strong to hold a sceptre, and over-sinewed to wield a common sword?

"Nay, I shall not command Syrian flesh against Roman. But you with my words shall wake that city, and my spirit shall speak to her second dawn.

"My words shall be an invisible army with horses and chariots, and without axe or spear I shall conquer the priests of Jerusalem, and the Caesars.

"I shall not sit upon a throne where slaves have sat and ruled other slaves. Nor will I rebel against the sons of Italy.

"But I shall be a tempest in their sky, and a song in their soul.

"And I shall be remembered.

"They shall call me Jesus the Anointed."

These things He said outside the walls of Jerusalem before He entered the city.

And His words are graven as with chisels.

Nathaniel:
Jesus was not Meek

THEY say that Jesus of Nazareth was humble and meek. They say that though He was a just man and righteous, He was a weakling, and was often confounded by the strong and the powerful; and that when He stood before men of authority He was but a lamb among lions.

But I say Jesus had authority over men, and that He knew His power and proclaimed it among the hills of Galilee, and in the cities of Judea and Phoenicia.

What man yielding and soft would say, "I am life, and I am the way to truth?"

What man meek and lowly would say, "I am in God, our Father; and our God, the Father, is in me?"

What man unmindful of His own strength would say, "He who believes not in me believes not in this life nor in the life everlasting?"

What man uncertain of tomorrow would proclaim, "Your world shall pass away and be naught but scattered ashes ere my words shall pass away?"

Was He doubtful of Himself when He said to those who would confound Him with a harlot, "He who is without sin, let him cast a stone?"

Did He fear authority when He drove the money-changers from the court of the temple, though they were licensed by the priests?

Were His wings shorn when He cried aloud, "My kingdom is above your earthly kingdoms?"

Was He seeking shelter in words when He repeated again and yet again, "Destroy this temple and I will rebuild it in three days?"

Was it a coward who shook His hand in the face of the authorities and pronounced them "liars, low, filthy, and degenerate?"

Shall a man bold enough to say these things to those who ruled Judea be deemed meek and humble?

Nay. The eagle builds not his nest in the weeping willow. And the lion seeks not his den among the ferns.

I am sickened and the bowels within me stir and rise when I hear the faint-hearted call Jesus humble and meek, that they may justify their own faint-heartedness; and when the downtrodden, for comfort and companionship, speak of Jesus as a worm shining by their side.

Yea, my heart is sickened by such men. It is the mighty hunter I would preach, and the mountainous spirit unconquerable.

Saba of Antioch:
On Saul of Tarsus

THIS day I heard Saul of Tarsus preaching the Christ unto the Jews of this city. He calls himself Paul now, the apostle to the Gentiles.

I knew him in my youth, and in those days he persecuted the friends of the Nazarene. Well do I remember his satisfaction when his fellows stoned the radiant youth called Stephen.

This Paul is indeed a strange man. His soul is not the soul of a free man.

At times he seems like an animal in the forest, hunted and wounded, seeking a cave wherein he would hide his pain from the world.

He speaks not of Jesus, nor does he repeat His words. He preaches the Messiah whom the prophets of old had foretold.

And though he himself is a learned Jew he addresses his fellow Jews in Greek; and his Greek is halting, and he ill chooses his words.

But he is a man of hidden powers and his presence is affirmed by those who gather around him. And at times he assures them of what he himself is not assured.

We who knew Jesus and heard his discourses say that He taught man how to break the chains of his bondage that he might be free from his yesterdays.

But Paul is forging chains for the man of tomorrow. He would strike with his own hammer upon the anvil in the name of one whom he does not know.

The Nazarene would have us live the hour in passion and ecstasy.

The man of Tarsus would have us be mindful of laws recorded in the ancient books.

Jesus gave His breath to the breathless dead. And in my lone nights I believe and I understand.

When He sat at the board, He told stories that gave happiness to the feasters, and spiced with His joy the meat and the wine.

But Paul would prescribe our loaf and our cup. Suffer me not to turn my eyes the other way.

Salome, To A Woman Friend:
A Desire Unfulfilled

HE was like poplars shimmering in the sun;
And like a lake among the lonely hills,
Shining in the sun.
And like snow upon the mountain heights,
White, white in the sun.

Yea, He was like unto all these,
And I loved Him. Yet I feared His presence.

And my feet would not carry my burden of love
That I might girdle His feet with my arms.

I would have said to Him,
"I have slain your friend in an hour of passion.
Will you forgive me my sin?
And will you not in mercy release my youth
From its blind deed,
That it may walk in your light?"

I know He would have forgiven my dancing
For the saintly head of His friend.
I know He would have seen in me
An object of His own teaching.
For there was no valley of hunger He could not bridge.
And no desert of thirst He could not cross.

Yea, He was even as the poplars.
And as the lakes among the hills.
And like snow upon Lebanon.
And I would have cooled my lips in the folds of His garment.

But He was far from me.
And I was ashamed.
And my mother held me back
When the desire to seek Him was upon me.

Whenever He passed by, my heart ached for his loveliness.
But my mother frowned at Him in contempt,
And would hasten me from the window
To my bedchamber.
And she would cry aloud saying:
"Who is He but another locust-eater from the desert?

"What is He but a scoffer and a renegade,
A seditious riot-monger, who would rob us of sceptre and
crown, And bid the foxes and the jackals of His accursed land

Howl in our halls and sit upon our throne?
Go hide your face from this day,
And await the day when His head shall fall down,
But not upon your platter."

These things my mother said.
But my heart would not keep her words.
I loved Him in secret,
And my sleep was girdled with flames.

He is gone now.
And something that was in me is gone also.
Perhaps it was my youth
That would not tarry here,
Since the God of youth was slain.

Rachael, A Woman Disciple:
On Jesus the Vision and the Man

I OFTEN wonder whether Jesus was a man of flesh and blood like ourselves, or a thought without a body, in the mind, or an idea that visits the vision of man.

Often it seems to me that He was but a dream dreamed by the countless men and women at the same time in a sleep deeper than sleep and a dawn more serene than all dawns.

And it seems that in relating the dream, the one to the other, we began to deem it a reality that had indeed come to pass; and in giving it body of our fancy and a voice of our longing we made it a substance of our own substance.

But in truth He was not a dream. We knew Him for three years and beheld Him with our open eyes in the high tide of noon.

We touched His hands, and we followed Him from one place to another. We heard His discourses and witnessed His deeds.

Think you that we were a thought seeking after more thought, or a dream in the region of dreams?

Great events always seem alien to our daily lives, though their nature may be rooted in our nature. But though they appear sudden in their coming and sudden in their passing, their true span is for years and for generations.

Jesus of Nazareth was Himself the Great Event. That man whose father and mother and brothers we know, was Himself a miracle wrought in Judea. Yea, all His own miracles, if placed at His feet, would not rise to the height of His ankles.

And all the rivers of all the years shall not carry away our remembrance of Him.

He was a mountain burning in the night, yet He was a soft glow beyond the hills. He was a tempest in the sky, yet He was a murmur in the mist of daybreak.

He was a torrent pouring from the heights to the plains to destroy all things in its path. And He was like the laughter of children.

Every year I had waited for spring to visit this valley. I had waited for the lilies and the cyclamen, and then every year my soul had been saddened within me; for ever I longed to rejoice with the spring, yet I could not.

But when Jesus came to my seasons He was indeed a spring, and in Him was the promise of all the years to come. He filled my heart with joy; and like the violets I grew, a shy thing, in the light of His coming.

And now the changing seasons of worlds not yet ours shall not erase His loveliness from this our world.

Nay, Jesus was not a phantom, nor a conception of the poets. He was man like yourself and myself. But only to sight and touch and hearing; in all other ways He was unlike us.

He was a man of joy; and it was upon the path of joy that He met the sorrows of all men. And it was from the high roofs of His sorrows that He beheld the joy of all men.

He saw visions that we did not see, and heard voices that we did not hear; and He spoke as if to invisible multitudes, and ofttimes He spoke through us to races yet unborn.

And Jesus was often alone. He was among us yet not one with us. He was upon the earth, yet He was of the sky. And only in our aloneness may we visit the land of His aloneness.

He loved us with tender love. His heart was a winepress. You and I could approach with a cup and drink therefrom.

One thing I did not use to understand in Jesus: He would make merry with His listeners; He would tell jests and play upon words, and laugh with all the fullness of His heart, even when there were distances in His eyes and sadness in His voice. But I understand now.

I often think of the earth as a woman heavy with her first child. When Jesus was born, He was the first child. And when He died, He was the first man to die.

For did it not appear to you that the earth was stilled on that dark Friday, and the heavens were at war with the heavens?

And felt you not when His face disappeared from our sight as if we were naught but memories in the mist?

Cleopas of Bethroune:
On the Law and the Prophets

WHEN Jesus spoke the whole world was hushed to listen. His words were not for our ears but rather for the elements of which God made this earth.

He spoke to the sea, our vast mother, that gave us birth. He spoke to the mountain, our elder brother whose summit is a promise.

And He spoke to the angels beyond the sea and the mountain to whom we entrusted our dreams ere the clay in us was made hard in the sun.

And still His speech slumbers within our breast like a love-song half forgotten, and sometimes it burns itself through to our memory.

His speech was simple and joyous, and the sound of His voice was like cool water in a land of drought.

Once He raised His hand against the sky, and His fingers were like the branches of a sycamore tree; and He said with a great voice:

"The prophets of old have spoken to you, and your ears are filled with their speech. But I say unto you, empty your ears of what you have heard."

And these words of Jesus, "But I say unto you," were not uttered by a man of our race nor of our world; but rather by a host of seraphim marching across the sky of Judea.

Again and yet again He would quote the law and the prophets, and then he would say, "But I say unto you."

Oh, what burning words, what waves of seas unknown to the shores of our mind, "But I say unto you."

What stars seeking the darkness of the soul, and what sleepless souls awaiting the dawn.

To tell of the speech of Jesus one must needs know of His speech or the echo thereof.

I have neither the speech nor the echo.

I beg you to forgive me for beginning a story that I cannot end. But the end is not yet upon my lips. It is still a love song in the wind

Naaman of the Gadarenes:
On the Death of Stephen

HIS disciples are dispersed. He gave them the legacy of pain ere He Himself was put to death. They are hunted like the deer, and the foxes of the fields, and the quiver of the hunter is yet full of arrows. But when they are caught and led to death, they are joyous, and their faces shine like the face of the bridegroom at the wedding-feast. For He gave them also the legacy of joy.

I had a friend from the North Country, and his name was Stephen; and because he proclaimed Jesus as the Son of God, he was led to the market-place and stoned.

And when Stephen fell to earth he outstretched his arms as if he would die as his Master had died. His arms were spread like wings ready for flight. And when the last gleam of light was fading in his eyes, with my own eyes I saw a smile upon his lips. It was a smile like the breath that comes before the end of winter for a pledge and a promise of spring.

How shall I describe it?

It seemed that Stephen was saying, "If I should go to another world, and other men should lead me to another market-place to stone me, even then I would proclaim Him for the truth which was in Him, and for that same truth which is in me now."

And I noticed that there was a man standing near, and looking with pleasure upon the stoning of Stephen.

His name was Saul of Tarsus, and it was he who had yielded Stephen to the priests and the Romans and the crowd, for stoning.

Saul was bald of head and short of stature. His shoulders were crooked and his features ill-sorted; and I liked him not.

I have been told that he is now preaching Jesus from the house tops. It is hard to believe.

But the grave halts not Jesus' walking to the enemies' camp to tame and take captive those who had opposed Him.

Still I do not like that man of Tarsus, though I have been told that after Stephen's death he was tamed and conquered on the road to Damascus. But his head is too large for his heart to be that of a true disciple.

And yet perhaps I am mistaken. I am often mistaken.

Thomas:
On the Forefathers of His Doubts

MY grandfather who was a lawyer once said, "Let us observe truth, but only when truth is made manifest unto us."

When Jesus called me I heeded Him, for His command was more potent than my will; yet I kept my counsel.

When He spoke and the others were swayed like branches in the wind, I listened immovable. Yet I loved Him.

Three years ago He left us, a scattered company to sing His name, and to be His witnesses unto the nations.

At that time I was called Thomas the Doubter. The shadow of my grandfather was still upon me, and always I would have truth made manifest.

I would even put my hand in my own wound to feel the blood ere I would believe in my pain.

Now a man who loves with his heart yet holds a doubt in his mind, is but a slave in a galley who sleeps at his oar and dreams of his freedom, till the lash of the master wakes him.

I myself was that slave, and I dreamed of freedom, but the sleep of my grandfather was upon me. My flesh needed the whip of my own day.

Even in the presence of the Nazarene I had closed my eyes to see my hands chained to the oar.

Doubt is a pain too lonely to know that faith is his twin brother.

Doubt is a foundling unhappy and astray, and though his own mother who gave him birth should find him and enfold him, he would withdraw in caution and in fear.

For Doubt will not know truth till his wounds are healed and restored.

I doubted Jesus until He made Himself manifest to me, and thrust my own hand into His very wounds.

Then indeed I believed, and after that I was rid of my yesterday and the yesterdays of my forefathers.

The dead in me buried their dead; and the living shall live for the Anointed King, even for Him who was the Son of Man.

Yesterday they told me that I must go and utter His name among the Persians and the Hindus.

I shall go. And from this day to my last day, at dawn and at eventide, I shall see my Lord rising in majesty and I shall hear Him speak.

Elmadam The Logician:
Jesus the Outcast

YOU bid me speak of Jesus the Nazarene, and much have I to tell, but the time has not come. Yet whatever I say of Him now is the truth; for all speech is worthless save when it discloses the truth.

Behold a man disorderly, against all order; a mendicant, opposed to all possessions; a drunkard who would only make merry with rogues and castaways.

He was not the proud son of the State, nor was He the protected citizen of the Empire; therefore He had contempt for both State and Empire.

He would live as free and dutiless as the fowls of the air, and for this the hunters brought Him to earth with arrows.

No man shall ram the towers of yesterday and escape the falling stones.

No one shall open the flood gates of his ancestors without

drowning. It is the law. And because the Nazarene broke the law, He and His witless followers were brought to naught.

And there lived many others like Him, men who would change the course of our destiny.

They themselves were changed, and they were the losers.

There is a grapeless vine that grows by the city walls. It creeps upward and clings to the stones. Should that vine say in her heart, "With my might and my weight I shall destroy these walls." what would other plants say? Surely they would laugh at her foolishness.

Now sir, I cannot but laugh at this man and His ill-advised disciples.

One of the Marys:
On His Sadness and His Smile

HIS head was always high, and the flame of God was in His eyes.

He was often sad, but His sadness was tenderness shown to those in pain, and comradeship given to the lonely.

When He smiled His smile was as the hunger of those who long after the unknown. It was like the dust of stars falling upon the eyelids of children. And it was like a morsel of bread in the throat.

He was sad, yet it was a sadness that would rise to the lips and become a smile.

It was like a golden veil in the forest when autumn is upon the world. And sometimes it seemed like moonlight upon the shores of the lake.

He smiled as if His lips would sing at the wedding-feast. Yet He was sad with the sadness of the winged who will not soar above his comrade

Rumanous a Greek poet:
Jesus the Poet

HE was a poet. He saw for our eyes and heard for our ears, and our silent words were upon His lips; and His fingers touched what we could not feel.

Out of His heart there flew countless singing birds to the north and to the south, and the little flowers on the hill-sides stayed His steps towards the heavens.

Oftentimes I have seen Him bending down to touch the blades of grass. And in my heart I have heard Him say: "Little green things, you shall be with me in my kingdom, even as the oaks of Besan, and the cedars of Lebanon." He loved all things of loveliness, the shy faces of children, and the myrrh and frankincense from the south.

He loved a pomegranate or a cup of wine given Him in kindness; it mattered not whether it was offered by a stranger in the inn or by a rich host.

And He loved the almond blossoms. I have seen Him gathering them into His hands and covering His face with the petals, as though He would embrace with His love all the trees in the world.

He knew the sea and the heavens; and He spoke of pearls which have light that is not of this light, and of stars that are beyond our night.

He knew the mountains as eagles know them, and the valleys as they are known by the brooks and the streams. And there was a desert in His silence and a garden in His speech.

Aye, He was a poet whose heart dwelt in a bower beyond the heights, and His songs though sung for our ears, were sung for other ears also, and to men in another land where life is for ever young and time is always dawn.

Once I too deemed myself a poet, but when I stood before Him in Bethany, I knew what it is to hold an instrument with but a single string before one who commands all instruments. For in His voice there was the laughter of thunder and the tears of rain, and the joyous dancing of trees in the wind.

And since I have known that my lyre has but one string, and that my voice weaves neither the memories of yesterday nor the hopes of tomorrow, I have put aside my lyre and I shall keep silence. But always at twilight I shall hearken, and I shall listen to the Poet who is the sovereign of all poets.

Levi, a Disciple:
On Those who would Confound Jesus

UPON an eventide He passed by my house, and my soul was quickened within me.

He spoke to me and said, "Come, Levi, and follow me."

And I followed Him that day.

And at eventide of the next day I begged Him to enter my house and be my guest. And He and His friends crossed my threshold and blessed me and my wife and my children.

And I had other guests. They were publicans and men of learning, but they were against Him in their hearts.

And when we were sitting about the board, one of the publicans questioned Jesus, saying, "Is it true that you and your disciples break the law, and make fire on the sabbath day?"

And Jesus answered him saying, "We do indeed make fire on the sabbath day. We would inflame the sabbath day, and we would burn with our touch the dry stubble of all days."

And another publican said, "It was brought to us that you drink wine with the unclean at the inn."

And Jesus answered, “Aye, these also we would comfort. Came we here except to share the loaf and the cup with the uncrowned and the unshod amongst you?

“Few, aye too few are the featherless who dare the wind, and many are the winged and fullfledged yet in the nest. “

And we would feed them all with our beak, both the sluggish and the swift.”

And another publican said, “Have I not been told that you would protect the harlots of Jerusalem?”

Then in the face of Jesus I saw, as it were, the rocky heights of Lebanon, and He said, “It is true.

“On the day of reckoning these women shall rise before the throne of my Father, and they shall be made pure by their own tears. But you shall be held down by the chains of your own judgment.

“Babylon was not put to waste by her prostitutes; Babylon fell to ashes that the eyes of her hypocrites might no longer see the light of day.”

And other publicans would have questioned Him, but I made a sign and bade them be silent, for I knew He would confound them; and they too were my guests, and I would not have them put to shame.

When it was midnight the publicans left my house, and their souls were limping.

Then I closed my eyes and I saw, as if in a vision, seven women in white raiment standing about Jesus. Their arms were crossed upon their bosoms, and their heads were bent down, and I looked deep into the mist of my dream and beheld the face of one of the seven women, and it shone in my darkness.

It was the face of a harlot who lived in Jerusalem.

Then I opened my eyes and looked at Him, and He was smiling at me and at the others who had not left the board.

And I closed my eyes again, and I saw in a light seven men in white garments standing around Him. And I beheld the face of one of them.

It was the face of the thief who was crucified afterward at His right hand.

And later Jesus and His comrades left my house for the road.

A Widow In Galilee:
Jesus the Cruel

MY son was my first and my only born. He laboured in our field and he was contented until he heard the man called Jesus speaking to the multitude.

Then my son suddenly became different, as if a new spirit, foreign and unwholesome, had embraced his spirit.

He abandoned the field and the garden; and he abandoned me also. He became worthless, a creature of the highways.

That man Jesus of Nazareth was evil, for what good man would separate a son from his mother?

The last thing my child said to me was this: "I am going with one of His disciples to the North Country. My life is established upon the Nazarene. You have given me birth, and for that I am grateful to you. But I needs must go. Am I not leaving with you our rich land, and all our silver and gold? I shall take naught but this garment and this staff."

Thus my son spoke, and departed.

And now the Romans and the priests have laid hold upon Jesus and crucified Him; and they have done well.

A man who would part mother and son could not be godly.

The man who sends our children to the cities of the Gentiles cannot be our friend.

I know my son will not return to me. I saw it in his eyes. And for this I hate Jesus of Nazareth who caused me to be alone in this unploughed field and this withered garden.

And I hate all those who praise Him.

Not many days ago they told me that Jesus once said, "My father and my mother and my brethren are those who hear my word and follow me."

But why should sons leave their mothers to follow His footsteps?

And why should the milk of my breast be forgotten for a fountain not yet tasted? And the warmth of my arms be forsaken for the Northland, cold and unfriendly?

Aye, I hate the Nazarene, and I shall hate Him to the end of my days, for He has robbed me of my first-born, my only son.

Judas The Cousin Of Jesus:
On the Death of John the Baptist

UPON a night in the month of August we were with the Master on a heath not far from the lake. The heath was called by the ancients the Meadow of Skulls.

And Jesus was reclining on the grass and gazing at the stars.

And of a sudden two men came rushing towards us breathless. They were as if in agony, and they fell prostrate at the feet of Jesus.

And Jesus stood up and He said, "Whence came you?"

And one of the men answered, "From Machaereus."

And Jesus looked upon him and was troubled, and He said, "What of John?"

And the man said, "He was slain this day. He was beheaded in his prison cell."

Then Jesus lifted up His head. And then He walked a little way from us. After a while He stood again in our midst.

And He said, "The king could have slain the prophet ere this day. Verily the king has tried the pleasure of His subjects. Kings of yore were not so slow in giving the head of a prophet to the head-hunters.

"I grieve not for John, but rather for Herod, who let fall the sword. Poor king, like an animal caught and led with a ring and a rope.

"Poor petty tetrarchs lost in their own darkness, they stumble and fall down. And what could you of the stagnant sea but dead fishes?"

"I hate not kings. Let them rule men, but only when they are wiser than men."

And the Master looked at the two sorrowful faces and then He looked at us, and He spoke again and said, "John was born wounded, and the blood of his wounds streamed forth with his words. He was freedom not yet free from itself, and patient only with the straight and the just.

"In truth he was a voice crying in the land of the deaf; and I loved him in his pain and his aloneness.

"And I loved his pride that would give its head to the sword ere it would yield it to the dust.

"Verily I say unto you that John, the son of Zachariah, was the last of his race, and like his forefathers he was slain between the threshold of the temple and the altar."

And again Jesus walked away from us.

Then He returned and He said, "Forever it has been that those who rule for an hour would slay the rulers of years. And forever they would hold a trial and pronounce condemnation upon a man not yet born, and decree his death ere he commits the crime.

"The son of Zachariah shall live with me in my kingdom and his day shall be long."

Then He turned to the disciples of John and said, "Every deed has its morrow. I myself may be the morrow of this deed. Go back to my friend's friends, and tell them I shall be with them."

And the two men walked away from us, and they seemed less heavy-hearted.

Then Jesus laid Himself down again upon the grass and outstretched His arms, and again He gazed at the stars.

Now it was late. And I lay not far from Him, and I would fain have rested, but there was a hand knocking upon the gate of my sleep, and I lay awake until Jesus and the dawn called me again to the road.

The Man From The Desert:
On the Money-changers

I WAS a stranger in Jerusalem. I had come to the Holy City to behold the great temple, and to sacrifice upon the altar, for my wife had given twin sons to my tribe.

And after I had made my offering, I stood in the portico of the temple looking down upon the money-changers and those who sold doves for sacrifice, and listening to the great noise in the court.

And as I stood there came of a sudden a man into the midst of the money-changers and those who sold doves.

He was a man of majesty, and He came swiftly.

In His hand He held a rope of goat's hide; and He began to overturn the tables of the money-changers and to beat the pedlars of birds with the rope.

And I heard Him saying with a loud voice, "Render these birds unto the sky which is their nest."

Men and women fled from before His face, and He moved amongst them as the whirling wind moves on the sand-hills.

All this came to pass in but a moment, and then the court of the temple was emptied of the money-changers. Only the man stood there alone, and His followers stood at a distance.

Then I turned my face and I saw another man in the portico of the temple. And I walked towards him and said, "Sir, who is this man who stands alone, even like another temple?" And he answered me, "This is Jesus of Nazareth, a prophet who has appeared of late in Galilee. Here in Jerusalem all men hate Him."

And I said, "My heart was strong enough to be with His whip, and yielding enough to be at His feet."

And Jesus turned towards His followers who were awaiting Him. But before He reached them, three of the temple doves flew back, and one alighted upon His left shoulder and the other two at His feet. And he touched each one tenderly. Then He walked on, and there were leagues in every step of His steps.

Now tell me, what power had He to attack and disperse hundreds of men and women without opposition? I was told that they all hate Him, yet no one stood before Him on that day. Had He plucked out the fangs of hate on His way to the court of the temple?

Peter:
On the Morrow of His Followers

ONCE at sundown Jesus led us into the village of Beithsaida. We were a tired company, and the dust of the road was upon us.

And we came to a great house in the midst of a garden, and the owner stood at the gate.

And Jesus said to him, "These men are weary and footsore. Let them sleep in your house. The night is cold and they are in need of warmth and rest."

And the rich man said, "They shall not sleep in my house."

And Jesus said, "Suffer them then to sleep in your garden."

And the man answered, "Nay, they shall not sleep in my garden."

Then Jesus turned to us and said, "This is what your tomorrow will be, and this present is like your future. All doors shall be closed in your face, and not even the gardens that lie under the stars may be your couch.

"Should your feet indeed be patient with the road and follow me, it may be you will find a basin and a bed, and perhaps bread and wine also. But if it should be that you find none of those things, forget not then that you have crossed one of my deserts. "Come, let us go forth."

And the rich man was disturbed, and his face was changed, and he muttered to himself words that I did not hear; and he shrank away from us and turned into his garden. And we followed Jesus upon the road.

Melachi Of Babylon, An Astronomer:
The Miracles of Jesus

YOU question me concerning the miracles of Jesus.

Every thousand thousand years the sun and the moon and this earth and all her sister planets meet in a straight line, and they confer for a moment together.

Then they slowly disperse and await the passing of another thousand thousand years.

There are no miracles beyond the seasons, yet you and I do not know all the seasons. And what if a season shall be made manifest in the shape of a man?

In Jesus the elements of our bodies and our dreams came together according to law. All that was timeless before Him became timeful in Him.

They say He gave sight to the blind and walking to the paralysed, and that He drove devils out of madmen.

Perchance blindness is but a dark thought that can be overcome by a burning thought. Perchance a withered limb is but idleness that can be quickened by energy. And perhaps the devils, these restless elements in our life, are driven out by the angels of peace and serenity.

They say He raised the dead to life. If you can tell me what is death, then I will tell you what is life.

In a field I have watched an acorn, a thing so still and seemingly useless. And in the spring I have seen that acorn take roots and rise, the beginning of an oak tree, towards the sun.

Surely you would deem this a miracle, yet that miracle is wrought a thousand thousand times in the drowsiness of every autumn and the passion of every spring.

Why shall it not be wrought in the heart of man? Shall not the seasons meet in the hand or upon the lips of a Man Anointed?

If our God has given to earth the art to nestle seed whilst the seed is seemingly dead, why shall He not give to the heart of man to breathe life into another heart, even a heart seemingly dead?

I have spoken of these miracles which I deem but little beside the greater miracle, which is the man Himself, the Wayfarer, the man who turned my dross into gold, who taught me how to love those who hate me, and in so doing brought me comfort and gave sweet dreams to my sleep.

This is the miracle in my own life.

My soul was blind, my soul was lame. I was possessed by restless spirits, and I was dead.

But now I see clearly, and I walk erect. I am at peace, and I live to witness and proclaim my own being every hour of the day.

And I am not one of His followers. I am but an old astronomer who visits the fields of space once a season, and who would be heedful of the law and the miracles thereof.

And I am at the twilight of my time, but whenever I would seek its dawning, I seek the youth of Jesus.

And for ever shall age seek youth. In me now it is knowledge that is seeking vision.

A Philosopher:
On Wonder and Beauty

WHEN he was with us He gazed at us and at our world with eyes of wonder, for His eyes were not veiled with the veil of years, and all that He saw was clear in the light of His youth.

Though He knew the depth of beauty, He was for ever surprised by its peace and its majesty; and He stood before the earth as the first man had stood before the first day.

We whose senses have been dulled, we gaze in full daylight and yet we do not see. We would cup our ears, but we do not hear; and stretch forth our hands, but we do not touch. And though all the incense of Arabia is burned, we go our way and do not smell.

We see not the ploughman returning from his field at eventide; nor hear the shepherd's flute when he leads his flock to the fold, nor do we stretch our arms to touch the sunset; and our nostrils hunger no longer for the roses of Sharon.

Nay, we honour no kings without kingdoms; nor hear the sound of harps save when the strings are plucked by hands; nor do we see a child playing in our olive grove as if he were a young olive tree. And all words must needs rise from lips of flesh, or else we deem each other dumb and deaf.

In truth we gaze but do not see, and hearken but do not hear; we eat and drink but do not taste. And there lies the difference between Jesus of Nazareth and ourselves.

His senses were all continually made new, and the world to Him was always a new world.

To Him the lisping of a babe was not less than the cry of all mankind, while to us it is only lisping.

To Him the root of a buttercup was a longing towards God, while to us it is naught but a root.

Uriah, An Old Man Of Nazareth:
He Was a Stranger in Our Midst

HE was a stranger in our midst, and His life was hidden with dark veils.

He walked not the path of our God, but followed the course of the foul and the infamous.

His childhood revolted, and rejected the sweet milk of our nature.

His youth was inflamed like dry grass that burns in the night.

And when He became a man, He took arms against us all.

Such men are conceived in the ebb tide of human kindness, and born in unholy tempests. And in tempests they live a day and the perish forever.

Do you not remember Him, a boy overweening, who would argue with our learned elders, and laugh at their dignity?

And remember you not His youth, when He lived by the saw and the chisel? He would not accompany our sons and daughters on their holidays. He would walk alone.

And He would not return the salutation of those who hailed Him, as though He were above us.

I myself met Him once in the field and greeted Him, and He only smiled, and in His smile I beheld arrogance and insult.

Not long afterward my daughter went with her companions to the vineyards to gather the grapes, and she spoke to Him and He did not answer her.

He spoke only to the whole company of grape-gatherers, as if my daughter had not been among them.

When He abandoned His people and turned vagabond He became naught but a babbler. His voice was like a claw in our flesh, and the sound of His voice is still a pain in our memory.

He would utter only evil of us and of our fathers and forefathers. And His tongue sought our bosoms like a poisoned arrow.

Such was Jesus.

If He had been my son, I would have committed Him with the Roman legions to Arabia, and I would have begged the captain to place Him in the forefront of the battle, so that the archer of the foe might mark Him, and free me of His insolence.

But I have no son. And mayhap I should be grateful. For what if my son had been an enemy of his own people, and my gray hairs were now seeking the dust with shame, my white beard humbled?

Nicodemus The Poet, The Youngest Of The Elders:
On Fools and Jugglers

MANY are the fools who say that Jesus stood in His own path and opposed Himself; that He knew not His own mind, and in the absence of that knowledge confounded Himself.

Many indeed are the owls who know no song unlike their own hooting.

You and I know the jugglers of words who would honour only a greater juggler, men who carry their heads in baskets to the market-place and sell them to the first bidder.

We know the pygmies who abuse the sky-man. And we know what the weed would say of the oak tree and the cedar.

I pity them that they cannot rise to the heights.

I pity the shrivelling thorn envying the elm that dares the seasons.

But pity, though enfolded by the regret of all the angels, can bring them no light.

I know the scarecrow whose rotting garments flutter in the corn, yet he himself is dead to the corn and to the singing wind.

I know the wingless spider that weaves a net for all who fly. I know the crafty, the blowers of horns and the beaters of drums, who in the abundance of their own noise cannot hear the skylark nor the east wind in the forest.

I know him who paddles against all streams, but never finds the source, who runs with all rivers, but never dares to the sea.

I know him who offers his unskilled hands to the builder of the temple, and when his unskilled hands are rejected, says in the darkness of his heart, "I will destroy all that shall be builded."

I know all these. They are the men who object that Jesus said on a certain day, "I bring peace unto you," and on another day, "I bring a sword."

They cannot understand that in truth He said, "I bring peace unto men of goodwill, and I lay a sword between him who would peace and him who would a sword."

They wonder that He who said, "My kingdom is not of this earth," said also, "Render unto Caesar that which is Caesar's"; and know not that if they would indeed be free to enter the kingdom of their passion, they must not resist the gate-keeper of their necessities. It behooves them gladly to pay that dole to enter into that city.

There are the men who say, "He preached tenderness and kindliness and filial love, yet He would not heed His mother and His brothers when they sought Him in the streets of Jerusalem."

They do not know that His mother and brothers in their loving fear would have had Him return to the bench of the carpenter, whereas He was opening our eyes to the dawn of a new day.

His mother and His brothers would have had Him live in the shadow of death, but He Himself was challenging death upon yonder hill that He might live in our sleepless memory.

I know these moles that dig paths to nowhere. Are they not the ones who accuse Jesus of glorifying Himself in that He said to the multitude, "I am the path and the gate to salvation," and even called Himself the life and the resurrection.

But Jesus was not claiming more than the month of May claims in her high tide.

Was He not to tell the shining truth because it was so shining?

He indeed said that He was the way and the life and the resurrection of the heart; and I myself as a testimony to His truth.

Do you not remember me, Nicodemus, who believed in naught but the laws and decrees and was in continual subjection to observances?

And behold me now, a man who walks with life and laughs with the sun from the first moment it smiles upon the mountain until it yields itself to bed behind the hills.

Why do you halt before the word salvation? I myself through Him have attained my salvation.

I care not for what shall befall me tomorrow, for I know that Jesus quickened my sleep and made my distant dreams my companions and my road-fellows.

Am I less man because I believe in a greater man?

The barriers of flesh and bone fell down when the Poet of Galilee spoke to me; and I was held by a spirit, and was lifted to the heights, and in midair my wings gathered the song of passion.

And when I dismounted from the wind and in the Sanhedrim my pinions were shorn, even then my ribs, my featherless wings, kept and guarded the song. And all the poverties of the lowlands cannot rob me of my treasure. I have said enough. Let the deaf bury the humming of life in their dead ears. I am content with the sound of His lyre, which He held and struck while the hands of His body were nailed and bleeding.

Joseph of Arimathea Ten Years After:
The Two Streams in Jesus' Heart

THERE were two streams running in the heart of the Nazarene: the stream of kinship to God whom He called Father, and the stream of rapture which He called the kingdom of the Above-world.

And in my solitude I thought of Him and I followed these two streams in His heart. Upon the banks of the one I met my own soul; and sometimes my soul was a beggar and a wanderer, and sometimes it was a princess in her garden.

Then I followed the other stream in His heart, and on my way I met one who had been beaten and robbed of his gold, and he was smiling. And farther on I saw the robber who had robbed him, and there were unshed tears upon his face.

Then I heard the murmur of these two streams in my own bosom also, and I was gladdened.

When I visited Jesus the day before Pontius Pilatus and the elders laid hands on Him, we talked long, and I asked Him many questions, and He answered my questionings with graciousness; and when I left Him I knew He was the Lord and Master of this our earth.

It is long since our cedar tree has fallen, but its fragrance endures, and will forever seek the four corners of the earth.

Georgus of Beirut:
On Strangers

HE and His friends were in the grove of pines beyond my hedge, and He was talking to them.

I stood near the hedge and listened. And I knew who He was, for His fame had reached these shores ere He Himself visited them.

When He ceased speaking I approached Him, and I said, "Sir, come with these men and honour me and my roof."

And He smiled upon me and said, "Not this day, my friend. Not this day."

And there was a blessing in His words, and His voice enfolded me like a garment on a cold night.

Then He turned to His friends and said, "Behold a man who deems us not strangers, and though He has not seen us ere this day, he bids us to His threshold.

"Verily in my kingdom there are no strangers. Our life is but the life of all other men, given us that we may know all men, and in that knowledge love them.

"The deeds of all men are but our deeds, both the hidden and the revealed.

"I charge you not to be one self but rather many selves, the householder and the homeless, the ploughman and the sparrow that picks the grain ere it slumber in the earth, the giver who gives in gratitude, and the receiver who receives in pride and recognition.

"The beauty of the day is not only in what you see, but in what other men see.

"For this I have chosen you from among the many who have chosen me."

Then He turned to me again and smiled and said, "I say these things to you also, and you also shall remember them."

Then I entreated Him and said, "Master, will you not visit in my house?"

And He answered, "I know your heart, and I have visited your larger house."

And as He walked away with His disciples He said, "Good-night, and may your house be large enough to shelter all the wanderers of the land."

Mary Magdalen:
His Mouth Was Like the Heart of a Pomegranate

HIS mouth was like the heart of a pomegranate, and the shadows in His eyes were deep.

And He was gentle, like a man mindful of his own strength.

In my dreams I beheld the kings of the earth standing in awe in His presence.

I would speak of His face, but how shall I?

It was like night without darkness, and like day without the noise of day.

It was a sad face, and it was a joyous face.

And well I remember how once He raised His hand towards the sky, and His parted fingers were like the branches of an elm.

And I remember Him pacing the evening. He was not walking. He Himself was a road above the road; even as a cloud above the earth that would descend to refresh the earth.

But when I stood before Him and spoke to him, He was a man, and His face was powerful to behold. And He said to me, "What would you, Miriam?"

I did not answer Him, but my wings enfolded my secret, and I was made warm.

And because I could bear His light no more, I turned and walked away, but not in shame. I was only shy, and I would be alone, with His fingers upon the strings of my heart.

Jotham of Nazareth, to a Roman:
On Living and Being

MY friend, you like all other Romans would conceive life rather than live it. You would rule lands rather than be ruled by the spirit.

You would conquer races and be cursed by them rather than stay in Rome and be blest and happy.

You think but of armies marching and of ships launched into the sea.

How shall you then understand Jesus of Nazareth, a man simple and alone, who came without armies or ships, to establish a kingdom in the heart and an empire in the free spaces of the soul?

How shall you understand the man who was not a warrior, but who came with the power of the mighty ether?

He was not a god, He was a man like unto ourselves; but in Him the myrrh of the earth rose to meet the frankincense of the sky; and in His words our lisping embraced the whispering of the unseen; and in His voice we heard a song unfathomable.

Aye, Jesus was a man and not a god, and therein lies our wonder and our surprise.

But you Romans wonder not save at the gods, and no man shall surprise you. Therefore you understand not the Nazarene.

He belonged to the youth of the mind and you belong to its old age.

You govern us today; but let us wait another day.

Who knows that this man with neither armies nor ships shall govern tomorrow?

We who follow the spirit shall sweat blood while journeying after Him. But Rome shall lie a white skeleton in the sun.

We shall suffer much, yet we shall endure and we shall live. But Rome must needs fall into the dust.

Yet if Rome, when humbled and made low, shall pronounce His name, He will heed her voice. And He will breathe new life into her bones that she may rise again, a city among the cities of the earth. But this He shall do without legions, nor with slaves to oar His galleys. He will be alone.

Ephraim of Jericho:
The Other Wedding-Feast

WHEN He came again to Jericho I sought Him out and said to Him, "Master, on the morrow my son will take a wife. I beg you come to the wedding-feast and do us honour, even as you honoured the wedding at Cana of Galilee."

And He answered, "It is true that I was once a guest at a wedding-feast, but I shall not be a guest again. I am myself now the Bridegroom"

And He smiled as though He would rebuke me, and said, "Why do you entreat me? Have you not wine enough?"

And I said, "My jugs are full, Master; yet I beseech you, come to my son's wedding-feast."

Then He said, "Who knows? I may come, I may surely come, if your heart is an altar in your temple." And I said, "I entreat you, Master, come to the wedding-feast of my son.

Upon the morrow my son was married, but Jesus came not to the wedding-feast. And though we had many guests, I felt that no one had come.

In very truth, I myself who welcomed the guests, was not there.

Perhaps my heart had not been an altar when I invited Him. Perhaps I desired another miracle.

Barca, A Merchant of Tyre:
On Buying and Selling

I BELIEVE that neither the Romans nor the Jews understood Jesus of Nazareth, nor did His disciples who now preach His name.

The Romans slew Him and that was a blunder. The Galileans would make a god of Him and that is a mistake.

Jesus was the heart of man.

I have sailed the Seven Seas with my ships, and bartered with kings and princes and with cheats and the wily in the market-places of distant cities; but never have I seen a man who understood merchants as He did.

I heard Him once tell this parable: "A merchant left his country for a foreign land. He had two servants, and he gave each a handful of gold, saying: 'Even as I go abroad, you also shall go forth and seek profit. Make just exchange, and see that you serve in giving and taking.'

"And after a year the merchant returned.

"And he asked his two servants what they had done with his gold.

"The first servant said, 'Behold, Master, I have bought and sold, and I have gained.'

"And the merchant answered, 'The gain shall be yours, for you have done well, and have been faithful to me and to yourself.'

"Then the other servant stood forth and said, 'Sir, I feared the loss of your money; and I did not buy nor sell. Behold, it is all here in this purse.'

"And the merchant took the gold, and said, 'Little is your faith. To barter and lose is better than not to go forth. For even as the wind scatters her seed and waits for the fruit, so must all merchants. It were fitter for you henceforth to serve others.'"

When Jesus spoke thus, though He was no merchant, He disclosed the secret of commerce.

Moreover, His parables often brought to my mind lands more distant than my journeys, and yet nearer than my house and my goods.

But the young Nazarene was not a god; and it is a pity His followers seek to make a god of such a sage.

Phumiah, The High Priestess of Sidon :
To the other Priestesses: An Invocation

TAKE your harps and let me sing.
Beat your strings, the silver and the gold;
For I would sing the dauntless Man
Who slew the dragon of the valley,
Then gazed down with pity
Upon the thing He had slain.
Take your harps and sing with me
The lofty Oak upon the height,
The sky-hearted and the ocean-handed Man,
Who kissed the pallid lips of death,
Yet quivers now upon the mouth of life.

Take your harps and let us sing
The fearless Hunter on the hill,
Who marked the beast, and shot His viewless arrow,
And brought the horn and tusk
Down to the earth.

Take your harps and sing with me
The valiant Youth who conquered the mountain cities,
And the cities of the plain that coiled like serpents in the sand.
He fought not against pygmies but against gods
Who hungered for our flesh and thirsted for our blood.

And like the first Golden Hawk
He would rival only eagles;
For His wings were vast and proud
And would not outwing the less winged.

Take your harps and sing with me
The joyous song of sea and cliff.
The gods are dead,
And they are lying still
In the forgotten isle of a forgotten sea.
And He who slew them sits upon His throne.

He was but a youth.
Spring had not yet given Him full beard,
And His summer was still young in His field.

Take your harps and sing with me
The tempest in the forest
That breaks the dry branch and the leafless twig,
Yet sends the living root to nestle deeper at the breast of earth.
Take your harps and sing with me
The deathless song of our Beloved.
Nay, my maidens, stay your hands.
Lay by your harps.
We cannot sing Him now.
The faint whisper of our song cannot reach His tempest,
Nor pierce the majesty of His silence.

Lay by your harps and gather close around me,
I would repeat His words to you,
And I would tell you of His deeds,
For the echo of His voice is deeper than our passion.

Benjamin the Scribe:
Let the Dead Bury Their Dead

IT has been said that Jesus was the enemy of Rome and Judea.

But I say that Jesus was the enemy of no man and no race.

I have heard Him say, "The birds of the air and the mountain tops are not mindful of the serpents in their dark holes.

"Let the dead bury their dead. Be you yourself among the living, and soar high."

I was not one of His disciples. I was but one of the many who went after Him to gaze upon His face.

He looked upon Rome and upon us who are the slaves of Rome, as a father looks upon his children playing with toys and fighting among themselves for the larger toy. And He laughed from His height.

He was greater than State and race; He was greater than revolution.

He was single and alone, and He was an awakening. He wept all our unshed tears and smiled all our revolts.

We knew it was in His power to be born with all who are not yet born, and to bid them see, not with their eyes but with His vision.

Jesus was the beginning of a new kingdom upon the earth, and that kingdom shall remain.

He was the son and the grandson of all the kings who builded the kingdom of the spirit. And only the kings of spirit have ruled our world.

Zacchaeus:
On the Fate of Jesus

YOU believe in what you hear said. Believe in the unsaid, for the silence of men is nearer the truth than their words.

You ask if Jesus could have escaped His shameful death and saved His followers from persecution.

I answer, He could indeed have escaped had He chosen, but He did not seek safety nor was He mindful of protecting His flock from wolves of the night.

He knew His fate and the morrow of His constant lovers. He foretold and prophesied what should befall every one of us. He sought not His death; but He accepted death as a husband-man shrouding his corn with earth, accepts the winter, and then awaits the spring and harvest; and as a builder lays the largest stone in the foundation.

We were men of Galilee and from the slopes of Lebanon. Our Master could have led us back to our country, to live with His youth in our gardens until old age should come and whisper us back into the years.

Was anything barring His path back to the temples of our villages where others were reading the prophets and then disclosing their hearts?

Could He not have said, "Now I go east with the west wind," and so saying dismiss us with a smile upon His lips?

Aye, He could have said, "Go back to your kin. The world is not ready for me. I shall return a thousand years hence. Teach your children to await my return."

He could have done this had He so chosen.

But He knew that to build the temple invisible He must needs lay Himself the corner-stone, and lay us around as little pebbles cemented close to Himself.

He knew that the sap of His sky-tree must rise from its roots, and He poured His blood upon its roots; and to Him it was not sacrifice but rather gain.

Death is the revealer. The death of Jesus revealed His life.

Had He escaped you and His enemies, you would have been the conquerors of the world. Therefore He did not escape.

Only He who desires all shall give all.

Aye, Jesus could have escaped His enemies and lived to old age. But He knew the passing of the seasons, and He would sing His song.

What man facing the armed world would not be conquered for the moment that he might overcome the ages?

And now you ask who, in very truth, slew Jesus, the Romans or the priests of Jerusalem?

Neither the Romans slew Him, nor the priests. The whole world stood to honour Him upon that hill.

Jonathan:
Among the Water-lilies

UPON a day my beloved and I were rowing upon the lake of sweet waters. And the hills of Lebanon were about us.
We moved beside the weeping willows, and the reflections of the willows were deep around us.
And while I steered the boat with an oar, my beloved took her lute and sang thus:

What flower save the lotus knows the waters and the sun?
What heart save the lotus heart shall know both earth and sky?
Behold my love, the golden flower that floats 'twixt deep and high
Even as you and I float betwixt a love that has for ever been
And shall for ever be.

Dip your oar, my love,
And let me touch my strings.
Let us follow the willows, and let us leave not the water-lilies.
In Nazareth there lives a Poet, and His heart is like the lotus.
He has visited the soul of woman,
He knows her thirst is growing out of the waters,
And her hunger for the sun, though all her lips are fed.
They say He walks in Galilee.
I say He is rowing with us.
Can you not see His face, my love?
Can you not see, where the willow bough and its reflection meet,
He is moving as we move?

Beloved, it is good to know the youth of life.
It is good to know its singing joy.
Would that you might always have the oar,
And I my stringed lute,
Where the lotus laughs in the sun,
And the willow is dipping to the waters,
And His voice is upon my strings.

Dip your oar, my beloved,
And let me touch my strings.
There is a Poet in Nazareth
Who knows and loves us both.
Dip your oar, my lover,
And let me touch my strings.

Hannah of Bethsaida: The Year 73
She Speaks of Her Father's Sister

THE sister of my father had left us in her youth to dwell in a hut beside her father's ancient vineyard.

She lived alone, and the people of the countryside sought her in their maladies, and she healed them with green herbs, and with roots and flowers dried in the sun.

And they deemed her a seeress; but there were those also who called her witch and sorceress.

One day my father said to me, "Take these loeaves of wheaten bread to my sister, and take this jug of wine and this basket of raisins."

And it was all put upon the back of a colt, and I followed the road until I reached the vineyard, and the hut of my father's sister. And she was gladdened.

Now as we sat together in the cool of the day, a man came by upon the road, and He greeted the sister of my father, saying, "Good-even to you, and the blessing of the night be upon you."

Then she rose up; and she stood as in awe before Him and said, "Good-even to you, master of all good spirits, and conqueror of all evil spirits."

The man looked at her with tender eyes, and then He passed on by.

But I laughed in my heart. Methought my father's sister was mad. But now I know that she was not mad. It was I who did not understand.

She knew of my laughter, though it was hidden.

And she spoke, but not in anger. She said, "Listen, my daughter, and hearken and keep my word in remembrance: the man who but now passed by, like the shadow of a bird flying between the sun and the earth, shall prevail against the Caesars and the empire of the Caesars. He shall wrestle with the crowned bull of Chaldea, and the man-headed lion of Egypt, and He shall overcome them; and He shall rule the world.

"But this land that now He walks shall come to naught; and Jerusalem, which sits proudly upon the hill, shall drift away in smoke upon the wind of desolation."

When she spoke thus, my laughter turned to stillness and I was quiet. Then I said, "Who is this man, and of what country and tribe does He come? And how shall He conquer the great kings and the empires of the great kings?"

And she answered, "He is one born here in this land, but we have conceived Him in our longing from the beginning of years. He is of all tribes and yet of none. He shall conquer by the word of His mouth and by the flame of His spirit."

Then suddenly she rose and stood up like a pinnacle of rock; and she said, "May the angel of the Lord forgive me for pronouncing this word also: He shall be slain, and His youth shall be shrouded, and He shall be laid in silence beside the tongueless heart of the earth. And the maidens of Judea shall weep for Him."

Then she lifted her hand skyward and spoke again, and she said, "But He shall be slain only in the body.

"In the spirit He shall rise and go forth leading His host from this land where the sun is born, to the land where the sun is slain at eventide.

"And His name shall be first among men."

She was an aged seeress when she said these things, and I was but a girl, a field unploughed, a stone not yet in a wall.

But all that she beheld in the mirror of her mind has come to pass even in my day.

Jesus of Nazareth rose from the dead and led men and women unto the people of the sunset. The city that yielded Him to judgment was given unto destruction; and in the Judgment Hall where He was tried and sentenced, the owl hoots a dirge while the night weeps the dew of her heart upon the fallen marble.

And I am an old woman, and the years bend me down. My people are no more and my race is vanished.

I saw Him but once again after that day, and once again heard His voice. It was upon a hill-top when He was talking to His friends and followers.

And now I am old and alone, yet still He visits my dreams.

He comes like a white angel with pinions; and with His grace He hushes my dread of darkness. And He uplifts me to dreams yet more distant.

I am still a field unploughed, a ripe fruit that would not fall. The most that I possess is the warmth of the sun, and the memory of that man.

I know that among my people these shall not rise again king nor prophet nor priest, even as the sister of my father foretold.

We shall pass with the flowing of the rivers, and we shall be nameless.

But those who crossed Him in mid-stream shall be remembered for crossing Him in mid-stream.

Manasseh, A Lawyer In Jerusalem:
On the Speech and Gesture of Jesus

YES, I used to hear Him speak. There was always a ready word upon His lips.

But I admired Him as a man rather than as a leader. He preached something beyond my liking, perhaps beyond my reason. And I would have no man preach to me.

I was taken by His voice and His gestures, not by the substance of His speech. He charmed me but never convinced me; for He was too vague, too distant and obscure to reach my mind.

I have known other men like Him. They are never constant nor are they consistent. It is with eloquence not with principles that they hold your ear and your passing thought, but never the core of your heart.

What a pity that His enemies confronted Him and forced the issue. It was not necessary. I believe their hostility will add to His stature and turn His mildness to power.

For is it not strange that in opposing a man you give Him courage? And in staying His feet you give Him wings?

I know not His enemies, yet I am certain that in their fear of a harmless man they have lent Him strength and made Him dangerous.

Jephtha of Caesarea:
A Man Weary of Jesus

THIS man who fills your day and haunts your night is repellent to me. Yet you would tire my eyes with His sayings and my mind with His deeds.

I am weary of His words, and all that He did. His very name offends me, and the name of His countryside. I will none of Him.

Why make you a prophet of a man who was but a shadow? Why see a tower in this sand-dune, or imagine a lake in the raindrops gathered together in this hoof-print?

I scorn not the echo of caves in valleys nor the long shadows of the sunset; but I would not listen to the deceptions that hum in your head, nor study the reflections in your eyes.

What word did Jesus utter that Halliel had not spoken? What wisdom did He reveal that was not of Gamaliel? What are His lispings to the voice of Philo? What cymbals did He beat that were not beaten ere ever He lived?

I hearken to the echo from the caves into the silent valleys, and I gaze upon the long shadows of sunset; but I would not have this man's heart echo the sound of another heart, nor would I have a shadow of the seers call himself a prophet.

What man shall speak since Isaiah has spoken? Who dares sing since David? And shall wisdom be born now, after Solomon has been gathered to his fathers?

And what of our prophets, whose tongues were swords and their lips flames?

Left they a straw behind for this gleaner of Galilee? Or a fallen fruit for the beggar from the North Country? There was naught for Him save to break the loaf already baked by our ancestors, and to pour the wine which their holy feet had already passed from the grapes of old.

It is the potter's hand I honour not the man who buys the ware.

I honour those who sit at the loom rather than the boor who wears the cloth.

Who was this Jesus of Nazareth, and what is He? A man who dared not live His mind. Therefore He faded into oblivion and that is His end.

I beg you, charge not my ears with His words or His deeds. My heart is overfull with the prophets of old, and that is enough.

John The Beloved Disciple: In His Old Age
On Jesus the Word

YOU would have me speak of Jesus, but how can I lure the passion-song of the world into a hollowed reed?

In every aspect of the day Jesus was aware of the Father. He beheld Him in the clouds and in the shadows of the clouds that pass over the earth. He saw the Father's face reflected in the quiet pools, and the faint print of His feet upon the sand; and He often closed His eyes to gaze into the Holy Eyes.

The night spoke to Him with the voice of the Father, and in solitude He heard the angel of the Lord calling to Him. And when He stilled Himself to sleep He heard the whispering of the heavens in His dreams.

He was often happy with us, and He would call us brothers.

Behold, He who was the first Word called us brothers, though we were but syllables uttered yesterday.

You ask why I call Him the first Word.

Listen, and I will answer:

In the beginning God moved in space, and out of His measureless stirring the earth was born and the seasons thereof.

Then God moved again, and life streamed forth, and the longing of life sought the height and the depth and would have more of itself.

Then God spoke thus, and His words were man, and man was a spirit begotten by God's Spirit.

And when God spoke thus, the Christ was His first Word and that Word was perfect; and when Jesus of Nazareth came to the world the first Word was uttered unto us and the sound was made flesh and blood.

Jesus the Anointed was the first Word of God uttered unto man, even as if an apple tree in an orchard should bud and blossom a day before the other trees. And in God's orchard that day was an aeon.

We are all sons and daughters of the Most High, but the Anointed One was His first-born, who dwelt in the body of Jesus of Nazareth, and He walked among us and we beheld Him.

All this I say that you may understand not only in the mind but rather in the spirit. The mind weighs and measures but it is the spirit that reaches the heart of life and embraces the secret; and the seed of the spirit is deathless.

The wind may blow and then cease, and the sea shall swell and then weary, but the heart of life is a sphere quiet and serene, and the star that shines therein is fixed for evermore.

Mannus The Pompeiian, To A Greek:
On the Semitic Deity

THE Jews, like their neighbours the Phoenicians and the Arabs, will not suffer their gods to rest for a moment upon the wind.

They are over-thoughtful of their deity, and over-observant of one another's prayer and worship and sacrifice.

While we Romans build marble temples to our gods, these people would discuss their god's nature. When we are in ecstasy we sing and dance round the altars of Jupiter and Juno, of Mars and Venus; but they in their rapture wear sackcloth and cover their heads with ashes – and even lament the day that gave them birth.

And Jesus, the man who revealed God as a being of joy, they tortured Him, and then put Him to death.

These people would not be happy with a happy god. They know only the gods of their pain.

Even Jesus' friends and disciples who knew His mirth and heard His laughter, make an image of His sorrow, and they worship that image.

And in such worship they rise not to their deity; they only bring their deity down to themselves.

I believe however that this philosopher, Jesus, who was not unlike Socrates, will have power over His race and mayhap over other races.

For we are all creatures of sadness and of small doubts. And when a man says to us, "Let us be joyous with the gods," we cannot but heed his voice. Strange that the pain of this man has been fashioned into a rite.

These people would discover another Adonis, a god slain in the forest, and they would celebrate his slaying. It is a pity they heed not His laughter.

But let us confess, as Roman to Greek. Do even we ourselves hear the laughter of Socrates in the streets of Athens? Is it ever in us to forget the cup of hemlock, even at the theatre of Dionysus?

Do not rather our fathers still stop at the street corners to chat of troubles and to have a happy moment remembering the doleful end of all our great men?

Pontius Pilatus:
Of Eastern Rites and Cults

MY wife spoke of Him many times ere He was brought before me, but I was not concerned.

My wife is a dreamer, and she is given, like so many Roman women of her rank, to Eastern cults and rituals. And these cults are dangerous to the Empire; and when they find a path to the hearts of our women they become destructive.

Egypt came to an end when the Hyskos of Arabia brought to her the one God of their desert. And Greece was overcome and fell to dust when Ashtarte and her seven maidens came from the Syrian shores.

As for Jesus, I never saw the man before He was delivered up to me as a malefactor, as an enemy of His own nation and also of Rome.

He was brought into the Hall of Judgment with His arms bound to His body with ropes.

I was sitting upon the dais, and He walked towards me with long, firm steps; then He stood erect and His head was held high.

And I cannot fathom what came over me at that moment; but it was suddenly my desire, though not my will, to rise and go down from the dais and fall before Him.

I felt as if Caesar had entered the Hall, a man greater than even Rome herself.

But this lasted only a moment. And then I saw simply a man who was accused of treason by His own people. And I was His governor and His judge.

I questioned Him but he would not answer. He only looked at me. And in His look was pity, as if it were He who was my governor and my judge.

Then there rose from without the cries of the people. But He remained silent, and still He was looking at me with pity in His eyes.

And I went out upon the steps of the palace, and when the people saw me they ceased to cry out. And I said, "What would you with this man?"

And they shouted as if with one throat, "We would crucify Him. He is our enemy and the enemy of Rome."

And some called out, "Did He not say He would destroy the temple? And was it not He who claimed the kingdom? We will have no king but Caesar."

Then I left them and went back into the Judgment Hall again, and I saw Him still standing there alone, and His head was still high.

And I remembered what I had read that a Greek philosopher said, "The lonely man is the strongest man." At that moment the Nazarene was greater than His race.

And I did not feel clement towards Him. He was beyond my clemency.

I asked Him then, "Are you the King of the Jews?"

And He said not a word.

And I asked Him again, "Have you not said that you are the King of the Jews?"

And He looked upon me.

Then He answered with a quiet voice, "You yourself proclaimed me king. Perhaps to this end I was born, and for this cause came to bear witness unto truth."

Behold a man speaking of truth at such a moment.

In my impatience I said aloud, to myself as much as to Him, "What is truth? And what is truth to the guiltless when the hand of the executioner is already upon him?"

Then Jesus said with power, "None shall rule the world save with the Spirit and truth."

And I asked Him saying, "Are you of the Spirit?"

He answered, "So are you also, though you know it not."

And what was the Spirit and what was truth, when I, for the sake of the State, and they from jealousy for their ancient rites, delivered an innocent man unto His death?

No man, no race, no empire would halt before a truth on its way towards self-fulfilment.

And I said again, "Are you the King of the Jews?"

And He answered, "You yourself say this. I have conquered the world ere this hour."

And this alone of all that He said was unseemly, inasmuch as only Rome has conquered the world.

But now the voices of the people rose again, and the noise was greater than before.

And I descended from my seat and said to Him, "Follow me."

And again I appeared upon the steps of the palace, and He stood there beside me.

When the people saw Him they roared like the roaring thunder. And in their clamour I heard naught save "Crucify Him, crucify Him."

Then I yielded Him to the priests who had yielded Him to me and I said to them, "Do what you will with this just man. And if it is your desire, take with you soldiers of Rome to guard Him."

Then they took Him, and I decreed that there be written upon the cross above His head, "Jesus of Nazareth, King of the Jews." I should have said instead, "Jesus of Nazareth, a King."

And the man was stripped and flogged and crucified.

It would have been within my power to save Him, but saving Him would have caused a revolution; and it is always wise for the governor of a Roman province not to be intolerant of the religious scruples of a conquered race.

I believe unto this hour that the man was more than an agitator. What I decreed was not my will, but rather for the sake of Rome.

Not long after, we left Syria, and from that day my wife has been a woman of sorrow. Sometimes even here in this garden I see a tragedy in her face. I am told she talks much of Jesus to other women of Rome.

Behold, the man whose death I decreed returns from the world of shadows and enters into my own house.

And within myself I ask again and again, What is truth and what is not truth?

Can it be that the Syrian is conquering us in the quiet hours of the night?

It should not indeed be so.

For Rome must needs prevail against the nightmares of our wives.

Bartholomew in Ephesus:
On Slaves and Outcasts

THE enemies of Jesus say that He addressed His appeal to slaves and outcasts, and would have incited them against their lords. They say that because He was of the lowly He invoked His own kind, yet that He sought to conceal His own origin.

But let us consider the followers of Jesus, and His leadership.

In the beginning He chose for companions few men from the North Country, and they were freemen. They were strong of body and bold of spirit, and in these past two score years they have had the courage to face death with willingness and defiance.

Think you that these men were slaves or outcasts? And think you that the proud princes of Lebanon and Armenia have forgotten their station in accepting Jesus as a prophet of God?

Or think you the high-born men and women of Antioch and Byzantium and Athens and Rome could be held by the voice of a leader of slaves?

Nay, the Nazarene was not with the servant against his master; neither was He with the master against his servant. He was with no man against another man.

He was a man above men, and the streams that ran in His sinews sang together with passion and with might.

If nobility lies in being protective, He was the noblest of all men. If freedom is in thought and word and action, He was the freest of all men. If high birth is in pride that yields only to love and in aloofness that is ever gentle and gracious, then He was of all men the highest born.

Forget not that only the strong and the swift shall win the race and the laurels, and that Jesus was crowned by those who loved Him, and also by His enemies though they knew it not.

Even now He is crowned every day by the priestesses of Artemis in the secret places of her temple.

Matthew:
On Jesus by a Prison Wall

UPON an evening Jesus passed by a prison that was in the Tower of David. And we were walking after Him.

Of a sudden He tarried and laid His cheek against the stones of the prison wall. And thus He spoke:

"Brothers of my ancient day, my heart beats with your hearts behind the bars. Would that you could be free in my freedom and walk with me and my comrades.

"You are confined, but not alone. Many are the prisoners who walk the open streets. Their wings are not shorn, but like the peacock they flutter yet cannot fly.

"Brothers of my second day, I shall soon visit you in your cells and yield my shoulder to your burden. For the innocent and the guilty are not parted, and like the two bones of the forearm they shall never be cleaved.

"Brothers of this day, which is my day, you swam against the current of their reasoning and you were caught. They say I too shall swim against that current. Perhaps I shall soon be with you, a law-breaker among the law-breakers.

"Brothers of a day not yet come, these walls shall fall down, and out of the stones other shapes shall be fashioned by Him whose mallet is light, and whose chisel is the wind, and you shall stand free in the freedom of my new day."

Thus spoke Jesus and He walked on, and His hand was upon the prison wall until He passed by the Tower of David.

Andrew:
On Prostitutes

THE bitterness of death is less bitter than life without Him. The days were hushed and made still when he was silenced. Only the echo in my memory repeats His words. But not His voice.

Once I heard Him say: "Go forth in your longing to the fields, and sit by the lilies, and you shall hear them humming in the sun. They weave not cloth for raiment, nor do they raise wood or stone for shelter; yet they sing.

"He who works in the night fulfils their needs and the dew of His grace is upon their petals.

"And are not you also His care who never wearies nor rests?"

And once I heard Him say, "The birds of the sky are counted and enrolled by Your Father even as the hairs of your head are numbered. Not a bird shall lie at the archer's feet, neither shall a hair of your head turn gray or fall into the emptiness of age without His will."

And once again He said, "I have heard you murmur in your hearts: 'Our God shall be more merciful unto us, children of Abraham, than unto those who knew Him not in the beginning.'

"But I say unto you that the owner of the vineyard who calls a labourer in the morning to reap, and calls another at sundown, and yet renders wages to the last even as to the first, that man is indeed justified. Does he not pay out of his own purse and with his own will?

"So shall my Father open the gate of His mansion at the knocking of the Gentiles even as at your knocking. For His ear heeds the new melody with the same love that it feels for the oft-heard song. And with a special welcome because it is the youngest string of His heart."

And once again I heard Him say, "Remember this: a thief is a man in need, a liar is a man in fear; the hunter who is hunted by the watchman of your night is also hunted by the watchman of his own darkness.

"I would have you pity them all.

"Should they seek your house, see that you open your door and bid them sit at your board. If you do not accept them you shall not be free from whatever they have committed."

And on a day I followed Him to the market-place of Jerusalem as the others followed Him. And He told us the parable of the prodigal son, and the parable of the merchant who sold all his possessions that he might buy a pearl.

But as He was speaking the Pharisees brought into the midst of the crowd a woman whom they called a harlot. And they confronted Jesus and said to Him, "She defiled her marriage vow, and she was taken in the act."

And He gazed at her; and He placed His hand upon her forehead and looked deep into her eyes.

Then he turned to the men who had brought her to Him, and He looked long at them; and He leaned down and with His finger He began to write upon the earth.

He wrote the name of every man, and beside the name He wrote the sin that every man had committed.

And as He wrote they escaped in shame into the streets.

And ere He had finished writing only that woman and ourselves stood before Him.

And again He looked into her eyes, and He said, "You have loved overmuch. They who brought you here loved but little. But they brought you as a snare for my ensnaring.

"And now go in peace.

"None of them is here to judge you. And if it is in your desire to be wise even as you are loving, then seek me; for the Son of Man will not judge you."

And I wondered then whether He said this to her because He Himself was not without sin.

But since that day I have pondered long, and I know now that only the pure of heart forgive the thirst that leads to dead waters.

And only the sure of foot can give a hand to him who stumbles.

And again and yet again I say, the bitterness of death is less bitter than life without Him.

A Rich Man:
On Possessions

HE spoke ill of rich men. And upon a day I questioned Him saying, "Sir, what shall I do to attain the peace of the spirit?"

And He bade me give my possessions to the poor and follow Him.

But He possessed nothing; therefore He knew not the assurance and the freedom of possessions, nor the dignity and the self-respect that lie within.

In my household there are seven score slaves and stewards; some labour in my groves and vineyards, and some direct my ships to distant isles.

Now had I heeded Him and given my possessions to the poor, what would have befallen my slaves and my servants and their wives and children? They too would have become beggars at the gate of the city or the portico of the temple.

Nay that good man did not fathom the secret of possessions. Because He and His followers lived on the bounty of others He thought all men should live likewise.

Behold a contradiction and a riddle: Should rich men bestow their riches upon the poor, and must the poor have the cup and the loaf of the rich man ere they welcome him to their board?

And must needs the holder of the tower be host to his tenants ere he calls himself lord of his own land?

The ant that stores food for the winter is wiser than a grasshopper that sings one day and hungers another.

Last sabbath one of His followers said in the market-place, "At the threshold of heaven where Jesus may leave His sandals, no other man is worthy to lay his head."

But I ask, at the threshold of whose house that honest vagabond could have left His sandals? He Himself never had a house nor a threshold; and often He went without sandals.

John At Patmos:
Jesus the Gracious

ONCE more I would speak of Him.

God gave me the voice and the burning lips though not the speech.

And unworthy am I for the fuller word, yet I would summon my heart to my lips.

Jesus loved me and I knew not why.

And I loved Him because He quickened my spirit to heights beyond my stature, and to depths beyond my sounding.

Love is a sacred mystery.

To those who love, it remains forever wordless;

But to those who do not love, it may be but a heartless jest.

Jesus called me and my brother when we were labouring in the field.

I was young then and only the voice of dawn had visited my ears.

But His voice and the trumpet of His voice was the end of my labour and the beginning of my passion.

And there were naught for me then but to walk in the sun and worship the loveliness of the hour.

Could you conceive a majesty too kind to be majestic? And a beauty too radiant to seem beautiful?

Could you hear in your dreams a voice shy of its own rapture?

He called me and I followed Him.

That evening I returned to my father's house to get my other cloak.

And I said to my mother, "Jesus of Nazareth would have me in His company."

And she said, "Go His way my son, even like your brother."

And I accompanied Him.

His fragrance called me and commanded me, but only to release me.

Love is a gracious host to his guests though to the unbidden his house is a mirage and a mockery.

Now you would have me explain the miracles of Jesus.

We are all the miraculous gesture of the moment; our Lord and Master was the centre of that moment.

Yet it was not in His desire that His gestures be known.

I have heard Him say to the lame, "Rise and go home, but say not to the priest that I have made you whole."

And Jesus' mind was not with the cripple; it was rather with the strong and the upright.

His mind sought and held other minds and His complete spirit visited other spirits.

And in so doing His spirit changed these minds and these spirits.

It seemed miraculous, but with our Lord and Master it was simply like breathing the air of every day.

And now let me speak of other things.

On a day when He and I were alone walking in a field, we were both hungry, and we came to a wild apple tree.

There were only two apples hanging on the bough. And He held the trunk of the tree with His arm and shook it, and the two apples fell down.

He picked them both up and gave one to me. The other He held in His hand.

In my hunger I ate the apple, and I ate it fast.

Then I looked at Him and I saw that He still held the other apple in His hand.

And He gave it to me saying, "Eat this also."

And I took the apple, and in my shameless hunger I ate it.

And as we walked on I looked upon His face.

But how shall I tell you of what I saw?

A night where candles burn in space,

A dream beyond our reaching;

A noon where all shepherds are at peace and happy that their flock are grazing;

An eventide, and a stillness, and a homecoming;

Then a sleep and a dream.

All these things I saw in His face.

He had given me the two apples. And I knew He was hungry even as I was hungry.

But I now know that in giving them to me He had been satisfied. He Himself ate of other fruit from another tree.

I would tell you more of Him, but how shall I?

When love becomes vast love becomes wordless.

And when memory is overladen it seeks the silent deep.

Peter:
On the Neighbour

ONCE in Capernaum my Lord and Master spoke thus:

"Your neighbour is your other self dwelling behind a wall. In understanding, all walls shall fall down.

"Who knows but that your neighbour is your better self wearing another body? See that you love him as you would love yourself.

"He too is a manifestation of the Most High, whom you do not know.

"Your neighbour is a field where the springs of your hope walk in their green garments, and where the winters of your desire dream of snowy heights.

"Your neighbour is a mirror wherein you shall behold your countenance made beautiful by a joy which you yourself did not know, and by a sorrow you yourself did not share.

"I would have you love your neighbour even as I have loved you." Then I asked Him saying: "How can I love a neighbour who loves me not, and who covets my property? One who would steal my possessions?"

And He answered, "When you are ploughing and your manservant is sowing the seed behind you, would you stop and look backward and put to flight a sparrow feeding upon a few of your seeds? Should you do this, you were not worthy of the riches of your harvest."

When Jesus had said this, I was ashamed and I was silent. But I was not in fear, for He smiled upon me.

A Cobbler In Jerusalem:
A Neutral

I LOVED Him not, yet I did not hate Him. I listened to Him not to hear His words but rather the sound of His voice; for His voice pleased me.

All that He said was vague to my mind, but the music thereof was clear to my ear.

Indeed were it not for what others have said to me of His teaching, I should not have known even so much as whether He was with Judea or against it.

Suzannah of Nazareth, A Neighbour:
Of the Youth and Manhood of Jesus

I KNEW Mary the mother of Jesus, before she became the wife of Joseph the carpenter, when we were both still unwedded.

In those days Mary would behold visions and hear voices, and she would speak of heavenly ministers who visited her dreams.

And the people of Nazareth were mindful of her, and they observed her going and her coming. And they gazed upon her brows and spaces in her steps.

But some said she was possessed. They said this because she would go only upon her own errands.

I deemed her old while she was young, for there was a harvest in her blossoming and ripe fruit in her spring.

She was born and reared amongst us yet she was like an alien from the North Country. In her eyes there was always the astonishment of one not yet familiar with our faces.

And she was as haughty as Miriam of old who marched with her brothers form the Nile to the wilderness.

Then Mary was betrothed to Joseph the carpenter.

When Mary was big with Jesus she would walk among the hills and return at eventide with loveliness and pain in her eyes.

And when Jesus was born I was told that Mary said to her mother, "I am but a tree unpruned. See you to this fruit." Martha the midwife heard her.

After three days I visited her. And there was wonder in her eyes, and her breasts heaved, and her arm was around her first-born like the shell that holds the pearl.

We all loved Mary's babe and we watched Him, for there was warmth in His being and He throbbed with the pace of His life.

The seasons passed, and He became a boy full of laughter and little wanderings. None of us knew what He would do for He seemed always outside of our race. But He was never rebuked though He was venturous and over-daring.

He played with the other children rather than they with Him.

When He was twelve years old, one day He led a blind man across the brook to the safety of the open road.

And in gratitude the blind man asked Him, "Little boy, who are you?"

And He answered, "I am not a little boy. I am Jesus."

And the blind man said, "Who is your father?"

And He answered, "God is my father."

And the blind man laughed and replied, "Well said, my little boy. But who is your mother?"

And Jesus answered, "I am not your little boy. And my mother is the earth."

And the blind man said, "Then behold, I was led by the Son of God and the earth across the stream."

And Jesus answered, "I will lead you wherever you would go, and my eyes will accompany your feet."

And He grew like a precious palm tree in our gardens.

When He was nineteen He was as comely as a hart, and His eyes were like honey and full of the surprise of day.

And upon His mouth there was the thirst of the desert flock for the lake.

He would walk the fields alone and our eyes would follow Him, and the eyes of all the maidens of Nazareth. But we were shy of Him.

Love is forever shy of beauty, yet beauty shall forever be pursued by love.

Then the years bade Him speak in the temple and in the gardens of Galilee.

And at times Mary followed Him to listen to His words and to hear the sound of her own heart. But when He and those who loved Him went down to Jerusalem she would not go. For we at the North Country are often mocked in the streets of Jerusalem, even when we go carrying our offerings to the temple. And Mary was too proud to yield to the South Country.

And Jesus visited other lands in the east and in the west. We knew not what lands He visited, yet our hearts followed Him.

But Mary awaited Him upon her threshold and every eventide her eyes sought the road for His home-coming.

Yet upon His return she would say to us, "He is too vast to be my Son, too eloquent for my silent heart. How shall I claim Him?"

It seemed to us that Mary could not believe that the plain had given birth to the mountain; in the whiteness of her heart she did not see that the ridge is a pathway to the summit.

She knew the man, but because He was her Son she dared not know Him.

And on a day when Jesus went to the lake to be with the fishermen she said to me, "What is man but this restless being that would rise from the earth, and who is man but a longing that desires the stars?

"My son is a longing. He is all of us longing for the stars.

"Did I say my son? May God forgive me. Yet in my heart I would be His mother."

Now, it is hard to tell more of Mary and her Son, but though there shall be husks in my throat, and my words shall reach you like cripples on crutches, I must needs relate what I have seen and heard.

It was in the youth of the year when the red anemones were upon the hills that Jesus called His disciples saying to them, "Come with me to Jerusalem and witness the slaying of the lamb for the passover."

Upon the selfsame day Mary came to my door and said, "He is seeking the Holy City. Will you come and follow Him with me and the other women?"

And we walked the long road behind Mary and her son till we reached Jerusalem. And there a company of men and women hailed us at the gate, for His coming had been heralded to those who loved Him.

But upon that very night Jesus left the city with His men.

We were told that He had gone to Bethany.

And Mary stayed with us in the inn, awaiting His return.

Upon the eve of the following Thursday He was caught without the walls, and was held prisoner.

And when we heard He was a prisoner, Mary uttered not a word, but there appeared in her eyes the fulfilment of that promised pain and joy which we had beheld when she was but a bride in Nazareth.

She did not weep. She only moved among us like the ghost of a mother who would not bewail the ghost of her son.

We sat low upon the floor but she was erect, walking up and down the room.

She would stand beside the window and gaze eastward, and then with the fingers of her two hands brush back her hair.

At dawn she was still standing among us, like a lone banner in the wilderness wherein there are no hosts.

We wept because we knew the morrow of her son; but she did not weep for she knew also what would befall Him.

Her bones were of bronze and her sinews of the ancient elms, and her eyes were like the sky, wide and daring.

Have you heard a thrush sing while its nest burns in the wind?

Have you seen a woman whose sorrow is too much for tears, or a wounded heart that would rise beyond its own pain?

You have not seen such a woman, for you have not stood in the presence of Mary; and you have not been enfolded by the Mother Invisible.

In that still moment when the muffled hoofs of silence beat upon the breasts of the sleepless, John the young son of Zebedee, came and said: "Mary Mother, Jesus is going forth. Come, let us follow Him."

And Mary laid her hand upon John's shoulder and they went out, and we followed them.

When we came to the Tower of David we saw Jesus carrying His cross. And there was a great crowd about Him.

And two other men were also carrying their crosses.

And Mary's head was held high, and she walked with us after her son. And her step was firm.

And behind her walked Zion and Rome, aye, the whole world, to revenge itself upon one free Man.

When we reached the hill, He was raised high upon the cross.

And I looked at Mary. And her face was not the face of a woman bereaved. It was the countenance of the fertile earth, forever giving birth, forever burying her children.

Then to her eyes came the remembrance of His childhood, and she said aloud, "My son, who is not my son; man who once visited my womb, I glory in your power. I know that every drop of blood that runs down from your hands shall be the well-stream of a nation.

"You die in this tempest even as my heart once died in the sunset, and I shall now sorrow."

At that moment I desired to cover my face with my cloak and run away to the North Country. But of a sudden I heard Mary say, "My son, who is not my son, what have you said to the man at your right hand that has made him happy in his agony? The shadow of death is light upon his face, and he cannot turn his eyes from you.

"Now you smile upon me, and because you smile I know you have conquered."

And Jesus looked upon His mother and said, "Mary, from this hour be you the mother of John."

And to John He said, "Be a loving son unto this woman. Go to her house and let your shadow cross the threshold where I once stood. Do this in remembrance of me."

And Mary raised her right hand towards Him, and she was like a tree with one branch. And again she cried, "My son, who is not my son, if this be of God may God give us patience and the knowledge thereof. And if it be of man may God forgive him forevermore.

"If it be of God, the snow of Lebanon shall be your shroud; and if it be only of the priests and soldiers, then I have this garment for your nakedness.

"My son, who is not my son, that which God builds here shall not perish; and that which man would destroy shall remain builded, but not in his sight."

And at that moment the heavens yielded Him to the earth, a cry and a breath.

And Mary yielded Him also unto man, a wound and a balsam.

And Mary said, "Now behold, He is gone. The battle is over. The star has shone forth. The ship has reached the harbour. He who once lay against my heart is throbbing in space."

And we came close to her, and she said to us, "Even in death He smiles. He has conquered. I would indeed be the mother of a conqueror." And Mary returned to Jerusalem leaning upon John the young disciple.

And she was a woman fulfiled.

And when we reached the gate of the city, I gazed upon her face and I was astonished, for on that day the head of Jesus was the highest among men, and yet Mary's head was not less high.

All this came to pass in the spring of the year.

And now it is autumn. And Mary the mother of Jesus has come again to her dwelling-place, and she is alone.

Two sabbaths ago my heart was as a stone in my breast, for my son had left me for a ship in Tyre. He would be a sailor.

And he said he would return no more.

And upon an evening I sought Mary.

When I entered her house she was sitting at her loom, but she was not weaving. She was looking into the sky beyond Nazareth.

And I said to her, "Hail, Mary."

And she stretched out her arm to me, and said, "Come and sit beside me, and let us watch the sun pour its blood upon the hills."

And I sat beside her on the bench and we gazed into the west through the window.

And after a moment Mary said, "I wonder who is crucifying the sun this eventide."

Then I said, "I came to you for comfort. My son has left me for the sea and I am alone in the house across the way."

Then Mary said, "I would comfort you but how shall I?"

And I said, "If you will only speak of your son I shall be comforted."

And Mary smiled upon me, and she laid her hand about my shoulder and she said, "I will speak of Him. That which will console you will give me consolation."

Then she spoke of Jesus, and she spoke long of all that was in the beginning.

And it seemed to me that in her speech she would have no difference between her son and mine.

For she said to me, "My son is also a seafarer. Why would you not trust your son to the waves even as I have trusted Him?

"Woman shall be forever the womb and the cradle but never the tomb. We die that we may give life unto life even as our fingers spin the thread for the raiment that we shall never wear.

"And we cast the net for the fish that we shall never taste.

"And for this we sorrow, yet in all this is our joy."

Thus spoke Mary to me.

And I left her and came to my house, and though the light of the day was spent I sat at my loom to weave more of the cloth.

Joseph Surnamed Justus:
Jesus the Wayfarer

THEY say He was vulgar, the common offspring of common seed, a man uncouth and violent. They say that only the wind combed His hair, and only the rain brought His clothes and His body together.

They deem Him mad, and they attribute His words to demons.

Yet behold, the Man despised sounded a challenge and the sound thereof shall never cease.

He sang a song and none shall arrest that melody. It shall hover from generation to generation and it shall rise from sphere to sphere remembering the lips that gave it birth and the ears that cradled it.

He was a stranger. Aye, He was a stranger, a wayfarer on His way to a shrine, a visitor who knocked at our door, a guest from a far country.

And because He found not a gracious host, He has returned to His own place.

Philip:
And When He Died All Mankind Died

WHEN our beloved died, all mankind died and all things for a space were still and gray. Then the east was darkened, and a tempest rushed out of it and swept the land. The eyes of the sky opened and shut, and the rain came down in torrents and carried away the blood that streamed from His hands and His feet.

I too died. But in the depth of my oblivion I heard Him speak and say, "Father forgive them, for they know not what they do."

And His voice sought my drowned spirit and I was brought back to the shore.

And I opened my eyes and I saw His white body hanging against the cloud, and His words that I had heard took the shape within me and became a new man. And I sorrowed no more.

Who would sorrow for a sea that is unveiling its face, or for a mountain that laughs in the sun?

Was it ever in the heart of man, when that heart was pierced, to say such words?

What other judge of men has released His judges? And did ever love challenge hate with power more certain of itself?

Was ever such a trumpet heard 'twixt heaven and earth?

Was it known before that the murdered had compassion on his murderers? Or that the meteor stayed his footsteps for the mole?

The seasons shall tire and the years grow old, ere they exhaust these words: "Father forgive them, for they know not what they do."

And you and I, though born again and again, shall keep them.

And now I would go into my house, and stand an exalted beggar, at His door.

Birbarah Of Yammouni:
On Jesus the Impatient

JESUS was patient with the dullard and the stupid, even as the winter awaits the spring.

He was patient like a mountain in the wind.

He answered with kindliness the harsh questionings of His foes.

He could even be silent to cavil and dispute, for He was strong and the strong can be forbearing.

But Jesus was also impatient.

He spared not the hypocrite.

He yielded not to men of cunning nor to the jugglers of words.

And He would not be governed.

He was impatient with those who believed not in light because they themselves dwelt in shadow; and with those who sought after signs in the sky rather than in their own hearts.

He was impatient with those who weighed and measured the day and the night before they would trust their dreams to dawn or eventide.

Jesus was patient.

Yet He was the most impatient of men. He would have you weave the cloth though you spend years between the loom and the linen.

But He would have none tear an inch off the woven fabric.

Pilate's Wife, To A Roman Lady

I WAS walking with my maidens in the groves outside of Jerusalem when I saw Him with a few men and women sitting about Him; and He was speaking to them in a language which I only half understood.

But one needs not a language to perceive a pillar of light or a mountain of crystal. The heart knows what the tongue may never utter and the ears may never hear.

He was speaking to His friends of love and strength. I know He spoke of love because there was melody in His voice; and I know He spoke of strength because there were armies in His gestures. And He was tender, though even my husband could not have spoken with such authority.

When He saw me passing by He stopped speaking for a moment and looked kindly upon me. And I was humbled; and in my soul I knew I had passed by a god.

After that day His image visited my privacy when I would not be visited by man or woman; and His eyes searched my soul when my own eyes were closed. And His voice governs the stillness of my nights.

I am held fast forevermore; and there is peace in my pain, and freedom in my tears.

Beloved friend, you have never seen that man, and you will never see Him.

He is gone beyond our senses, but of all men He is now the nearest to me.

A Man Outside Of Jerusalem:
Of Judas

JUDAS came to my house that Friday, upon the eve of the passover; and he knocked at my door with force.

When he entered I looked at him, and his face was ashen. His hands trembled like dry twigs in the wind, and his clothes were as wet as if he had stepped out from a river; for on that evening there were great tempests.

He looked at me, and the sockets of his eyes were like dark caves and his eyes were blood-sodden.

And he said, "I have delivered Jesus of Nazareth to His enemies and to my enemies."

Then Judas wrung his hands and he said, "Jesus declared that He would overcome all His foes and the foes of our people. And I believed and I followed Him.

"When first He called us to Him He promised us a kingdom mighty and vast, and in our faith we sought His favour that we might have honourable stations in His court.

"We beheld ourselves princes dealing with these Romans as they have dealt with us. And Jesus said much about His kingdom, and

I thought He had chosen me a captain of His chariots, and a chief man of his warriors. And I followed His footsteps willingly.

"But I found it was not a kingdom that Jesus sought, nor was it from the Romans He would have had us free. His kingdom was but the kingdom of the heart. I heard Him talk of love and charity and forgiveness, and the wayside women listened gladly, but my heart grew bitter and I was hardened.

"My promised king of Judea seemed suddenly to have turned flute-player, to soothe the mind of wanderers and vagabonds.

"I had loved Him as others of my tribe had loved Him. I had beheld Him a hope and a deliverance from the yoke of the aliens. But when He would not utter a word or move a hand to free us from that yoke, and when He would even have rendered unto Caesar that which is Caesar's, then despair filled me and my hopes died. And I said, 'He who murders my hopes shall be murdered, for my hopes and expectations are more precious than the life of any man.'"

Then Judas gnashed his teeth; and he bent down his head. And when he spoke again, he said, "I have delivered Him up. And He was crucified this day. ...Yet when He died upon the cross, He died a king. He died in the tempest as deliverers die, like vast men who live beyond the shroud and the stone.

"And all the while He was dying, He was gracious, and He was kindly; and His heart was full of pity. He felt pity even for me who had delivered Him up."

And I said, "Judas, you have committed a grave wrong."

And Judas answered, "But He died a king. Why did He not live a king?"

And I said again, "You have committed a grave crime."

And he sat down there, upon that bench, and he was as still as a stone.

But I walked to and fro in the room, and once more I said, "You have committed a great sin."

But Judas said not a word. He remained as silent as the earth.

And after a while he stood up and faced me and he seemed taller, and when he spoke his voice was like the sound of a cracked vessel; and he said, "Sin was not in my heart. This very night I shall seek His kingdom, and I shall stand in His presence and beg His forgiveness.

"He died a king, and I shall die a felon. But in my heart I know He will forgive me."

After saying these words he folded his wet cloak around him and he said, "It was good that I came to you this night even though I have brought you trouble. Will you also forgive me?

"Say to your sons and to your sons' sons: 'Judas Iscariot delivered Jesus of Nazareth to His enemies because he believed Jesus was an enemy to His own race.'

"And say also that Judas upon the selfsame day of his great error followed the King to the steps of His throne to deliver up his own soul and to be judged.

"I shall tell Him that my blood also was impatient for the sod, and my crippled spirit would be free."

Then Judas leaned his head back against the wall and he cried out, "O God whose dreaded name no man shall utter ere his lips are touched by the fingers of death, why did you burn me with a fire that had no light?

"Why did you give the Galilean a passion for a land unknown and burden me with desire that would not escape kin or hearth? And who is this man Judas, whose hands are dipped in blood?

"Lend me a hand to cast him off, an old garment and a tattered harness.

"Help me to do this tonight.

"And let me stand again outside of these walls.

"I am weary of this wingless liberty. I would a larger dungeon.

"I would flow a stream of tears to the bitter sea. I would be a man of your mercy rather than one knocking at the gate of his own heart."

Thus Judas spoke, and thereupon he opened the door and went out again into the tempest.

Three days afterwards I visited Jerusalem and heard of all that had come to pass. And I also heard that Judas had flung himself from the summit of the High Rock.

I have pondered long since that day, and I understand Judas. He fulfiled his little life, which hovered like a mist on this land and enslaved by the Romans, while the great prophet was ascending the heights.

One man longed for a kingdom in which he was to be a prince.

Another man desired a kingdom in which all men shall be princes.

Sarkis, An Old Greek Shepherd, Called The Madman:
Jesus and Pan

IN a dream I saw Jesus and My God Pan sitting together in the heart of the forest.

They laughed at each other's speech, with the brook that ran near them, and the laughter of Jesus was the merrier. And they conversed long.

Pan spoke of earth and her secrets, and of his hoofed brothers and his horned sisters; and of dreams. And he spoke of roots and their nestlings, and of the sap that wakes and rises and sings to summer.

And Jesus told of the young shoots in the forest, and of flowers and fruit, and the seed that they shall bear in a season not yet come.

He spoke of birds in space and their singing in the upper world.

And He told of white harts in the desert wherein God shepherds them.

And Pan was pleased with the speech of the new God, and his nostrils quivered.

And in the same dream I beheld Pan and Jesus grow quiet and still in the stillness of the green shadows.

And then Pan took his reeds and played to Jesus.

The trees were shaken and the ferns trembled, and there was a fear upon me.

And Jesus said, "Good brother, you have the glade and the rocky height in your reeds."

Then Pan gave the reeds to Jesus and said, "You play now. It is your turn."

And Jesus said, "These reeds are too many for my mouth. I have this flute."

And He took His flute and He played. And I heard the sound of rain in the leaves, and the singing of streams among the hills, and the falling of snow on the mountain-top.

The pulse of my heart, that had once beaten with the wind, was restored again to the wind, and all the waves of my yesterdays were upon my shore, and I was again Sarkis the shepherd, and the flute of Jesus became the pipes of countless shepherds calling to countless flocks.

Then Pan said to Jesus, "Your youth is more kin to the reed than my years. And long ere this in my stillness I have heard your song and the murmur of your name.

"Your name has a goodly sound; well shall it rise with the sap to the branches, and well shall it run with the hoofs among the hills.

"And it is not strange to me, though my father called me not by that name. It was your flute that brought it back to my memory.

"And now let us play our reeds together."

And they played together.

And their music smote heaven and earth, and a terror struck all living things.

I heard the bellow of beasts and the hunger of the forest. And I heard the cry of lonely men, and the plaint of those who long for what they know not.

I heard the sighing of the maiden for her lover, and the panting of the luckless hunter for his prey.

And then there came peace into their music, and the heavens and the earth sang together.

All this I saw in my dream, and all this I heard.

Annas, The High Priest:
On Jesus the Rabble

HE was of the rabble, a brigand, a mountebank and a self-trumpeter. He appealed only to the unclean and the disinherited, and for this He had to go the way of all the tainted and the defiled.

He made sport of us and of our laws; He mocked at our honour and jeered at our dignity. He even said He would destroy the temple and desecrate the holy places. He was shameless, and for this He had to die a shameful death.

He was a man from Galilee of the Gentiles, an alien, from the North Country where Adonis and Ashtarte still claim power against Israel and the God of Israel.

He whose tongue halted when He spoke the speech of our prophets was loud and ear-splitting when he spoke the bastard language of the low-born and the vulgar.

What else was there for me but to decree His death?

Am I not a guardian of the temple? Am I not a keeper of the law? Could I have turned my back on Him, saying in all tranquillity: "He is a madman among madmen. Let Him alone to exhaust Himself raving; for the mad and the crazed and those possessed with devils shall be naught in the path of Israel" ?

Could I have been deaf unto Him when he called us liars. hypocrites, wolves, vipers, and the sons of vipers?

Nay I could not be deaf to Him, for He was not a madman. He was self-possessed; and in His big-sounding sanity He denounced and challenged us all.

For this I had Him crucified, and His crucifixion was a signal and warning unto the others who are stamped with the same damned seal.

I know well I have been blamed for this, even by some of the elders in the Sanhedrim. But I was mindful then as I am mindful now, that one man should die for the people rather than the people be led astray by one man.

Judea was conquered by an enemy from without. I shall see that Judea is not conquered again, by an enemy from within.

No man from the cursed North shall reach our Holy of Holies nor lay His shadow across the Ark of the Covenant.

A Woman, One Of Mary's Neighbours:
A Lamentation

ON the fortieth day after His death, all the women neighbours came to the house of Mary to console her and to sing threnodies. And one of them sang this song:

Whereto my Spring, whereto?
And to what other space your perfume ascending?
In what other fields shall you walk?
And to what sky shall you lift up your head to speak your heart?

These valleys shall be barren,
And we shall have naught but dried fields and arid.
All green things will parch in the sun,
And our orchards will bring forth sour apples,
And our vineyards bitter grapes.
We shall thirst for your wine,
And our nostrils will long for your fragrance.

Where to Flower of our first spring, whereto?
And will you return no more?
Will not your jasmine visit us again,
And your cyclamen stand by our wayside
To tell us that we too have our roots deep in earth,
And that our ceaseless breath would forever climb the sky?

Whereto Jesus, whereto,
Son of my neighbour Mary,
And comrade to my son?
Whither, our first Spring, and to what other fields?
Will you return to us again?
Will you in your love-tide visit the barren shores of our dreams?

Ahaz, The Portly:
The Keeper of the Inn

WELL do I remember the last time I saw Jesus the Nazarene. Judas had come to me at the noon hour of that Thursday, and bidden me prepare supper for Jesus and His friends.

He gave me two silver pieces and said, "Buy all that you deem needful for the meal."

And after He was gone my wife said to me, "This is indeed a distinction." For Jesus had become a prophet and He had wrought many miracles.

At twilight He came and His followers, and they sat in the upper chamber around the board, but they were silent and quiet.

Last year also and the year before they had come and then they had been joyous. They broke the bread and drank the wine and sang our ancient strains; and Jesus would talk to them till midnight.

After that they would leave Him alone in the upper chamber and go to sleep in other rooms; for after midnight it was His desire to be alone.

And He would remain awake; I would hear His steps as I lay upon my bed.

But this last time He and His friends were not happy.

My wife had prepared fishes from the Lake of Galilee, and pheasants from Houran stuffed with rice and pomegranate seeds, and I had carried them a jug of my cypress wine.

And then I had left them for I felt that they wished to be alone.

They stayed until it was full dark, and then they all descended together from the upper chamber, but at the foot of the stairs Jesus tarried awhile. And He looked at me and my wife, and He placed His hand upon the head of my daughter and He said, "Good night to you all. We shall come back again to your upper chamber, but we shall not leave you at this early hour. We shall stay until the sun rises above the horizon.

"In a little while we shall return and ask for more bread and more wine. You and your wife have been good hosts to us, and we shall remember you when we come to our mansion and sit at our own board."

And I said, "Sir, it was an honour to serve you. The other innkeepers envy me because of your visits, and in my pride I smile at them in the market-place. Sometimes I even make a grimace."

And He said, "All innkeepers should be proud in serving. For he who gives bread and wine is the brother of him who reaps and gathers the sheaves for the threshing-floor, and of him who crushes the grapes at the winepress. And you are all kindly. You give of your bounty even to those who come with naught but hunger and thirst."

Then He turned to Judas Iscariot who kept the purse of the company, and He said, "Give me two shekels."

And Judas gave Him two shekels saying: "These are the last silver pieces in my purse."

Jesus looked at him and said, "Soon, oversoon, your purse shall be filled with silver."

Then He put the two pieces into my hand and said, "With these buy a silken girdle for your daughter, and bid her wear it on the day of the passover, in remembrance of me."

And looking again into the face of my daughter, He leaned down and kissed her brow. And then He said once more, "Good-night to you all."

And He walked away.

I have been told that what He said to us has been recorded upon a parchment by one of His friends, but I repeat it to you even as I heard it from His own lips.

Never shall I forget the sound of His voice as He said those words, "Good night to you all."

If you would know more of Him, ask my daughter. She is a woman now, but she cherishes the memory of her girlhood. And her words are more ready than mine.

Barabbas:
The Last Words of Jesus

THEY released me and chose Him. Then He rose and I fell down.

And they held Him a victim and a sacrifice for the passover.

I was freed from my chains, and walked with the throng behind Him, but I was a living man going to my own grave.

I should have fled to the desert where shame is burned out by the sun.

Yet I walked with those who had chosen Him to bear my crime.

When they nailed Him on His cross I stood there.

I saw and I heard but I seemed outside of my body.

The thief who was crucified on His right said to Him, "Are you bleeding with me, even you, Jesus of Nazareth?"

And Jesus answered and said, "Were it not for this nail that stays my hand I would reach forth and clasp your hand.

"We are crucified together. Would they had raised your cross nearer to mine."

Then He looked down and gazed upon His mother and a young man who stood beside her.

He said, "Mother, behold your son standing beside you.

"Woman, behold a man who shall carry these drops of my blood to the North Country."

And when he heard the wailing of the women of Galilee He said, "Behold, they weep and I thirst.

"I am held too high to reach their tears.

"I will not take vinegar and gall to quench this thirst."

Then His eyes opened wide to the sky, and He said, "Father, why hast Thou foresaken us?"

And then He said in compassion, "Father, forgive them, for they know not what they do."

When He uttered those words methought I saw all men prostrated before God beseeching forgiveness for the crucifixion of this one man.

Then again He said with a great voice: "Father, into Thy hand I yield back my spirit."

And at last He lifted up His head and said, "Now it is finished, but only upon this hill."

And He closed His eyes.

Then lightning cracked the dark skies, and there was a great thunder.

I know now that those who slew Him in my stead achieved my endless torment.

His crucifixion endured but for an hour.

But I shall be crucified unto the end of my years.

Claudius, A Roman Sentinel:
Jesus the Stoic

AFTER He was taken, they entrusted Him to me. And I was ordered by Pontius Pilatus to keep Him in custody until the following morning.

My soldiers led Him prisoner, and He was obedient to them.

At midnight I left my wife and children and visited the arsenal. It was my habit to go about and see all that was well with my battalions in Jerusalem; and that night I visited the arsenal where He was held.

My soldiers and some of the young Jews were making sport of Him. They had stripped Him of His garment, and they had put a crown of last year's brier-thorns upon His head.

They had seated Him against a pillar, and they were dancing and shouting before Him.

And they had given Him a reed to hold in His hand.

As I entered someone shouted, "Behold, O Captain, the King of the Jews."

I stood before Him and looked at Him, and I was ashamed. I knew not why.

I had fought in Gallia and in Spain, and with my men I had faced death. Yet never had I been in fear, nor been a coward. But when I stood before that man and He looked at me I lost heart. It seemed as though my lips were sealed, and I could not utter no word.

And straightway I left the arsenal.

This chanced thirty years ago. My sons who were babes then are men now. And they are serving Caesar and Rome.

But often in counselling them I have spoken of Him, a man facing death with the sap of life upon His lips, and with compassion for His slayers in His eyes.

And now I am old. I have lived the years fully. And I think truly that neither Pompey nor Caesar was so great a commander as that Man of Galilee.

For since His unresisting death an army has risen out of the earth to fight for Him. . . . And He is better served by them, though dead, than ever Pompey or Caesar was served, though living.

James, The Brother Of The Lord:
The Last Supper

A THOUSAND times I have been visited by the memory of that night. And I know now that I shall be visited a thousand times again.

The earth shall forget the furrows ploughed upon her breast, and a woman the pain and joy of childbirth, ere I shall forget that night.

In the afternoon we had been outside the walls of Jerusalem, and Jesus had said, "Let us go into the city now and take supper at the inn."

It was dark when we reached the inn, and we were hungry. The innkeeper greeted us and led us to an upper chamber.

And Jesus bade us sit around the board, but He himself remained standing, and His eyes rested upon us.

And He spoke to the keeper of the inn and said, "Bring me a basin and a pitcher full of water, and a towel."

And He looked at us again and said gently, "Cast off your sandals."

We did not understand, but at His command we cast them off.

Then the keeper of the inn brought the basin and the pitcher; and Jesus said, "Now I will wash your feet. For I must needs free your feet from the dust of the ancient road, and give them the freedom of the new way."

And we were all abashed and shy.

Then Simon Peter stood up and said: "How shall I suffer my Master and my Lord to wash my feet?"

And Jesus answered, "I will wash your feet that you may remember that he who serves men shall be the greatest among men."

Then He looked at each one of us and He said: "The Son of Man who has chosen you for His brethren, He whose feet were anointed yesterday with myrrh of Arabia and dried with a women's hair, desires now to wash your feet."

And He took the basin and the pitcher and kneeled down and washed our feet, beginning with Judas Iscariot.

Then He sat down with us at the board; and His face was like the dawn rising upon a battlefield after a night of strife and blood-shedding.

And the keeper of the inn came with his wife, bringing food and wine.

And though I had been hungry before Jesus knelt at my feet, now I had no stomach for food. And there was a flame in my throat which I would not quench with wine.

Then Jesus took a loaf of bread and gave to us, saying, "Perhaps we shall not break bread again. Let us eat this morsel in remembrance of our days in Galilee."

And He poured wine from the jug into a cup and He drank, and gave to us, and He said, "Drink this in remembrance of a thirst we have known together. And drink it also in hope for the new vintage. When I am enfolded and am no more among you, and when you meet here or elsewhere, break the bread and pour the wine, and eat and drink even as you are doing now. Then look about you; and perchance you may see me sitting with you at the board."

After saying this He began to distribute among us morsels of fish and pheasant, like a bird feeding its fledglings.

We ate little yet we were filled; and we drank but a drop, for we felt that the cup was like a space between this land and another land.

Then Jesus said, "Ere we leave this board let us rise and sing the joyous hymns of Galilee."

And we rose and sang together, and His voice was above our voices, and there was a ringing in every word of His words.

And He looked at our faces, each and every one, and He said, "Now I bid you farewell. Let us go beyond these walls. Let us go unto Gethsemane."

And John the Son of Zebedee said, "Master, why do you say farewell to us this night?"

And Jesus said, "Let not your heart be troubled. I only leave you to prepare a place for you in my Father's house. But if you shall be in need of me, I will come back to you. Where you call me, there I shall hear you, and wherever your spirit shall seek me, there I will be.

"Forget not that thirst leads to the winepress, and hunger to the wedding-feast.

"It is in your longing that you shall find the Son of Man. For longing is the fountain-head of ecstasy, and it is the path to the Father."

And John spoke again and said, "If you would indeed leave us, how shall we be of good cheer? And why speak you of separation?"

And Jesus said, "The hunted stag knows the arrow of the hunter before it feels it in his breast; and the river is aware of the sea ere it comes to her shore. And the Son of Man has travelled the ways of men.

Before another almond tree renders her blossoms to the sun, my roots shall be reaching into the heart of another field."

Then Simon Peter said: "Master, leave us not now, and deny us not the joy of your presence. Where you go we too will go; and wherever you abide there we will be also."

And Jesus put His hand upon Simon Peter's shoulder, and smiled upon him, and He said, "Who knows but that you may deny me before this night is over, and leave me before I leave you?"

Then of a sudden He said, "Now let us go hence."

And He left the inn and we followed Him. But when we reached the gate of the city, Judas of Iscariot was no longer with us. And we crossed the Valley of Jahannam. Jesus walked far ahead of us, and we walked close to one another.

When He reached an olive grove he stopped and turned towards us saying, "Rest here for an hour." The evening was cool, though it was full spring with the mulberries unfolding their shoots and the apple trees in bloom. And the gardens were sweet.

Each one of us sought the trunk of a tree, and we lay down. I myself gathered my cloak around me and lay under a pine tree.

But Jesus left us and walked by Himself in the olive grove. And I watched Him while the others slept.

He would suddenly stand still, and again He would walk up and down. This He did many times.

Then I saw Him lift His face towards the sky and outstretch His arms to east and west.

Once He had said, "Heaven and earth, and hell too, are of man." And now I remembered His saying, and I knew that He who was pacing the olive grove was heaven made man; and I bethought me that the womb of the earth is not a beginning nor an end, but rather a chariot, a pause; and a moment of wonder and surprise; and hell I saw also, in the valley called Jahannam, which lay between Him and the Holy City.

And as He stood there and I lay wrapped in my garment, I heard His voice speaking. But He was not speaking to us. Thrice I heard Him pronounce the word Father. And that was all I heard.

After a while His arms dropped down, and He stood still like a cypress tree between my eyes and the sky. At last He came over among us again, and He said to us, "Wake and rise. My hour has come. The world is already upon us, armed for battle."

And then He said, "A moment ago I heard the voice of my Father. If I see you not again, remember that the conqueror shall not have peace until he is conquered."

And when we had risen and come close to Him, His face was like the starry heaven above the desert.

Then He kissed each one of us upon the cheek. And when His lips touched my cheek, they were hot, like the hand of a child in fever.

Suddenly we heard a great noise in the distance, as of numbers, and when it came near it was a company of men approaching with lanterns and slaves. And they came in haste.

As they reached the hedge of the grove Jesus left us and went forth and met them. And Judas of Iscariot was leading them.

There were Roman soldiers with swords and spears, and men of Jerusalem with clubs and pickaxes.

And Judas came up to Jesus and kissed Him. And then he said to the armed men, "This is the Man."

And Jesus said to Judas, "Judas, you were patient with me. This could have been yesterday."

Then He turned to the armed men and said: "Take me now. But see that your cage is large enough for these wings."

Then they fell upon Him and held Him, and they were all shouting.

But we in our fear ran away and sought to escape. I ran alone through the olive groves, nor had I power to be mindful, nor did any voice speak in me except my fear.

Through the two or three hours that remained of that night I was fleeing and hiding, and at dawn I found myself in a village near Jericho.

Why had I left Him? I do not know. But to my sorrow I did leave Him. I was a coward and I fled from the face of His enemies.

Then I was sick and ashamed at heart, and I returned to Jerusalem, but He was a prisoner, and no friend could have speech with Him.

He was crucified, and His blood has made new clay of the earth.

And I am living still; I am living upon the honeycomb of His sweet life.

Simon, The Cyrene:
He who Carried the Cross

I WAS on my way to the fields when I saw Him carrying His cross; and multitudes were following Him.

Then I too walked beside Him.

His burden stopped Him many a time, for His body was exhausted.

Then a Roman soldier approached me, saying, "Come, you are strong and firm built; carry the cross of this man."

When I heard these words my heart swelled within me and I was grateful.

And I carried His cross.

It was heavy, for it was made of poplar soaked through with the rains of winter.

And Jesus looked at me. And the sweat of His forehead was running down upon His beard.

Again He looked at me and He said, "Do you too drink this cup? You shall indeed sip its rim with me to the end of time."

So saying He placed His hand upon my free shoulder. And we walked together towards the Hill of the Skull.

But now I felt not the weight of the cross. I felt only His hand. And it was like the wing of a bird upon my shoulder.

Then we reached the hill top, and there they were to crucify Him.

And then I felt the weight of the tree.

He uttered no word when they drove the nails into His hands and feet, nor made He any sound.

And His limbs did not quiver under the hammer.

It seemed as if His hands and feet had died and would only live again when bathed in blood. Yet it seemed also as if He sought the nails as the prince would seek the sceptre; and that He craved to be raised to the heights.

And my heart did not think to pity Him, for I was too filled to wonder.

Now, the man whose cross I carried has become my cross.

Should they say to me again, "Carry the cross of this man," I would carry it till my road ended at the grave.

But I would beg Him to place His hand upon my shoulder.

This happened many years ago; and still whenever I follow the furrow in the field, and in that drowsy moment before sleep, I think always of that Beloved Man.

And I feel His winged hand, here, on my left shoulder.

Cyborea:
The Mother of Judas

MY son was a good man and upright. He was tender and kind to me, and he loved his kin and his countrymen. And he hated our enemies, the cursed Romans, who wear purple cloth though they spin no thread nor sit at any loom; and who reap and gather where they have not ploughed nor sowed the seed.

My son was but seventeen when he was caught shooting arrows at the Roman legion passing through our vineyard.

Even at that age he would speak to the other youths of the glory of Israel, and he would utter many strange things that I did not understand.

He was my son, my only son.

He drank life from these breasts now dry, and he took his first steps in this garden, grasping these fingers that are now like trembling reeds.

With these selfsame hands, young and fresh then like the grapes of Lebanon, I put away his first sandals in a linen kerchief that my mother had given me. I still keep them there in that chest, beside the window.

He was my first-born, and when he took his first step, I too took my first step. For women travel not save when led by their children.

And now they tell me he is dead by his own hand; that he flung himself from the High Rock in remorse because he had betrayed his friend Jesus of Nazareth.

I know my son is dead. But I know he betrayed no one; for he loved his kin and hated none but the Romans.

My son sought the glory of Israel, and naught but that glory was upon his lips and in his deeds.

When he met Jesus on the highway he left me to follow Him. And in my heart I knew that he was wrong to follow any man.

When he bade me farewell I told him that he was wrong, but he listened not.

Our children do not heed us; like the high tide of today, they take no counsel with the high tide of yesterday.

I beg you question me no further about my son.

I loved him and I shall love him forevermore.

If love were in the flesh I would burn it out with hot irons and be at peace. But it is in the soul, unreachable.

And now I would speak no more. Go question another woman more honoured than the mother of Judas.

Go to the mother of Jesus. The sword is in her heart also; she will tell you of me, and you will understand.

The Woman In Byblos:
A Lamentation

WEEP with me, ye daughters of Ashtarte, and all ye lovers of Tamouz.
Bid your heart melt and rise and run blood-tears,
For He who was made of gold and ivory is no more.
In the dark forest the boar overcame Him,
And the tusks of the boar pierced His flesh.
Now He lies stained with the leaves of yesteryear,
And no longer shall His footsteps wake the seeds that sleep in the bosom of the spring.
His voice will not come with the dawn to my window,
And I shall be forever alone.

Weep with me, ye daughters of Ashtarte, and all ye lovers of Tamouz,
For my Beloved has escaped me;

He who spoke as the rivers speak;
He whose voice and time were twins;
He whose mouth was a red pain made sweet;
He on whose lips gall would turn to honey.

Weep with me, daughters of Ashtarte, and ye lovers of Tamouz.
Weep with me around His bier as the stars weep,
And as the moon-petals fall upon His wounded body.
Wet with your tears the silken covers of my bed,
Where my Beloved once lay in my dream,
And was gone away in my awakening.
I charge ye, daughters od Ashtarte, and all ye lovers of Tamouz,
Bare your breasts and weep and comfort me,
For Jesus of Nazareth is dead.

Mary Magdalen (Thirty years later):
On the Resurrection of the Spirit

ONCE again I say that with death Jesus conquered death, and rose from the grave a spirit and a power. And He walked in our solitude and visited the gardens of our passion.

He lies not there in that cleft rock behind the stone.

We who love Him beheld Him with these our eyes which He made to see; and we touched Him with these our hands which He taught to reach forth.

I know you who believe not in Him. I was one of you, and you are many; but your number shall be diminished.

Must you break your harp and your lyre to find the music therein?

Or must you fell a tree ere you can believe it bears fruit?

You hate Jesus because someone from the North Country said He was the Son of God. But you hate one another because each of you deems himself too great to be the brother of the next man.

You hate Him because someone said He was born of a virgin, and not of man's seed.

But you know not the mothers who go to the tomb in virginity, nor the men who go down to the grave choked with their own thirst.

You know not that the earth was given in marriage to the sun, and that earth it is who sends us forth to the mountain and the desert.

There is a gulf that yawns between those who love Him and those who hate Him, between those who believe and those who do not believe.

But when the years have bridged that gulf you shall know that He who lived in us is deathless, that He was the Son of God even as we are the children of God; that He was born of a virgin even as we are born of the husbandless earth.

It is passing strange that the earth gives not to the unbelievers the roots that would suck at her breast, nor the wings wherewith to fly high and drink, and be filled with the dews of her space. But I know what I know, and it is enough.

A Man From Lebanon:
Nineteen Centuries Afterward

MASTER, Master singer,
Master of words unspoken,
Seven times was I born, and seven times have I died,
Since your last hasty visit and our brief welcome.
And behold I live again,
Remembering a day and a night among the hills,
When your tide lifted us up.
Thereafter many lands and many seas did I cross,
And wherever I was led by saddle or sail
Your name was prayer or argument.
Men would bless you or curse you;

The curse, a protest against failure,
The blessing, a hymn of the hunter
Who comes back from the hills
With provision for his mate.

Your friends are yet with us for comfort and support,
And your enemies also, for strength and assurance.
Your mother is with us;
I have beheld the sheen of her face in the
countenance of all mothers;
Her hand rocks cradles with gentleness,
Her hand folds shrouds with tenderness.
And Mary Magdalen is yet in our midst,
She who drank the vinegar of life, and then its wine.
And Judas, the man of pain and small ambitions,
He too walks the earth;
Even now he preys upon himself when his hunger
find naught else,
And seeks his larger self in self-destruction.

And John, he whose youth loved beauty, is here,
And he sings though unheeded.
And Simon Peter the impetuous, who denied you
that he might live longer for you,
He too sits by our fire.
He may deny you again ere the dawn of another day,
Yet he would be crucified for your purpose, and
deem himself unworthy of the honour.
And Caiaphas and Annas still live their day,
And judge the guilty and the innocent.
They sleep upon their feathered bed
Whilst he whom they have judged is whipped with the rods.

And the woman who was taken in adultery,
She too walks the streets of our cities,
And hungers for bread not yet baked,
And she is alone in an empty house.

And Pontius Pilatus is here also:
He stands in awe before you,
And still questions you,
But he dares not risk his station or defy an alien race;
And he is still washing his hands.
Even now Jerusalem holds the basin and Rome the ewer,
And betwixt the two thousand thousand hands
would be washed to whiteness.

Master, Master Poet,
Master of words sung and spoken,
They have builded temples to house your name,
And upon every height they have raised your cross,
A sign and a symbol to guide their wayward feet,
But not unto your joy.
Your joy is a hill beyond their vision,
And it does not comfort them.
They would honour the man unknown to them.
And what consolation is there in a man like
themselves, a man whose kindliness is like their own
kindliness, A god whose love is like their own love,
And whose mercy is in their own mercy?
They honour not the man, the living man,
The first man who opened His eyes and gazed at the sun
With eyelids unquivering.
Nay, they do not know Him, and they would not be like Him.

They would be unknown, walking in the procession of the
unknown.
They would bear sorrow, their sorrow,
And they would not find comfort in your joy.
Their aching heart seeks not consolation in your words and the
song thereof.
And their pain, silent and unshapen,
Makes them creatures lonely and unvisited.
Though hemmed about my kin and kind,
They live in fear, uncomraded;

Yet they would not be alone.
They would bend eastward when the west wind blows.
They call you king,
And they would be in your court.
They pronounce you the Messiah,
And they would themselves be anointed with the holy oil.
Yea, they would live upon your life.

Master, Master Singer,
Your tears were like the showers of May,
And your laughter like the waves of the white sea.
When you spoke your words were the far-off whisper of their lips when those lips should be kindled with fire;
You laughed for the marrow in their bones that was not yet ready for laughter;
And you wept for their eyes that yet were dry.
Your voice fathered their thoughts and their understanding.
Your voice mothered their words and their breath.

Seven times was I born and seven times have I died,
And now I live again, and I behold you,
The fighter among fighters,
The poet of poets,
King above all kings,
A man half-naked with your road-fellows.
Every day the bishop bends down his head
When he pronounces your name.
And every day the beggars say:
"For Jesus' sake
give us a penny to buy bread."
We call upon each other, But in truth we call upon you, Like the flood tide in the spring of our want and desire, And when our autumn comes, like the ebb tide. High or low, your name is upon our lips, The Master of infinite compassion.

Master, Master of our lonely hours,
Here and there, betwixt the cradle and the coffin, I

meet your silent brothers,
The free men, unshackled,
Sons of your mother earth and space.
They are like the birds of the sky,
And like the lilies of the field.
They live your life and think your thoughts,
And they echo your song.
But they are empty-handed,
And they are not crucified with the great crucifixion,
And therein is their pain.
The world crucifies them every day,
But only in little ways.
The sky is not shaken,
And the earth travails not with her dead.
They are crucified and there is none to witness their agony;
They turn their face to right and left
And find not one to promise them a station in his kingdom.
Yet they would be crucified again and yet again,
That your God may be their God,
And your Father their Father.

Master, Master Lover,
The Princess awaits your coming in her fragrant chamber,
And the married unmarried woman in her cage;
The harlot who seeks bread in the streets of her shame,
And the nun in her cloister who has no husband;
The childless woman too at her window,
Where frost designs the forest on the pane,
She finds you in that symmetry,
And she would mother you, and be comforted.

Master, Master Poet,
Master of our silent desires,
The heart of the world quivers with the throbbing of your heart,
But it burns not with your song.
The world sits listening to your voice in tranquil delight,

But it rises not from its seat
To scale the ridges of your hills.
Man would dream your dream but he would not wake to your dawn,
Which is his greater dream.
He would see with your vision,
But he would not drag his heavy feet to your throne;
Yet many have been enthroned in your name
And mitred with your power,
And have turned your golden visit
Into crowns for their head and sceptres for their hand.
Master, Master of Light,
Whose eye dwells in the seeking fingers of the blind,
You are still despised and mocked,
A man too weak and infirm to be God,
A God too much man to call forth adoration.
Their mass and their hymn,
Their sacrament and their rosary, are for their imprisoned self.
You are their yet distant self, their far-off cry, and their passion.
But Master, Sky-heart, Knight of our fairer dream,
You do still tread this day;
Nor bows nor spears shall stay your steps;
You walk through all our arrows.
You smile down upon us,
And though you are the youngest of us all
You father us all.
Poet, Singer, Great Heart,
May our God bless your name,
And the womb that held you, and the breasts that gave you milk.
And may God forgive us all.

The Forerunner

The Forerunner

You are your own forerunner, and the towers you have builded are but the foundation of your giant-self. And that self too shall be a foundation.

And I too am my own forerunner, for the long shadow stretching before me at sunrise shall gather under my feet at the noon hour. Yet another sunrise shall lay another shadow before me, and that also shall be gathered at another noon.

Always have we been our own forerunners, and always shall we be. And all that we have gathered and shall gather shall be but seeds for fields yet unploughed. We are the fields and the ploughmen, the gatherers and the gathered.

When you were a wandering desire in the mist, I too was there a wandering desire. Then we sought one another, and out of our eagerness dreams were born. And dreams were time limitless, and dreams were space without measure.

And when you were a silent word upon life's quivering lips, I too was there, another silent word. Then life uttered us and we came down the years throbbing with memories of yesterday and with longing for tomorrow, for yesterday was death conquered and tomorrow was birth pursued.

And now we are in God's hands. You are a sun in His right hand and I an earth in His left hand. Yet you are not more, shining, than I, shone upon.

And we, sun and earth, are but the beginning of a greater sun and a greater earth. And always shall we be the beginning.

You are your own forerunner, you the stranger passing by the gate of my garden.

And I too am my own forerunner, though I sit in the shadows of my trees and seem motionless.

God's Fool

Once there came from the desert to the great city of Sharia a man who was a dreamer, and he had naught but his garment and staff.

And as he walked through the streets he gazed with awe and wonder at the temples and towers and palaces, for the city of Sharia was of surpassing beauty. And he spoke often to the passers-by, questioning them about their city—but they understood not his language, nor he their language.

At the noon hour he stopped before a vast inn. It was built of yellow marble, and people were going in and coming out unhindered.

"This must be a shrine,' he said to himself, and he too went in. But what was his surprise to find himself in a hall of great splendour and a large company of men and women seated about many tables. They were eating and drinking and listening to the musicians.

'Nay,' said the dreamer. 'This is no worshipping. It must be a feast given by the prince to the people, in celebration of a great event.'

At that moment a man, whom he took to be the slave of the prince, approached him, and bade him be seated. And he was served with meat and wine and most excellent sweets.

When he was satisfied, the dreamer rose to depart. At the door he was stopped by a large man magnificently arrayed.

'Surely this is the prince himself,' said the dreamer in his heart, and he bowed to him and thanked him.

Then the large man said in the language of the city:

'Sir, you have not paid for your dinner.' And the dreamer did not understand, and again thanked him heartily. Then the large man bethought him, and he looked more closely upon the dreamer. And he saw that he was a stranger, clad in but a poor garment, and that indeed he had not wherewith to pay for his meal. Then the large man clapped his hands and called—and there came four watchmen of the city. And they listened to the large man. Then they took the dreamer between them, and they were two on each side of him. And the dreamer noted the ceremoniousness of their dress and of their manner and he looked upon them with delight. 'These,' said he, 'are men of distinction.'

And they walked all together until they came to the House of Judgement and they entered.

The dreamer saw before him, seated upon a throne, a venerable man with flowing beard, robed majestically. And he thought he was the king. And he rejoiced to be brought before him.

Now the watchmen related to the judge, who was the venerable man, the charge against the dreamer, and the judge appointed two advocates, one to present the charge and the other to defend the stranger. And the advocates rose, the one after the other, and delivered each his argument. And the dreamer thought himself to be listening to addresses of welcome, and his heart filled with gratitude to the king and the prince for all that was done for him.

Then sentence was passed upon the dreamer, that upon a tablet about his neck his crime should be written, and that he should ride through the city on a naked horse, with a trumpeter and a drummer before him. And the sentence was carried out forthwith.

Now as the dreamer rode through the city upon the naked horse, with the trumpeter and the drummer before him, the inhabitants of the city came running forth at the sound of the noise, and when they saw him they laughed one and all, and the children ran after him in companies from street to street. And the dreamer's heart was filled with ecstasy, and his eyes shone upon them. For to him the tablet was a sign of the king's blessing and the procession was in his honour.

Now as he rode, he saw among the crowd a man who was from the desert like himself and his heart swelled with joy, and he cried out to him with a shout:

'Friend! Friend! Where are we? What city of the heart's desire is this? What race of lavish hosts, who feast the chance guest in their palaces, whose princes companion him, whose kings hangs a token upon his breast and opens to him the hospitality of a city descended from heaven?'

And he who was also of the desert replied not. He only smiled and slightly shook his head. And the procession passed on.

And the dreamer's face was uplifted and his eyes were overflowing with light.

Love

They say the jackal and the mole
Drink from the selfsame stream
Where the lion comes to drink.
And they say the eagle and the vulture
Dig their beaks into the same carcass,
And are at peace, one with the other,

In the presence of the dead thing.
O love, whose lordly hand
Has bridled my desires,
And raised my hunger and my thirst
To dignity and pride,
Let not the strong in me and the constant
Eat the bread or drink the wine
That tempt my weaker self.
Let me rather starve,
And let my heart parch with thirst,
And let me die and perish,
Ere I stretch my hand
To a cup you did not fill,
Or a bowl you did not bless.

The King Hermit

They told me that in a forest among the mountains lives a young man in solitude who once was a king of a vast country beyond the Two Rivers. And they also said that he, of his own will, had left his throne and the land of his glory and come to dwell in the wilderness.

And I said, "I would seek that man, and learn the secret of his heart; for he who renounces a kingdom must needs be greater than a kingdom."

On that very day I went to the forest where he dwells. And I found him sitting under a white cypress, and in his hand a reed as if it were a sceptre. And I greeted him even as I would greet a king. And he turned to me and said gently, "What would you in this forest of serenity? Seek you a lost self in the green shadows, or is it a home-coming in your twilight?"

And I answered, "I sought but you—for I fain would know that which made you leave a kingdom for a forest."

And he said, "Brief is my story, for sudden was the bursting of the bubble. It happened thus: one day as I sat at a window in my palace, my chamberlain and an envoy from a foreign land were walking in my garden. And as they approached my window, the lord chamberlain was speaking of himself and saying, 'I am like the king; I have a thirst for strong wine and a hunger for all games of chance. And like my lord the king I have storms of temper.' And the lord chamberlain and the envoy disappeared among the trees. But in a few minutes they returned, and this time the lord chamberlain was speaking of me, and he was saying, 'My lord the king is like myself—a good marksman; and like me he loves music and bathes thrice a day.' "

After a moment he added, "On the eve of that day I left my palace with but my garment, for I would no longer be ruler over those who assume my vices and attribute to me their virtues."

And I said, "This is indeed a wonder, and passing strange."

And he said, "Nay, my friend, you knocked at the gate of my silences and received but a trifle. For who would not leave a kingdom for a forest where the seasons sing and dance ceaselessly? Many are those who have given their kingdom for less than solitude and the sweet fellowship of aloneness. Countless are the eagles who descend from the upper air to live with moles that they may know the secrets of the earth. There are those who renounce the kingdom of dreams that they may not seem distant from the dreamless. And those who renounce the kingdom of nakedness and cover their souls that others may not be ashamed in beholding truth uncovered and beauty unveiled. And greater yet than all of these is he who renounces the kingdom of sorrow that he may not seem proud and vainglorious."

Then rising he leaned upon his reed and said, "Go now to the great city and sit at its gate and watch all those who enter into it and those who go out. And see that you find him who, though born a king, is without kingdom; and him who though ruled in flesh rules in spirit—though neither he nor his subjects know this; and him also who but seems to rule yet is in truth slave of his own slaves."

After he had said these things he smiled on me, and there were a thousand dawns upon his lips. Then he turned and walked away into the heart of the forest.

And I returned to the city, and I sat at its gate to watch the passers-by even as he had told me. And from that day to this numberless are the kings whose shadows have passed over me and few are the subjects over whom my shadow passed.

The Lion's Daughter

Four slaves stood fanning an old queen who was asleep upon her throne. And she was snoring. And upon the queen's lap a cat lay purring and gazing lazily at the slaves.

The first slave spoke, and said, "How ugly this old woman is in her sleep. See her mouth droop; and she breathes as if the devil were choking her."

Then the cat said, purring, "Not half so ugly in her sleep as you in your waking slavery."

And the second slave said, "You would think sleep would smooth her wrinkles instead of deepening them. She must be dreaming of something evil."

And the cat purred, "Would that you might sleep also and dream of your freedom."

And the third slave said, "Perhaps she is seeing the procession of all those that she has slain."

And the cat purred, "Aye, she sees the procession of your forefathers and your descendants."

And the fourth slave said, "It is all very well to talk about her, but it does not make me less weary of standing and fanning."

And the cat purred, "You shall be fanning to all eternity; for as it is on earth, so it is in heaven."

At this moment the old queen nodded in her sleep, and her crown fell to the floor.

And one of the slaves said, "That is a bad omen."

And the cat purred, "The bad omen of one is the good omen of another."

And the second slave said, "What if she should wake, and find her crown fallen! She would surely slay us."

And the cat purred, "Daily from your birth she has slain you and you know it not."

And the third slave said, "Yes, she would slay us and she would call it making a sacrifice to the gods."

And the cat purred, "Only the weak are sacrificed to the gods."

And the fourth slave silenced the others, and softly he picked up the crown and replaced it, without waking her, on the old queen's head.

And the cat purred, "Only a slave restores a crown that has fallen."

And after a while the old queen woke, and she looked about her and yawned. Then she said, "Methought I dreamed, and I saw four caterpillars chased by a scorpion around the trunk of an ancient oak tree. I like not my dream."

Then she closed her eyes and went to sleep again. And she snored. And the four slaves went on fanning her.

And the cat purred, "Fan on, fan on, stupids. You fan but the fire that consumes you."

Tyranny

Thus sings the she-dragon that guards the seven caves by the sea:

"My mate shall come riding on the waves. His thundering roar shall fill the earth with fear, and the flames of his nostrils shall set the sky afire. At the eclipse of the moon we shall be wedded, and at the eclipse of the sun I shall give birth to a Saint George, who shall slay me."

Thus sings the she-dragon that guards the seven caves by the sea.

The Saint

In my youth I once visited a saint in his silent grove beyond the hills; and as we were conversing upon the nature of virtue a brigand came limping wearily up the ridge. When he reached the grove he knelt down before the saint and said, "O saint, I would be comforted! My sins are heavy upon me."

And the saint replied, "My sins, too, are heavy upon me."

And the brigand said, "But I am a thief and a plunderer."

And the saint replied, "I too am a thief and a plunderer."

And the brigand said, "But I am a murderer, and the blood of many men cries in my ears."

And the saint replied, "I am a murderer, and in my ears cries the blood of many men."

And the brigand said, "I have committed countless crimes."

And the saint replied, "I too have committed crimes without number."

Then the brigand stood up and gazed at the saint, and there was a strange look in his eyes. And when he left us he went skipping down the hill.

And I turned to the saint and said, "Wherefore did you accuse yourself of uncommitted crimes? See you not this man went away no longer believing in you?"

And the saint answered, "It is true he no longer believes in me. But he went away much comforted."

At that moment we heard the brigand singing in the distance, and the echo of his song filled the valley with gladness.

The Plutocrat

In my wanderings I once saw upon an island a man-headed, iron-hoofed monster who ate of the earth and drank of the sea incessantly. And for a long while I watched him. Then I approached him and said, "Have you never enough; is your hunger never satisfied and your thirst never quenched?"

And he answered saying, "Yes, I am satisfied, nay, I am weary of eating and drinking; but I am afraid that tomorrow there will be no more earth to eat and no more sea to drink."

The Greater Self

This came to pass. After the coronation of Nufsibaal King of Byblus, he retired to his bed-chamber—the very room which the three hermit-magicians of the mountains had built for him. He took off his crown and his royal raiment, and stood in the centre of the room thinking of himself, now the all-powerful ruler of Byblus.

Suddenly he turned; and he saw stepping out of the silver mirror which his mother had given him, a naked man.

The king was startled, and he cried out to the man, "What would you?"

And the naked man answered, "Naught but this: Why have they crowned you king?"

And the king answered, "Because I am the noblest man in the land."

Then the naked man said, "If you were still more noble, you would not be king."

And the king said, "Because I am the mightiest man in the land they crowned me."

And the naked man said, "If you were mightier yet, you would not be king."

Then the king said, "Because I am the wisest man they crowned me king."

And the naked man said, "If you were still wiser you would not choose to be king."

Then the king fell to the floor and wept bitterly.

The naked man looked down upon him. Then he took up the crown and with tenderness replaced it upon the king's bent head.

And the naked man, gazing lovingly upon the king, entered into the mirror.

And the king roused, and straightway he looked into the mirror. And he saw there but himself crowned.

War And The Small Nations

Once, high above a pasture, where a sheep and a lamb were grazing, an eagle was circling and gazing hungrily down upon the lamb. And as he was about to descend and seize his prey, another eagle appeared and hovered above the sheep and her young with the same hungry intent. Then the two rivals began to fight, filling the sky with their fierce cries.

The sheep looked up and was much astonished. She turned to the lamb and said:

"How strange, my child, that these two noble birds should attack one another. Is not the vast sky large enough for both of them? Pray, my little one, pray in your heart that God may make peace between your winged brothers."

And the lamb prayed in his heart.

Critics

One nightfall a man travelling on horseback towards the sea reached an inn by the roadside. He dismounted and, confident in man and night like all riders towards the sea, he tied his horse to a tree beside the door and entered into the inn.

At midnight, when all were asleep, a thief came and stole the traveller's horse.

In the morning the man awoke, and discovered that his horse was stolen. And he grieved for his horse, and that a man had found it in his heart to steal.

Then his fellow lodgers came and stood around him and began to talk.

And the first man said, "How foolish of you to tie your horse outside the stable."

And the second said, " Still more foolish, without even hobbling the horse!"

And the third man said, "It is stupid at best to travel to the sea on horseback."

And the fourth said, "Only the indolent and the slow of foot own horses."

Then the traveller was much astonished. At last he cried, "My friends, because my horse was stolen, you have hastened one and all to tell me my faults and my shortcomings. But strange, not one word of reproach have you uttered about the man who stole my horse."

Poets

Four poets were sitting around a bowl of punch that stood on a table.

Said the first poet, "Methinks I see with my third eye the fragrance of this wine hovering in space like a cloud of birds in an enchanted forest."

The second poet raised his head and said, "With my inner ear I can hear those mist-birds singing. And the melody holds my heart as the white rose imprisons the bee within her petals."

The third poet closed his eyes and stretched his arm upwards, and said, "I touch them with my hand. I feel their wings, like the breath of a sleeping fairy, brushing against my fingers."

Then the fourth poet rose and lifted up the bowl, and he said, "Alas, friends! I am too dull of sight and of hearing and of touch. I cannot see the fragrance of this wine, nor hear its song, nor feel the beating of its wings. I perceive but the wine itself. Now therefore must I drink it, that it may sharpen my senses and raise me to your blissful heights."

And putting the bowl to his lips, he drank the punch to the very last drop.

The three poets, with their mouths open, looked at him aghast, and there was a thirsty yet unlyrical hatred in their eyes.

The Weather-Cock

Said the weather-cock to the wind, "How tedious and monotonous you are! Can you not blow any other way but in my face? You disturb my God-given stability."

And the wind did not answer. It only laughed in space.

The King of Aradus

Once the elders of the city of Aradus presented themselves before the king, and besought of him a decree to forbid to men all wine and all intoxicants within their city.

And the king turned his back upon them and went out from them laughing.

Then the elders departed in dismay.

At the door of the palace they met the lord chamberlain. And the lord chamberlain observed that they were troubled, and he understood their case.

Then he said, "Pity, my friends! Had you found the king drunk, surely he would have granted you your petition."

Out Of My Deeper Heart

Out of my deeper heart a bird rose and flew skywards.

Higher and higher did it rise, yet larger and larger did it grow.

At first it was but like a swallow, then a lark, then an eagle, then as vast as a spring cloud, and then it filled the starry heavens.

Out of my heart a bird flew skywards. And it waxed larger as it flew. Yet it left not my heart.

O my faith, my untamed knowledge, how shall I fly to your height and see with you man's larger self pencilled upon the sky?

How shall I turn this sea within me into mist, and move with you in space immeasurable?

How can a prisoner within the temple behold its golden domes?

How shall the heart of a fruit be stretched to envelop the fruit also?

O my faith, I am in chains behind these bars of silver and ebony, and I cannot fly with you.

Yet out of my heart you rise skyward, and it is my heart that holds you, and I shall be content.

Dynasties

The queen of Ishana was in travail of childbirth; and the king and the mighty men of his court were waiting in breathless anxiety in the great hall of the Winged Bulls.

At eventide there came suddenly a messenger in haste and prostrated himself before the king, and said, "I bring glad tidings unto my lord the king, and unto the kingdom and the slaves of the king. Mihrab the Cruel, thy life-long enemy, the king of Bethroun, is dead."

When the king and the mighty men heard this, they all rose and shouted for joy; for the powerful Mihrab, had he lived longer, had assuredly overcome Ishana and carried the inhabitants captive.

At this moment the court physician also entered the hall of Winged Bulls, and behind him came the royal midwives. And the physician prostrated himself before the king, and said, "My lord the king shall live for ever, and through countless generations shall he rule over the people of Ishana. For unto thee, O King, is born this very hour a son, who shall be thy heir."

Then indeed was the soul of the king intoxicated with joy, that in the same moment his foe was dead and the royal line was established.

Now in the city of Ishana lived a true prophet. And the prophet was young, and bold of spirit. And the king that very night ordered that the prophet should be brought before him. And when he was brought, the king said unto him, "Prophesy now, and foretell what shall be the future of my son who is this day born unto the kingdom."

And the prophet hesitated not, but said, "Hearken, O King, and I will indeed prophesy of the future of thy son that is this day born. The soul of thy enemy, even of thy enemy King Mihrab, who died yester-eve, lingered but a day upon the wind. Then it sought for itself a body to enter into. And that which it entered into was the body of thy son that is born unto thee this hour."

Then the king was enraged, and with his sword he slew the prophet.

And from that day to this, the wise men of Ishana say one to another secretly, "Is it not known, and has it not been said from of old, that Ishana is ruled by an enemy?"

Knowledge and Half-Knowledge

Four frogs sat upon a log that lay floating on the edge of a river. Suddenly the log was caught by the current and swept slowly down the stream. The frogs were delighted and absorbed, for never before had they sailed.

At length the first frog spoke, and said, "This is indeed a most marvellous log. It moves as if alive. No such log was ever known before."

Then the second frog spoke, and said, "Nay, my friend, the log is like other logs, and does not move. It is the river that is walking to the sea, and carries us and the log with it."

And the third frog spoke, and said, "It is neither the log nor the river that moves. The moving is in our thinking. For without thought nothing moves."

And the three frogs began to wrangle about what was really moving. The quarrel grew hotter and louder, but they could not agree.

Then they turned to the fourth frog, who up to this time had been listening attentively but holding his peace, and they asked his opinion.

And the fourth frog said, "Each of you is right, and none of you is wrong. The moving is in the log and the water and our thinking also."

And the three frogs became very angry, for none of them was willing to admit that his was not the whole truth, and that the other two were not wholly wrong.

Then a strange thing happened. The three frogs got together and pushed the fourth frog off the log into the river.

Said A Sheet Of Snow White Paper...

Said a sheet of snow-white paper, "Pure was I created, and pure will I remain for ever. I would rather be burnt and turn to white ashes than suffer darkness to touch me or the unclean to come near me."

The ink-bottle heard what the paper was saying, and it laughed in its dark heart; but it never dared to approach her. And the multicoloured pencils heard her also, and they too never came near her.

And the snow-white sheet of paper did remain pure and chaste for ever, pure and chaste—and empty.

The Scholar And The Poet

Said the serpent to the lark, "Thou flyest, yet thou canst not visit the recesses of the earth where the sap of life moveth in perfect silence."

And the lark answered, "Aye, thou knowest over much, nay thou art wiser then all things wise—pity thou canst not fly."

And as if he did not hear, the serpent said, "Thou canst not see the secrets of the deep, nor move among the treasures of the hidden empire. It was but yesterday I lay in a cave of rubies. It is like the heart of a ripe pomegranate, and the faintest ray of light turns into a flame-rose. Who but me can behold such marvels?"

And the lark said, "None, none but thee can lie among the crystal memories of the cycles—pity thou canst not sing."

And the serpent said, "I know a plant whose root descends to the bowels of the earth, and he who eats of that root becomes fairer than Ashtarte."

And the lark said, "No one, no one but thee could inveil the magic thought of the earth—pity thou canst not fly."

And the serpent said, "There is a purple stream that runneth under a mountain, and he who drinketh of it shall become immortal even as the gods. Surely no bird or beast can discover that purple stream."

And the lark answered, "If thou willest thou canst become deathless even as the gods—pity thou canst not sing."

And the serpent said, "I know a buried temple, which I visit once a moon. It was built by a forgotten race of giants, and upon its walls are graven the secrets of time and space, and he who reads them shall understand that which passeth all understanding."

And the lark said, "Verily, if thou so desirest thou canst encircle with thy pliant body all knowledge of time and space—pity thou canst not fly."

Then the serpent was disgusted, and as he turned and entered into his hole he muttered, "Empty-headed songster!"

And the lark flew away singing, "Pity thou canst not sing. Pity, pity, my wise one, thou canst not fly."

Values

Once a man unearthed in his field a marble statue of great beauty. And he took it to a collector who loved all beautiful things and offered it to him for sale, and the collector bought it for a large price. And they parted.

And as the man walked home with his money he thought, and he said to himself, "How much life this money means! How can anyone give all this for a dead carved stone buried and undreamed of in the earth for a thousand years?"

And now the collector was looking at his statue, and he was thinking, and he said to himself, "What beauty! What life! The dream of what a soul!—and fresh with the sweet sleep of a thousand years. How can anyone give all this for money, dead and dreamless?"

Other Seas

A fish said to another fish, "Above this sea of ours there is another sea, with creatures swimming in it—and they live there even as we live here."

The fish replied, "Pure fancy! Pure fancy! When you know that everything that leaves our sea by even an inch, and stays out of it, dies. What proof have you of other lives in other seas?"

Repentance

On a moonless night a man entered into his neighbour's garden and stole the largest melon he could find and brought it home.

He opened it and found it still unripe.

Then behold a marvel!

The man's conscience woke and smote him with remorse; and he repented having stolen the melon.

The Dying Man And The Vulture

Wait, wait yet awhile, my eager friend.
I shall yield but too soon this wasted thing,
Whose agony overwrought and useless
Exhausts your patience.
I would not have your honest hunger
Wait upon these moments:
But this chain, though made of breath,
Is hard to break.
And the will to die,
Stronger than all things strong,
Is stayed by a will to live

Feebler than all things feeble.
Forgive me, comrade; I tarry too long.
It is memory that holds my spirit;
A procession of distant days,
A vision of youth spent in a dream,
A face that bids my eyelids not to sleep,
A voice that lingers in my ears,
A hand that touches my hand.
Forgive me that you have waited too long.
It is over now, and all is faded:
The face, the voice, the hand and the mist that brought them hither.
The knot is untied.
The cord is cleaved.
And that which is neither food nor drink is withdrawn.
Approach, my hungry comrade;
The board is made ready.
And the fare, frugal and spare,
Is given with love.
Come, and dig your beak here, into the left side,
And tear out of its cage this smaller bird,
Whose wings can beat no more:
I would have it soar with you into the sky.
Come now, my friend, I am your host tonight,
And you my welcome guest.

Beyond My Solitude

Beyond my solitude is another solitude, and to him who dwells therein my aloneness is a crowded market-place and my silence a confusion of sounds.

Too young am I and too restless to seek that above-solitude. The voices of yonder valley still hold my ears and its shadows bar my way and I cannot go.

Beyond these hills is a grove of enchantment and to him who dwells therein my peace is but a whirlwind and my enchantment an illusion.

Too young am I and too riotous to seek that sacred grove. The taste of blood is clinging in my mouth, and the bow and the arrows of my fathers yet linger in my hand and I cannot go.

Beyond this burdened self lives my freer self; and to him my dreams are a battle fought in twilight and my desires the rattling of bones.

Too young am I and too outraged to be my freer self.

And how shall I become my freer self unless I slay my burdened selves, or unless all men become free?

How shall the eagle in me soar against the sun until my fledglings leave the nest which I with my own beak have built for them?

The Last Watch

At high tide of night, when the first breath of dawn came upon the wind, the forerunner, he who calls himself echo to a voice yet unheard, left his bed-chamber and ascended to the roof of his house. Long he stood and looked down upon the slumbering city. Then he raised his head, and even as if the sleepless spirits of all those asleep had gathered around him, he opened his lips and spoke, and he said:

"My friends and neighbours and you who daily pass my gate, I would speak to you in your sleep, and in the valley of your dreams I would walk naked and unrestrained; for heedless are your waking hours and deaf are your sound-burdened ears.

"Long did I love you and overmuch.

"I love the one among you as though he were all, and all as if you were one. And in the spring of my heart I sang in your gardens, and in the summer of my heart I watched at your threshing-floors.

"Yea, I loved you all, the giant and the pygmy, the leper and the anointed, and him who gropes in the dark even as him who dances his days upon the mountains.

"You, the strong, have I loved, though the marks of your iron hoofs are yet upon my flesh; and you the weak, though you have drained my faith and wasted my patience.

"You the rich have I loved, while bitter was your honey to my mouth; and you the poor, though you knew my empty-handed shame.

"You the poet with the bowed lute and blind fingers, you have I loved in self-indulgence; and you the scholar ever gathering rotted shrouds in potters' fields.

"You the priest I have loved, who sit in the silences of yesterday questioning the fate of my tomorrow; and you the worshippers of gods the images of your own desires.

"You the thirsting woman whose cup is ever full, I have loved in understanding; and you the woman of restless nights, you too I have loved in pity.

"You the talkative have I loved, saying, 'Life hath much to say'; and you the dumb have I loved, whispering to myself, 'Says he not in silence that which I fain would hear in words?"

"And you the judge and the critic, I have loved also; yet when you have seen me crucified, you said, 'He bleeds rhythmically, and the pattern his blood makes upon his white skin is beautiful to behold.'

"Yea, I have loved you all, the young and the old, the trembling reed and the oak.

"But, alas, it was the over-abundance of my heart that turned you from me. You would drink love from a cup, but not from a surging river. You would hear love's faint murmur, but when love shouts you would muffle your ears.

"And because I have loved you all you have said, 'Too soft and yielding is his heart, and too undiscerning is his path. It is the love of a needy one, who picks crumbs even as he sits at kingly feasts. And it is the love of a weakling, for the strong loves only the strong."

"And because I have loved you overmuch you have said, 'It is but the love of a blind man who knows not the beauty of one nor the ugliness of another. And it is the love of the tasteless who drinks vinegar even as wine. And it is the love of the impertinent and the overweening, for what stranger could be our mother and father and sister and brother?'

"This you have said, and more. For often in the market-place you pointed your fingers at me and said mockingly, 'There goes the ageless one, the man without seasons, who at the noon hour plays games with our children and at eventide sits with our elders and assumes wisdom and understanding.'

"And I said, 'I will love them more. Aye, even more. I will hide my love with seeming to hate, and disguise my tenderness as bitterness. I will wear an iron mask, and only when armed and mailed shall I seek them.'

"Then I laid a heavy hand upon your bruises, and like a tempest in the night I thundered in your ears.

"From the housetop I proclaimed you hypocrites, Pharisees, tricksters, false and empty earth-bubbles.

"The short-sighted among you I cursed for blind bats, and those too near the earth I likened to soulless moles.

"The eloquent I pronounced fork-tongued, the silent, stone-lipped, and the simple and artless I called the dead never weary of death.

"The seekers after world knowledge I condemned as offenders of the holy spirit and those who would naught but the spirit I branded as hunters of shadows who cast their nets in flat waters and catch but their own images.

"Thus with my lips have I denounced you, while my heart, bleeding within me, called you tender names.

"It was love lashed by its own self that spoke. It was pride half slain that fluttered in the dust. It was my hunger for your love that raged from the housetop, while my own love, kneeling in silence, prayed your forgiveness.

"But behold a miracle!

"It was my disguise that opened your eyes, and my seeming to hate that woke your hearts.

"And now you love me.

"You love the swords that stroke you and the arrows that crave your breast. For it comforts you to be wounded and only when you drink of your own blood can you be intoxicated.

"Like moths that seek destruction in the flame you gather daily in my garden; and with faces uplifted and eyes enchanted you watch me tear the fabric of your days. And in whispers you say the one to the other, 'He sees with the light of God. He speaks like the prophets of old. He unveils our souls and unlocks our hearts, and like the eagle that knows the way of foxes he knows our ways.'

"Aye, in truth, I know your ways, but only as an eagle knows the ways of his fledglings. And I fain would disclose my secret. Yet in my need for your nearness I feign remoteness, and in fear of the ebb tide of your love I guard the floodgates of my love."

After saying these things the forerunner covered his face with his hands and wept bitterly. For he knew in his heart that love humiliated in its nakedness is greater than love that seeks triumph in disguise; and he was ashamed.

But suddenly he raised his head, and like one waking from sleep he outstretched his arms and said, "Night is over, and we children of night must die when dawn comes leaping upon the hills; and out of our ashes a mightier love shall rise. And it shall laugh in the sun, and it shall be deathless."

The Wanderer

The Wanderer

I met him at the crossroads, a man with but a cloak and a staff, and a veil of pain upon his face. And we greeted one another, and I said to him, "Come to my house and be my guest."

And he came.

My wife and my children met us at the threshold, and he smiled at them, and they loved his coming.

Then we all sat together at the board and we were happy with the man for there was a silence and a mystery in him.

And after supper we gathered to the fire and I asked him about his wanderings.

He told us many a tale that night and also the next day, but what I now record was born out of the bitterness of his days though he himself was kindly, and these tales are of the dust and patience of his road.

And when he left us after three days we did not feel that a guest had departed but rather that one of us was still out in the garden and had not yet come in.

Garments

Upon a day Beauty and Ugliness met on the shore of a sea. And they said to one another, "Let us bathe in the sea."

Then they disrobed and swam in the waters. And after a while Ugliness came back to shore and garmented himself with the garments of Beauty and walked away.

And Beauty too came out of the sea, and found not her raiment, and she was too shy to be naked, therefore she dressed herself with the raiment of Ugliness. And Beauty walked her way.

And to this very day men and women mistake the one for the other.

Yet some there are who have beheld the face of Beauty, and they know her notwithstanding her garments. And some there be who know the face of Ugliness, and the cloth conceals him not from their eyes.

The Eagle And The Skylark

A skylark and an eagle met on a rock upon a high hill. The skylark said, "Good morrow to you, Sir." And the eagle looked down upon him and said faintly, "Good morrow."

And the skylark said, "I hope all things are well with you, Sir."

"Aye," said the eagle, "all is well with us. But do you not know that we are the king of birds, and that you shall not address us before we ourselves have spoken?"

Said the skylark, "Methinks we are of the same family."

The eagle looked upon him with disdain and he said, "Who ever has said that you and I are of the same family?"

Then said the skylark, "But I would remind you of this, I can fly even as high as you, and I can sing and give delight to the other creatures of this earth. And you give neither pleasure nor delight."

Then the eagle was angered, and he said, "Pleasure and delight! You little presumptuous creature! With one thrust of my beak I could destroy you. You are but the size of my foot."

Then the skylark flew up and alighted upon the back of the eagle and began to pick at his feathers. The eagle was annoyed, and he flew swift and high that he might rid himself of the little bird. But he failed to do so. At last he dropped back to that very rock upon the high hill, more fretted than ever, with the little creature still upon his back, and cursing the fate of the hour.

Now at that moment a small turtle came by and laughed at the sight, and laughed so hard the she almost turned upon her back.

And the eagle looked down upon the turtle and he said, "You slow creeping thing, ever one with the earth, what are you laughing at?"

And the turtle said, "Why I see that you are turned horse, and that you have a small bird riding you, but the small bird is the better bird."

And the eagle said to her, "Go you about your business. This is a family affair between my brother, the lark, and myself."

The Love Song

A poet once wrote a love song and it was beautiful. And he made many copies of it, and sent them to his friends and his acquaintances, both men and women, and even to a young woman whom he had met but once, who lived beyond the mountains.

And in a day or two a messenger came from the young woman bringing a letter. And in the letter she said, "Let me assure you, I am deeply touched by the love song that you have written to me. Come now, and see my father and my mother, and we shall make arrangements for the betrothal."

And the poet answered the letter, and he said to her, "My friend, it was but a song of love out of a poet's heart, sung by every man to every woman."

And she wrote again to him saying, "Hypocrite and liar in words! From this day unto my coffin-day I shall hate all poets for your sake."

Tears And Laughter

Upon the bank of the Nile at eventide, a hyena met a crocodile and they stopped and greeted one another.

The hyena spoke and said, "How goes the day with you, Sir?" And the crocodile answered saying, "It goes badly with me. Sometimes in my pain and sorrow I weep, and then the creatures always say, 'They are but crocodile tears.' And this wounds me beyond all telling."

Then the hyena said, "You speak of your pain and your sorrow, but think of me also, for a moment. I gaze at the beauty of the world, its wonders and its miracles, and out of sheer joy I laugh even as the day laughs. And then the people of the jungle say, 'It is but the laughter of a hyena.'"

At The Fair

There came to the Fair a girl from the country-side, most comely. There was a lily and a rose in her face. There was a sunset in her hair, and dawn smiled upon her lips.

No sooner did the lovely stranger appear in their sight than the young men sought her and surrounded her. One would dance with her, and another would cut a cake in her honour. And they all desired to kiss her cheek. For after all, was it not the Fair?

But the girl was shocked and started, and she thought ill of the young men. She rebuked them, and she even struck one or two of them in the face. Then she ran away from them.

And on her way home that evening she was saying in her heart, "I am disgusted. How unmannerly and ill bred are these men. It is beyond all patience."

A year passed during which that very comely girl thought much of Fairs and men. Then she came again to the Fair with the lily and the rose in her face, the sunset in her hair and the smile of dawn upon her lips.

But now the young men, seeing her, turned from her. And all the day long she was unsought and alone.

And at eventide as she walked the road toward her home she cried in her heart, "I am disgusted. How unmannerly and ill bred are these youths. It is beyond all patience."

The Two Princesses

In the city of Shawakis lived a prince, and he was loved by everyone, men and women and children. Even the animals of the field came unto him in greeting.

But all the people said that his wife, the princess, loved him not; nay, that she even hated him.

And upon a day the princess of a neighbouring city came to visit the princess of Shawakis. And they sat and talked together, and their words led to their husbands.

And the princess of Sharakis said with passion, "I envy you your happiness with the prince, your husband, though you have been married these many years. I hate my husband. He belongs not to me alone, and I am indeed a woman most unhappy."

Then the visiting princess gazed at her and said, "My friend, the truth is that you love your husband. Aye, and you still have him for a passion unspent, and that is life in woman like unto Spring in a garden. But pity me, and my husband, for we do but endure one another in silent patience. And yet you and others deem this happiness."

The Lightning Flash

There was a Christian bishop in his cathedral on a stormy day, and an un-Christian woman came and stood before him, and she said, "I am not a Christian. Is there salvation for me from hell-fire?"

And the bishop looked upon the woman, and he answered her saying, "Nay, there is salvation for those only who are baptised of water and of the spirit."

And even as he spoke a bolt from the sky fell with thunder upon the cathedral and it was filled with fire.

And the men of the city came running, and they saved the woman, but the bishop was consumed, food of the fire.

The Hermit And The Beasts

Once there lived among the green hills a hermit. He was pure of spirit and white of heart. And all the animals of the land and all the fowls of the air came to him in pairs and he spoke unto them. They heard him gladly, and they would gather near unto him, and would not go until nightfall, when he would send them away, entrusting them to the wind and the woods with his blessing.

Upon an evening as he was speaking of love, a leopard raised her head and said to the hermit, "You speak to us of loving. Tell us, Sir, where is your mate?"

And the hermit said, "I have no mate."

Then a great cry of surprise rose from the company of beasts and fowls, and they began to say among themselves, "How can he tell us of loving and mating when he himself knows naught thereof?" And quietly and in distain they left him alone.

That night the hermit lay upon his mat with his face earthward, and he wept bitterly and beat his hands upon his breast.

The Prophet And The Child

Once on a day the prophet Sharia met a child in a garden. The child ran to him and said, "Good morrow to you, Sir," and the prophet said, "Good morrow to you, Sir." And in a moment, "I see that you are alone."

Then the child said, in laughter and delight, "It took a long time to lose my nurse. She thinks I am behind those hedges; but can't you see that I am here?" Then he gazed at the prophet's face and spoke again. "You are alone, too. What did you do with your nurse?"

The prophet answered and said, "Ah, that is a different thing. In very truth I cannot lose her oftentime. But now, when I came into this garden, she was seeking after me behind the hedges."

The child clapped his hands and cried out, "So you are like me! Isn't it good to be lost?" And then he said, "Who are you?"

And the man answered, "They call me the prophet Sharia. And tell me, who are you?"

"I am only myself," said the child, "and my nurse is seeking after me, and she does not know where I am."

Then the prophet gazed into space saying, "I too have escaped my nurse for awhile, but she will find me out."

And the child said, "I know mine will find me out too."

At that moment a woman's voice was heard calling the child's name, "See," said the child, "I told you she would be finding me."

And at the same moment another voice was heard, "Where art thou, Sharia?"

And the prophet said, "See my child, they have found me also."

And turning his face upward, Sharia answered, "Here I am."

The Pearl

Said one oyster to a neighbouring oyster, "I have a very great pain within me. It is heavy and round and I am in distress."

And the other oyster replied with haughty complacence, "Praise be to the heavens and to the sea, I have no pain within me. I am well and whole both within and without."

At that moment a crab was passing by and heard the two oysters, and he said to the one who was well and whole both within and without, "Yes, you are well and whole; but the pain that your neighbour bears is a pearl of exceeding beauty."

Body And Soul

A man and a woman sat by a window that opened upon Spring. They sat close one unto the other. And the woman said, "I love you. You are handsome, and you are rich, and you are always well-attired."

And the man said, "I love you. You are a beautiful thought, a thing too apart to hold in the hand, and a song in my dreaming."

But the woman turned from him in anger, and she said, "Sir, please leave me now. I am not a thought, and I am not a thing that passes in your dreams. I am a woman. I would have you desire me, a wife, and the mother of unborn children."

And they parted.

And the man was saying in his heart, "Behold another dream is even now turned into mist."

And the woman was saying, "Well, what of a man who turns me into a mist and a dream?"

The King

The people of the kingdom of Sadik surrounded the palace of their king shouting in rebellion against him. And he came down the steps of the palace carrying his crown in one hand and his sceptre in the other. The majesty of his appearance silenced the multitude, and he stood before them and said, "My friends, who are no longer my subjects, here I yield my crown and sceptre unto you. I would be one of you. I am only one man, but as a man I would work together with you that our lot may be made better. There is no need for king. Let us go therefore to the fields and the vineyards and labour hand with hand. Only you must tell me to what field or vineyard I should go. All of you now are king."

And the people marvelled, and stillness was upon them, for the king whom they had deemed the source of their discontent now yielding his crown and sceptre to them and became as one of them.

Then each and every one of them went his way, and the king walked with one man to a field.

But the Kingdom of Sadik fared not better without a king, and the mist of discontent was still upon the land. The people cried out in the market places saying that they have a king to rule them. And the elders and the youths said as if with one voice, "We will have our king."

And they sought the king and found him toiling in the field, and they brought him to his seat, and yielded unto his crown and his sceptre. And they said, "Now rule us, with might and with justice."

And he said, "I will indeed rule you with might, and may the gods of the heaven and the earth help me that I may also rule with justice."

Now, there came to his presence men and women and spoke unto him of a baron who mistreated them, and to whom they were but serfs.

And straightway the king brought the baron before him and said, "The life of one man is as weighty in the scales of God as the life of another. And because you know not how to weigh the lives of those who work in your fiends and your vineyards, you are banished, and you shall leave this kingdom forever."

The following day came another company to the king and spoke of the cruelty of a countess beyond the hills, and how she brought them down to misery. Instantly the countess was brought to court, and the king sentenced her also to banishment, saying, "Those who till our fields and care for our vineyards are nobler than we who eat the bread they prepare and drink the wine of their wine-press. And because you know not this, you shall leave this land and be afar from this kingdom."

Then came men and women who said that the bishop made them bring stones and hew the stones for the cathedral, yet he gave them naught, though they knew the bishop's coffer was full of gold and silver while they themselves were empty with hunger.

And the king called for the bishop, and when the bishop came the king spoke and said unto his, "That cross you wear upon your bosom should mean giving life unto life. But you have taken life from life and you have given none. Therefore you shall leave this kingdom never to return."

Thus each day for a full moon men and women came to the king to tell him of the burdens laid upon them. And each and every day a full moon some oppressor was exiled from the land.

And the people of Sadik were amazed, and there was cheer in their heart.

And upon a day the elders and the youths came and surrounded the tower of the king and called for him. And he came down holding his crown with one hand and his sceptre with the other.

And he spoke unto and said, "Now, what would you do of me? Behold, I yield back to you that which you desired me to hold."

But they cried. "Nay, nay, you are our rightful king. You have made clean the land of vipers, and you have brought the wolves to naught, and we welcome to sing our thanksgiving unto you. The crown is yours in majesty and the sceptre is yours in glory."

Then the king said, "Not I, not I. You yourselves are king. When you deemed me weak and a misruler, you yourselves were weak and misruling. And now the land fares well because it is in your will. I am but a thought in the mind of you all, and I exist not save in your actions. There is no such person as governor. Only the governed exist to govern themselves."

And the king re-entered his tower with his crown and his sceptre. And the elders and the youths went their various ways and they were content.

And each and every one thought of himself as king with a crown in one hand and a sceptre in the other.

Upon The Sand

Said one man to another, "At the high tide of the sea, long ago, with the point of my staff I wrote a line upon the sand; and the people still pause to read it, and they are careful that naught shall erase it."

And the other man said, "And I to wrote a line upon the sand, but it was at low tide, and the waves of the vast sea washed it away. But tell me, what did you write?"

And the first man answered and said, "I wrote this: 'I am he who is.' But what did you write?"

And the other man said, "This I wrote: 'I am but a drop of this great ocean.'"

The Three Gifts

Once in the city of Becharre there lived a gracious prince who was loved and honoured by all his subjects.

But there was one exceedingly poor man who was bitter against the prince, and who wagged continually a pestilent tongue in his dispraise.

The prince knew this, yet he was patient.

But at last he bethought him; and upon a wintry night there came to the door of the man a servant of the prince, bearing a sack of flour, a bag of soap and a cone of sugar.

And the servant said, "The prince sends you these gifts in token of remembrance."

The man was elated, for he thought the gifts were an homage from the prince. And in his pride we went to the bishop and told him what the prince had done, saying, "Can you not see how the prince desires my goodwill?"

But the bishop said, "Oh, how wise a prince, and how little you understand. He speaks in symbols. The flour is for your empty stomach; the soap is for your dirty hide; and the sugar is to sweeten your bitter tongue."

From that day forward the man became shy even of himself. His hatred of the prince was greater than ever, and even more he hated the bishop who had revealed the prince unto him.

But thereafter he kept silent.

Peace And War

Three dogs were basking in the sun and conversing. The first dog said dreamily, "It is indeed wondrous to be living in this day of dogdom. Consider the ease with which we travel under the sea, upon the earth and even in the sky. And meditate for a moment upon the inventions brought forth for the comfort of dogs, even for our eyes and ears and noses."

And the second dog spoke and he said, "We are more heedful of the arts. We bark at the moon more rhythmically than did our forefathers. And when we gaze at ourselves in the water we see that our features are clearer than the features of yesterday."

Then the third dog spoke and said, "But what interests me most and beguiles my mind is the tranquil understanding existing between dogdoms."

At that very moment they looked, and lo, the dog-catcher was approaching.

The three dogs sprang up and scampered down the street; and as they ran the third dog said, "For God's sake, run for your lives. Civilisation is after us."

The Dancer

Once there came to the court of the Prince of Birkasha a dancer with her musicians. And she was admitted to the court, and she danced before the prince to the music the lute and the flute and the zither.

She danced the dance of flames, and the dance of swords and spears; she danced the dance of stars and the dance of space. And then she danced the dance of flowers in the wind.

After this she stood before the throne of the prince and bowed her body before him. And the prince bade her to come nearer, and he said unto her, "Beautiful woman, daughter of grace and delight, whence comes your art? And how is it that you command all the elements in your rhythms and your rhymes?"

And the dancer bowed again before the prince, and she answered, "Mighty and gracious Majesty, I know not the answer to your questionings. Only this I know: The philosopher's soul dwells in his head, the poet's soul is in the heart; the singer's soul lingers about his throat, but the soul of the dancer abides in all her body."

The Two Guardian Angels

On an evening two angels met at the city gate, and they greeted one another, and they conversed.

The one angel said, "What are you doing these days, and what work is given you?"

And the other answered, "It was been assigned me to be the guardian of a fallen man who lives down in the valley, a great sinner, most degraded. Let me assure you it is an important task, and I work hard."

The first fallen angel said, "That is an easy commission. I have often known sinners, and have been their guardian many a time. But it has now been assigned me to be the guardian of the good saint who lives in a bower out yonder. And I assure you that is an exceedingly difficult work, and most subtle."

Said the first angel, "This is but assumption. How can guarding a saint be harder than guarding a sinner?"

And the other answered, "What impertinence, to call me assumptious! I have stated but the truth. Methinks it is you who are assumptious!"

Then the angels wrangled and fought, first with words and then with fists and wings.

While they were fighting an archangel came by. And he stopped them, and said, "Why do you fight? And what is it all about? Know you not that it is most unbecoming for guardian angels to fight at the city gate? Tell me, what is your disagreement?"

Then both angels spoke at once, each claiming that the work given him was the harder, and that he deserved the greater recognition.

The archangel shook his head and bethought him.

Then he said, "My friends, I cannot say now which one of you has the greater claim upon honour and reward. But since the power is bestowed in me, therefore for peace' sake and for good guardianship, I give each of you the other's occupation, since each of you insists that the other's task is the easier one. Now go hence and be happy at your work."

The angels thus ordered went their ways. But each one looked backward with greater anger at the archangel. And in his heart each was saying, "Oh, these archangels! Every day they make life harder and still harder for us angels!"

But the archangel stood there, and once more he bethought him. And he said in his heart, "We have indeed, to be watchful and to keep guard over our guardian angels."

The Statue

Once there lived a man among the hills who possessed a statue wrought by an ancient master. It lay at his door face downward and he was not mindful of it.

One day there passed by his house a man from the city, a man of knowledge, and seeing the statue he inquired of the owner if he would sell it.

The owner laughed and said, "And pray who would want to buy that dull and dirty stone?"

The man from the city said, "I will give you this piece of silver for it."

And the other man was astonished and delighted.

The statue was removed to the city, upon the back of and elephant. And after many moons the man from the hills visited the city, and as he walked the streets he saw a crowd before a shop, and a man with a loud voice was crying, "Come ye in and behold the most beautiful, the most wonderful statue in all the world. Only two silver pieces to look upon this most marvellous work of a master."

Thereupon the man from the hills paid two silver pieces and entered the shop to see the statue that he himself had sold for one piece of silver.

The Exchange

Once upon a crossroad a poor Poet met a rich Stupid, and they conversed. And all that they said revealed but their discontent.

Then the Angel of the Road passed by, and he laid his hand upon the shoulder of the two men.

And behold, a miracle: The two men had now exchanged their possessions.

And they parted. But strange to relate, the Poet looked and found naught in his hand but dry moving sand; and the Stupid closed his eyes and felt naught but moving cloud in his heart.

Love And Hate

A woman said unto a man, "I love you." And the man said, "It is in my heart to be worthy of your love."

Ant he woman said, "You love me not?"

And the man only gazed upon her and said nothing.

Then the woman cried aloud, "I hate you."

And the man said, "Then it is also in my heart to be worthy of your hate."

Dreams

A man dreamed a dream, and when he awoke he went to his soothsayer and desired that his dream be made plain unto him.

And the soothsayer said to the man, "Come to me with the dreams that you behold in your wakefulness and I will tell you their meaning. But the dreams of your sleep belong neither to my wisdom nor to your imagination."

The Madman

It was in the garden of a madhouse that I met a youth with a face pale and lovely and full of wonder. And I sat beside him upon the bench, and I said, "Why are you here?"

And he looked at me in astonishment, and he said, "It is an unseemly question, yet I will answer you. My father would make of me a reproduction of himself; so also would my uncle. My mother would have me the image of her seafaring husband as the perfect example for me to follow. My brother thinks I should be like him, a fine athlete.

"And my teachers also, the doctor of philosophy, and the music-master, and the logician, they too were determined, and each would have me but a reflection of his own face in a mirror.

"Therefore I came to this place. I find it more sane here. At least, I can be myself."

Then of a sudden he turned to me and he said, "But tell me, were you also driven to this place by education and good counsel?"

And I answered, "No, I am a visitor."

And he answered, "Oh, you are one of those who live in the madhouse on the other side of the wall."

The Frogs

Upon a summer day a frog said to his mate, "I fear those people living in that house on the shore are disturbed by our night-songs."

And his mate answered and said, "Well, do they not annoy our silence during the day with their talking?"

The frog said, "Let us not forget that we may sing too much in the night."

And his mate answered, "Let us not forget that they chatter and shout overmuch during the day."

Said the frog, "How about the bullfrog who that they clatter and shout overmuch during the day."

Said the frog, "How about the bullfrog who disturbs the whole neighbourhood with his God-forbidden booming?"

And his mate replied, "Aye, and what say you of the politician and the priest and the scientist who come to these shores and fill the air with noisy and rhymeless sound?"

Then the frog said, "Well, let us be better than these human beings. Let us be quiet at night, and keep our songs in our hearts, even though the moon calls for our rhythm and the stars for our rhyme. At least, let us be silent for a night or two, or even for three nights."

And his mate said, "Very well, I agree. We shall see what your bountiful heart will bring forth."

That night the frogs were silent; and they were silent the following night also, and again upon the third night.

And strange to relate, the talkative woman who lived in the house beside the lake came down to breakfast on that third day and shouted to her husband, "I have not slept these three nights. I was secure with sleep when the noise of the frogs was in my ear. But something must have happened. They have not sung now for three nights; and I am almost maddened with sleeplessness."

The frog heard this and turned to his mate and said, winking his eye, "And we were almost maddened with our silence, were we not?"

And his mate answered, "Yes, the silence of the night was heavy upon us. And I can see now that there is no need for us to cease our singing for the comfort of those who must needs fill their emptiness with noise."

And that night the moon called not in vain for their rhythm nor the stars for their rhyme.

Laws And Law-Giving

Ages ago there was a great king, and he was wise. And he desired to lay laws unto his subjects.

He called upon one thousand wise men of one thousand different tribes to his capitol and lay down the laws.

And all this came to pass.

But when the thousand laws written upon parchment were put before the king and he read them, he wept bitterly in his soul, for he had not known that there were one thousand forms of crime in his kingdom.

Then he called his scribe, and with a smile upon his mouth he himself dictated laws. And his laws were but seven.

And the one thousand wise men left him in anger and returned to their tribes with the laws they had laid down. And every tribe followed the laws of its wise men.

Therefore they have a thousand laws even to our own day.

It is a great country, but it has one thousand prisons, and the prisons are full of women and men, breakers of a thousand laws.

It is indeed a great country, but the people thereof are descendants of one thousand law-givers and of only one wise king.

Yesterday, Today And tomorrow

I said to my friend, "You see her leaning upon the arm of that man. It was but yesterday that she leaned thus upon my arm."

And my friend said, "And tomorrow she will lean upon mine."

I said, "Behold her sitting close at his side. It was but yesterday she sat close beside me."

And he answered, "tomorrow she will sit beside me."

I said, "See, she drinks wine from his cup, and yesterday she drank from mine."

And he said, "tomorrow, from my cup."

Then I said, "See how she gazes at him with love, and with yielding eyes. Yesterday she gazed thus upon me."

And my friend said, "It will be upon me she gazes tomorrow."

I said, "Do you not hear her now murmuring songs of love into his ears? Those very songs of love she murmured but yesterday into my ears."

And my friend said, "And tomorrow she will murmur them in mine."

I said, "Why see, she is embracing him. It was but yesterday that she embraced me."

And my friend said, "She will embrace me tomorrow."

Then I said, "What a strange woman."

But he answered, "She is like unto life, possessed by all men; and like death, she conquers all men; and like eternity, she enfolds all men."

The Philosopher And The Cobbler

There came to a cobbler's shop a philosopher with worn shoes. And the philosopher said to the cobbler, "Please mend my shoes."

And the cobbler said, "I am mending another man's shoes now, and there are still other shoes to patch before I can come to yours. But leave your shoes here, and wear this other pair today, and come tomorrow for your own."

Then the philosopher was indignant, and he said, "I wear no shoes that are not mine own."

And the cobbler said, "Well then, are you in truth a philosopher, and cannot enfold your feet with the shoes of another man? Upon this very street there is another cobbler who understands philosophers better than I do. Go you to him for mending."

Builders Of Bridges

In Antioch where the river Assi goes to meet the sea, a bridge was built to bring one half of the city nearer to the other half. It was built of large stones carried down from among the hills, on the backs of the mules of Antioch.

When the bridge was finished, upon a pillar thereof was engraved in Greek and in Aramaic, "This bridge was builded by King Antiochus II."

And all the people walked across the good bridge over the goodly river Assi.

And upon an evening, a youth, deemed by some a little mad, descended to the pillar where the words were engraven, and he covered over the graving with charcoal, and above it wrote, "The stones of this bridge were brought down from the hills by the mules. In passing to and fro over it you are riding upon the backs of the mules of Antioch, builders of this bridge."

And when the people read what the youth had written, some of them laughed and some marvelled. And some said, "Ah yes, we know who has done this. Is he not a little mad?"

But one mule said, laughing, to another mule, "Do you not remember that we did carry those stones? And yet until now it has been said that the bridge was builded by King Antiochus."

The Field Of Zaad

Upon the road of Zaad a traveller met a man who lived in a nearby village, and the traveller, pointing with his hand to a vast field, asked the man saying, "Was not this the battle-ground where King Ahlam overcame his enemies?"

And the man answered and said, "This has never been a battle-ground. There once stood on this field the great city of Zaad, and it was burnt down to ashes. But now it is a good field, is it not?"

And the traveller and the man parted.

Not a half mile farther the traveller met another man, and pointing to the field again, he said, "So that is where the great city of Zaad once stood?'

And the man said, "There has never been a city in this place. But once there was a monastery here, and it was destroyed by the people of the South Country."

Shortly after, on that very road of Zaad, the traveller met a third man, and pointing once more to the vast field he said, "Is it not true that this is the place where once there stood a great monastery?"

But the man answered, "There has never been a monastery in this neighbourhood, but our fathers and our forefathers have told us that once there fell a great meteor on this field."

Then the traveller walked on, wondering in his heart. And he met a very old man, and saluting his he said, "Sir, upon this road I have met three men who live in the neighbourhood and I have asked each of them about this field, and each one denied what the other had said, and each one told me a new tale that the other had not told."

Then the old man raised his head, and answered, "My friend, each and every one of these men told you what was indeed so; but few of us are able to add fact to different fact and make a truth thereof."

The Golden Belt

Once upon a day two men who met on the road were walking together toward Salamis, the City of Columns. In the mid-afternoon they came to a wide river and there was no bridge to cross it. They must needs swim, or seek another road unknown to them.

And they said to one another, "Let us swim. After all, the river is not so wide." And they threw themselves into the water and swam.

And one of the men who had always known rivers and the ways of rivers, in mid-stream suddenly began to lose himself; and to be carried away by the rushing waters; while the other who had never swum before crossed the river straight-way and stood upon the farther bank. Then seeing his companion still wrestling with the stream, he threw himself again into the waters and brought him also safely to the shore.

And the man who had been swept away by the current said, "But you told me you could not swim. How then did you cross that river with such assurance?"

And the second man answered, "My friend, do you see this belt which girdles me? It is full of golden coins that I have earned for my wife and my children, a full year's work. It is the weight of this belt of gold that carried me across the river, to my wife and my children. And my wife and my children were upon my shoulders as I swam."

And the two men walked on together toward Salamis.

The Red Earth

Said a tree to a man, "My roots are in the deep red earth, and I shall give you of my fruit."

And the man said to the tree, "How alike we are. My roots are also deep in the red earth. And the red earth gives you power to bestow upon me of your fruit, and the red earth teaches me to receive from you with thanksgiving."

The Full Moon

The full moon rose in glory upon the town, and all the dogs of that town began to bark at the moon.

Only one dog did not bark, and he said to them in a grave voice, "Awake not stillness from her sleep, nor bring you the moon to the earth with your barking."

Then all the dogs ceased barking, in awful silence. But the dog who had spoken to them continued barking for silence, the rest of the night.

The Hermit Prophet

Once there lived a hermit prophet, and thrice a moon he would go down to the great city and in the market places he would preach giving and sharing to the people. And he was eloquent, and his fame was upon the land.

Upon an evening three men came to his hermitage and he greeted them. And they said, "You have been preaching giving and sharing, and you have sought to teach those who have much to give unto those who have little; and we doubt not that your fame has brought you riches. Now come and give us of your riches, for we are in need."

And the hermit answered and said, "My friends, I have naught but this bed and this mat and this jug of water. Take them if it is in your desire. I have neither gold nor silver."

Then they looked down with distain upon him, and turned their faces from him, and the last man stood at the door for a moment, and said, "Oh, you cheat! You fraud! You teach and preach that which you yourself do not perform."

The Old, Old Wine

Once there lived a rich man who was justly proud of his cellar and the wine therein. And there was one jug of ancient vintage kept for some occasion known only to himself.

The governor of the state visited him, and he bethought him and said, "That jug shall not be opened for a mere governor."

And a bishop of the diocese visited him, but he said to himself, "Nay, I will not open that jug. He would not know its value, nor would its aroma reach his nostrils."

The prince of the realm came and supped with him. But he thought, "It is too royal a wine for a mere princeling."

And even on the day when his own nephew was married, he said to himself, "No, not to these guests shall that jug be brought forth."

And the years passed by, and he died, an old man, and he was buried like unto every seed and acorn.

And upon the day that he was buried the ancient jug was brought out together with other jugs of wine, and it was shared by the peasants of the neighbourhood. And none knew its great age.

To them, all that is poured into a cup is only wine.

The Two Poems

Many centuries ago, on a road to Athens, two poets met, and they were glad to see one another.

And one poet asked the other saying, "What have you composed of late, and how goes it with your lyre?"

And the other poet answered and said with pride, "I have but now finished the greatest of my poems, perchance the greatest poem yet written in Greek. It is an invocation to Zeus the Supreme."

Then he took from beneath his cloak a parchment, saying, "Here, behold, I have it with me, and I would fain read it to you. Come, let us sit in the shade of that white cypress."

And the poet read his poem. And it was a long poem.

And the other poet said in kindliness, "This is a great poem. It will live through the ages, and in it you shall be glorified."

And the first poet said calmly, "And what have you been writing these late days?"

And the other another, "I have written but little. Only eight lines in remembrance of a child playing in a garden." And he recited the lines.

The first poet said, "Not so bad; not so bad."

And they parted.

And now after two thousand years the eight lines of the one poet are read in every tongue, and are loved and cherished.

And though the other poem has indeed come down through the ages in libraries and in the cells of scholars, and though it is remembered, it is neither loved nor read.

Lady Ruth

Three men once looked from afar upon a white house that stood alone on a green hill. One of them said, "That is the house of Lady Ruth. She is an old witch."

The second man said, "You are wrong. Lady Ruth is a beautiful woman who lives there consecrated unto her dreams."

The third man said, "You are both wrong. Lady Ruth is the holder of this vast land, and she draws blood from her serfs."

And they walked on discussing Lady Ruth. Then when they came to a crossroad they met an old man, and one of them asked him, saying, "Would you please tell us about the Lady Ruth who lives in that white house upon the hill?"

And the old man raised his head and smiled upon them, and said, "I am ninety of years, and I remember Lady Ruth when I was but a boy. But Lady Ruth died eighty years ago, and now the house is empty. The owls hoot therein, sometimes, and people say the place is haunted."

The Mouse And The Cat

Once on an evening a poet met a peasant. The poet was distant and the peasant was shy, yet they conversed.

And the peasant said, "Let me tell you a little story which I heard of late. A mouse was caught in a trap, and while he was happily eating the cheese that lay therein, a cat stood by. The mouse trembled awhile, but he knew he was safe within the trap.

"Then the cat said, 'You are eating your last meal, my friend.'

"'Yes,' answered the mouse, 'one life have I, therefore one death. But what of you? They tell me you have nine lives. Doesn't that mean that you will have to die nine times?'"

And the peasant looked at the poet and he said, "Is not this a strange story?"

And the poet answered him not, but he walked away saying in his soul, "To be sure, nine lives have we, nine lives to be sure. And we shall die nine times, nine times shall we die. Perhaps it were better to have but one life, caught in a trap—the life of a peasant with a bit of cheese for the last meal. And yet, are we not kin unto the lions of the desert and the jungle?"

The Curse

And old man of the sea once said to me, "It was thirty years ago that a sailor ran away with my daughter. And I cursed them both in my heart, for of all the world I loved but my daughter.

"Not long after that, the sailor youth went down with his ship to the bottom of the sea, and with him my lovely daughter was lost unto me.

"Now therefore behold in me the murderer of a youth and a maid. It was my curse that destroyed them. And now on my way to the grave I seek God's forgiveness."

This the old man said. But there was a tone of bragging in his words, and it seems that he is still proud of the power of his curse.

The Pomegranates

There was once a man who had many pomegranate trees in his orchard. And for many an autumn he would put his pomegranates on silvery trays outside of his dwelling, and upon the trays he would place signs upon which he himself had written, "Take one for aught. You are welcome."

But people passed by and no one took of the fruit.

Then the man bethought him, and one autumn he placed no pomegranates on silvery trays outside of his dwelling, but he raised this sign in large lettering: "Here we have the best pomegranates in the land, but we sell them for more silver than any other pomegranates."

And now behold, all the men and women of the neighbourhood came rushing to buy.

God And Many Gods

In the city of Kilafis a sophist stood on the steps of the Temple and preached many gods. And the people said in their hearts, "We know all this. Do they not live with us and follow us wherever we go?"

Not long after, another man stood in the market place and spoke unto the people and said, "There is no god." And many who heard him were glad of his tidings, for they were afraid of gods.

And upon another day there came a man of great eloquence, an he said, "There is but one God." And now the people were dismayed for in their hearts they feared the judgment of one God more than that of many gods.

That same season there came yet another man, and he said to the people, "There are three gods, and they dwell upon the wind as one, and they have a vast and gracious mother who is also their mate and their sister."

Then everyone was comforted, for they said in their secret, "three gods in one must needs disagree over our failings, and besides, their gracious mother will surely be an advocate for us poor weaklings."

Yet even to this day there are those in the city of Kilafis who wrangle and argue with each other about many gods and no god, and one god and three gods in one, and a gracious mother of gods.

She Who Was Deaf

Once there lived a rich man who had a young wife, and she was stone deaf.

And upon a morning when they were breaking their feast, she spoke to him and she said, "Yesterday I visited the market place, and there were exhibited silken raiment from Damascus, and coverchiefs from India, necklaces from Persia, and bracelets from Yamman. It seems that the caravans had but just brought these things to our city. And now behold me, in rags, yet the wife of a rich man. I would have some of those beautiful things."

The husband, still busy with his morning coffee said, "My dear, there is no reason why you should not go down to the Street and buy all that your heart may desire."

And the deaf wife said, "'No!' You always say, 'No, no.' Must I needs appear in tatters among our friends to shame your wealth and my people?"

And the husband said, "I did not say, 'No.' You may go forth freely to the market place and purchase the most beautiful apparel and jewels that have come to our city."

But again the wife mis-read his words, and she replied, "Of all rich men you are the most miserly. You would deny me everything of beauty and loveliness, while other women of my age walk the gardens of the city clothed in rich raiment."

And she began to weep. And as her tears fell upon her breast she cried out again, "You always say, 'Nay, nay' to me when I desire a garment or a jewel."

Then the husband was moved, and he stood up and took out of his purse a handful of gold and placed it before her, saying in a kindly voice, "Go down to the market place, my dear, and buy all that you will."

From that day onward the deaf young wife, whenever she desired anything, would appear before her husband with a pearly tear in her eye, and he in silence would take out a handful of gold and place it in her lap.

Now, it changed that the young woman fell in love with a youth whose habit it was to make long journeys. And whenever he was away she would sit in her casement and weep.

When her husband found her thus weeping, he would say in his heart, "There must be some new caravan, and some silken garments and rare jewels in the Street."

And he would take a handful of gold and place it before her.

The Quest

A thousand years ago two philosophers met on a slope of Lebanon, and one said to the other, "Where goest thou?"

And the other answered, "I am seeking after the fountain of youth which I know wells out among these hills. I have found writings which tell of that fountain flowering toward the sun. And you, what are you seeking?"

The first man answered, "I am seeking after the mystery of death."

Then each of the two philosophers conceived that the other was lacking in his great science, and they began to wrangle, and to accuse each other of spiritual blindness.

Now while the two philosophers were loud upon the wind, a stranger, a man who was deemed a simpleton in his own village, passed by, and when he heard the two in hot dispute, he stood awhile and listened to their argument.

Then he came near to them and said, "My good men, it seems that you both really belong to the same school of philosophy, and that you are speaking of the same thing, only you speak in different words. One of you is seeks the fountain of youth, and the other seeks the mystery of death. Yet indeed they are but one, and as they dwell in you both."

Then the stranger turned away saying, "Farewell sages." And as he departed he laughed a patient laughter.

The two philosophers looked at each other in silence for a moment, and then they laughed also. And one of them said, "Well now, shall we not walk and seek together."

The Sceptre

Said a king to his wife, "Madame, you are not truly a queen. You are too vulgar and ungracious to be my mate."

Said his wife, "Sir, you deem yourself king, but indeed you are only a poor soundling."

Now these words angered the king, and he took his sceptre with his hand, and struck the queen upon her forehead with his golden sceptre.

At that moment the lord chamberlain entered, and he said, "Well, well, Majesty! That sceptre was fashioned by the greatest artist of the land. Alas! Some day you and the queen shall be forgotten, but this sceptre shall be kept, a thing of beauty from generation to generation. And now that you have drawn blood from her Majesty's head, Sire, the sceptre shall be the more considered and remembered."

The Path

There lived among the hills a woman and her son, and he was her first-born and her only child.

And the boy died of a fever whilst the physician stood by.

The mother was distraught with sorrow, and she cried to the physician and besought him saying, "Tell me, tell me, what was it that made quiet his striving and silent his song?"

And the physician said, "It was the fever."

And the mother said, "What is the fever?"

And the physician answered, "I cannot explain it. It is a thing infinitely small that visits the body, and we cannot see it with the human eye."

The physician left her. And she kept repeating to herself, "Something infinitely small. We cannot see it with our human eye."

And at evening the priest came to console her. And she wept and she cried out saying, "Oh, why have I lost my son, my only son, my first-born?"

And the priest answered, "My child, it is the will of God."

And the woman said, "What is God and where is God? I would see God that I may tear my bosom before Him, and pour the blood of my heart at His feet. Tell me where I shall find Him."

And the priest said, ""God is infinitely vast. He is not to be seen with our human eye."

Then the woman cried out, "The infinitely small has slain my son through the will of the infinitely great! Then what are we? What are we?"

At that moment the woman's mother came into the room with the shroud for the dead boy, and she heard the words of the priest and also her daughter's cry. And she laid down the shroud, and took her daughter's hand in her own hand, and she said, "My daughter, we ourselves are the infinitely small and the infinitely great; and we are the path between the two."

The Whale And The Butterfly

Once on an evening a man and a woman found themselves together in a stagecoach. They had met before.

The man was a poet, and as he sat beside the woman he sought to amuse her with stories, some that were of his own weaving, and some that were not his own.

But even while he was speaking the lady went to sleep. Then suddenly the coach lurched, and she awoke, and she said, "I admire your interpretation of the story of Jonah and the whale."

And the poet said, "But Madame, I have been telling you a story of mine own about a butterfly and a white rose, and how they behaved the one to the other!"

The Shadow

Upon a June day the grass said to the shadow of an elm tree, "You move to right and left over-often, and you disturb my peace."

And the shadow answered and said, "Not I, not I. Look skyward. There is a tree that moves in the wind to the east and to the west, between the sun and the earth."

And the grass looked up, and for the first time beheld the tree. And it said in its heart, "Why, behold, there is a larger grass than myself."

And the grass was silent.

Peace Contagious

One branch in bloom said to his neighbouring branch, "This is a dull and empty day." And the other branch answered, "It is indeed empty and dull."

At that moment a sparrow alighted on one of the branches, and the another sparrow, nearby.

And one of the sparrows chirped and said, "My mate has left me."

And the other sparrow cried, "My mate has also gone, and she will not return. And what care I?"

Then the two birds began to twitter and scold, and soon they were fighting and making harsh noise upon the air.

All of a sudden two other sparrows came sailing from the sky, and they sat quietly beside the restless two. And there was calm, and there was peace.

Then the four flew away together in pairs.

And the first branch said to his neighbouring branch, "That was a mighty zig-zag of sound."

And the other branch answered, "Call it what you will, it is now both peaceful and spacious. And if the upper air makes peace it seems to me that those who dwell in the lower might make peace also. Will you not wave in the wind a little nearer to me?"

And the first branch said, "Oh, perchance, for peace' sake, ere the Spring is over."

And then he waved himself with the strong wind to embrace her.

Seventy

The poet youth said to the princess, "I love you." And the princess answered, "And I love you too, my child."

"But I am not your child. I am a man and I love you."

And she said, "I am the mother of sons and daughters, and they are fathers and mothers of sons and daughters; and one of the sons of my sons is older than you."

And the poet youth said, "But I love you."

It was not long after that the princess died. But ere her last breath was received again by the greater breath of earth, she said within her soul, "My beloved, mine only son, my youth-poet, it may yet be that some day we shall meet again, and I shall not be seventy."

Finding God

Two men were walking in the valley, and one man pointed with his finger toward the mountain side, and said, "See you that hermitage? There lives a man who has long divorced the world. He seeks but after God, and naught else upon this earth."

And the other man said, "He shall not find God until he leaves his hermitage, and the aloneness of his hermitage, and returns to our world, to share our joy and pain, to dance with our dancers at the wedding feast, and to weep with those who weep around the coffins of our dead."

And the other man was convinced in his heart, though in spite of his conviction he answered, "I agree with all that you say, yet I believe the hermit is a good man. And it may it not well be that one good man by his absence does better than the seeming goodness of these many men?"

The River

In the valley of Kadisha where the mighty river flows, two little streams met and spoke to one another.

One stream said, "How came you, my friend, and how was your path?"

And the other answered, "My path was most encumbered. The wheel of the mill was broken, and the master farmer who used to conduct me from my channel to his plants, is dead. I struggled down oozing with the filth of laziness in the sun. But how was your path, my brother?"

And the other stream answered and said, "Mine was a different path. I came down the hills among fragrant flowers and shy willows; men and women drank of me with silvery cups, and little children paddled their rosy feet at my edges, and there was laughter all about me, and there were sweet songs. What a pity that your path was not so happy."

At that moment the river spoke with a loud voice and said, "Come in, come in, we are going to the sea. Come in, come in, speak no more. Be with me now. We are going to the sea. Come in, come in, for in me you shall forget you wanderings, sad or gay. Come in, come in. And you and I will forget all our ways when we reach the heart of our mother the sea."

The Two Hunters

Upon a day in May, Joy and Sorrow met beside a lake. They greeted one another, and they sat down near the quiet waters and conversed.

Joy spoke of the beauty which is upon the earth, and the daily wonder of life in the forest and among the hills, and of the songs heard at dawn and eventide.

And sorrow spoke, and agreed with all that Joy had said; for Sorrow knew the magic of the hour and the beauty thereof. And Sorrow was eloquent when he spoke of may in the fields and among the hills.

And Joy and Sorrow talked long together, and they agreed upon all things of which they knew.

Now there passed by on the other side of the lake two hunters. And as they looked across the water one of them said, "I wonder who are those two persons?" And the other said, "Did you say two? I see only one."

The first hunter said, "But there are two." And the second said, "There is only one that I can see, and the reflection in the lake is only one."

"Nay, there are two," said the first hunter, "and the reflection in the still water is of two persons."

But the second man said again, "Only one do I see." And again the other said, "But I see two so plainly."

And even unto this day one hunter says that the other sees double; while the other says, "My friend is somewhat blind."

The Other Wanderer

Once on a time I met another man of the roads. He too was a little mad, and thus spoke to me:

"I am a wanderer. Oftentimes it seems that I walk the earth among pygmies. And because my head is seventy cubits farther from the earth than theirs, it creates higher and freer thoughts.

"But in truth I walk not among men but above them, and all they can see of me is my footprints in their open fields.

"And often have I heard them discuss and disagree over the shape and size of my footprints. For there are some who say,

'These are the tracks of a mammoth that roamed the earth in the far past.' And others say, 'Nay, these are places where meteors have fallen from the distant stars.'

"But you, my friend, you know full well that they are naught save the footprints of a wanderer."

The Broken Wings

Silent Sorrow

My neighbours, you remember the dawn of youth with pleasure and regret its passing; but I remember it like a prisoner who recalls the bars and shackles of his jail. You speak of those years between infancy and youth as a golden era free from confinement and cares, but I call those years an era of silent sorrow which dropped as a seed into my heart and grew with it and could find no outlet to the world of Knowledge and wisdom until love came and opened the heart's doors and lighted its corners. Love provided me with a tongue and tears. You people remember the gardens and orchids and the meeting places and street corners that witnessed your games and heard your innocent whispering; and I remember, too, the beautiful spot in North Lebanon. Every time I close my eyes I see those valleys full of magic and dignity and those mountains covered with glory and greatness trying to reach the sky. Every time I shut my ears to the clamour of the city I hear the murmur of the rivulets and the rustling of the branches. All those beauties which I speak of now and which I long to see, as a child longs for his mother's breast, wounded my spirit, imprisoned in the darkness of youth, as a falcon suffers in its cage when it sees a flock of birds flying freely in the spacious sky. Those valleys and hills fired my imagination, but bitter thoughts wove round my heart a net of hopelessness.

Every time I went to the fields I returned disappointed, without understanding the cause of my disappointment. Every time I looked at the grey sky I felt my heart contract. Every time I heard the singing of the birds and babbling of the spring I suffered without understanding the reason for my suffering. It is said that unsophistication makes a man empty and that emptiness makes him carefree. It may be true among those who were born dead and who exist like frozen corpses; but the sensitive boy who feels much and knows little is the most unfortunate creature under the sun, because he is torn by two forces. the first force elevates him and shows him the beauty of existence through a cloud of dreams; the second ties him down to the earth and fills his eyes with dust and overpowers him with fears and darkness.

Solitude has soft, silky hands, but with strong fingers it grasps the heart and makes it ache with sorrow. Solitude is the ally of sorrow as well as a companion of spiritual exaltation.

The boy's soul undergoing the buffeting of sorrow is like a white lily just unfolding. It trembles before the breeze and opens its heart to day break and folds its leaves back when the shadow of night comes. If that boy does not have diversion or friends or companions in his games his life will be like a narrow prison in which he sees nothing but spider webs and hears nothing but the crawling of insects.

That sorrow which obsessed me during my youth was not caused by lack of amusement, because I could have had it; neither from lack of friends, because I could have found them. That sorrow was caused by an inward ailment which made me love solitude. It killed in me the inclination for games and amusement. It removed from my shoulders the wings of youth and made me like a pond of water between mountains which reflects in its calm surface the shadows of ghosts and the colours of clouds and trees, but cannot find an outlet by which to pass singing to the sea.

Thus was my life before I attained the age of eighteen. That year is like a mountain peak in my life, for it awakened knowledge in me and made me understand the vicissitudes of mankind. In that year I was reborn and unless a person is born again his life will remain like a blank sheet in the book of existence. In that year, I saw the angels of heaven looking at me through the eyes of a beautiful woman. I also saw the devils of hell raging in the heart of an evil man. He who does not see the angels and devils in the beauty and malice of life will be far removed from knowledge, and his spirit will be empty of affection.

The Hand of Destiny

In the spring of the that wonderful year, I was in Beirut. The gardens were full of Nisan flowers and the earth was carpeted with green grass, and like a secret of earth revealed to Heaven. The orange trees and apple trees, looking like houris or brides sent by nature to inspire poets and excite the imagination, were wearing white garments of perfumed blossoms.

Spring is beautiful everywhere, but it is most beautiful in Lebanon. It is a spirit that roams round the earth but hovers over Lebanon, conversing with kings and prophets, singing with the rives the songs of Solomon, and repeating with the Holy Cedars of Lebanon the memory of ancient glory. Beirut, free from the mud of winter and the dust of summer, is like a bride in the spring, or like a mermaid sitting by the side of a brook drying her smooth skin in the rays of the sun.

One day, in the month of Nisan, I went to visit a friend whose home was at some distance from the glamourous city. As we were conversing, a dignified man of about sixty-five entered the house. As I rose to greet him, my friend introduced him to me as Farris Effandi Karamy and then gave him my name with flattering words. The old man looked at me a moment, touching his forehead with the ends of his fingers as if he were trying to regain his memory. Then he smilingly approached me saying, "You are the son of a very dear friend of mine, and I am happy to see that friend in your person."

Much affected by his words, I was attracted to him like a bird whose instinct leads him to his nest before the coming of the tempest. As we sat down, he told us about his friendship with my father, recalling the time which they spent together. An old man likes to return in memory to the days of his youth like a stranger who longs to go back to his own country. He delights to tell stories of the past like a poet who takes pleasure in reciting his best poem. He lives spiritually in the past because the present passes swiftly, and the future seems to him an approach to the oblivion of the grave. An hour full of old memories passed like the shadows of the trees over the grass. When Farris Effandi started to leave, he put his left hand on my shoulder and shook my right hand, saying, " I have not seen your father for twenty years. I hope you will l take his place in frequent visits to my house." I promised gratefully to do my duty toward a dear friend of my father.

Then the old man left the house, I asked my friend to tell me more about him. He said, "I do not know any other man in Beirut whose wealth has made him kind and whose kindness has made him wealthy. He is one of the few who come to this world and leave it without harming any one, but people of that kind are usually miserable and oppressed because they are not clever enough to save themselves from the crookedness of others. Farris Effandi has one daughter whose character is similar to his and whose beauty and gracefulness are beyond description, and she will also be miserable because her father's wealth is placing her already at the edge of a horrible precipice."

As he uttered these words, I noticed that his face clouded. Then he continued, "Farris Effandi is a good old man with a noble heart, but he lacks will power. People lead him like a blind man.

His daughter obeys him in spite of her pride and intelligence, and this is the secret which lurks in the life of father and daughter. This secret was discovered by an evil man who is a bishop and whose wickedness hides in the shadow of his Gospel. He makes the people believe that he is kind and noble. He is the head of religion in this land of the religions. The people obey and worship him. he leads them like a flock of lambs to the slaughter house. This bishop has a nephew who is full of hatefulness and corruption. The day will come sooner or later when he will place his nephew on his right and Farris Effandi's daughter on this left, and, holding with his evil hand the wreath of matrimony over their heads, will tie a pure virgin to a filthy degenerate, placing the heart of the day in the bosom of the night.

That is all I can tell you about Farris Effandi and his daughter, so do not ask me any more questions."

Saying this, he turned his head toward the window as if he were trying to solve the problems of human existence by concentrating on the beauty of the universe.

As I left the house I told my friend that I was going to visit Farris Effandi in a few days for the purpose of fulfiling my promise and for the sake of the friendship which had joined him and my father. He stared at me for a moment, and I noticed a change in his expression as if my few simple words had revealed to him a new idea. Then he looked straight through my eyes in a strange manner, a look of love, mercy, and fear—the look of a prophet who foresees what no one else can divine. Then his lips trembled a little, but he said nothing when I started towards the door. That strange look followed me, the meaning of which I could not understand until I grew up in the world of experience, where hearts understand each other intuitively and where spirits are mature with knowledge.

Entrance to the Shrine

In a few days, loneliness overcame me; and I tired of the grim faces of books; I hired a carriage and started for the house of Farris Effandi. As I reached the pine woods where people went for picnics, the driver took a private way, shaded with willow trees on each side. Passing through , we could see the beauty of the green grass, the grapevines, and the many coloured flowers of Nisan just blossoming.

In a few minutes the carriage stopped before a solitary house in the midst of a beautiful garden. The scent of roses, gardenia, and jasmine filled the air. As I dismounted and entered the spacious garden, I saw Farris Effandi coming to meet me. He ushered me into his house with a hearty welcome and sat by me, like a happy father when he sees his son, showering me with questions on my life, future and education. I answered him, my voice full of ambition and zeal; for I heard ringing in my ears the hymn of glory, and I was sailing the calm sea of hopeful dreams. Just then a beautiful young woman, dressed in a gorgeous white silk gown, appeared from behind the velvet curtains of the door and walked toward me. Farris Effandi and I rose from our seats.

This is my daughter Selma," said the old man. Then he introduced me to her, saying, "Fate has brought back to me a dear old friend of mine in the person of his son." Selma stared at me a moment as if doubting that a visitor could have entered their house. Her hand, when I touched it, was like a white lily, and a strange pang pierced my heart.

We all sat silent as if Selma had brought into the room with her heavenly spirit worthy of mute respect. As she felt the silence she smiled at me and said, "Many a times my father has repeated to me the stories of his youth and of the old days he and your father spent together. If your father spoke to you in the same way, then this meeting is not the first one between us."

The old man was delighted to hear his daughter talking in such a manner and said, "Selma is very sentimental. She sees everything through the eyes of the spirit." Then he resumed his conversation with care and tact as if he had found in me a magic which took him on the wings of memory to the days of the past.

As I considered him, dreaming of my own later years, he looked upon me, as a lofty old tree that has withstood storms and sunshine throws its shadow upon a small sapling which shakes before the breeze of dawn.

But Selma was silent. Occasionally, she looked first at me and then at her father as if reading the first and last chapters of life's drama. The day passed faster in that garden, and I could see through the window the ghostly yellow kiss of sunset on the mountains of Lebanon. Farris Effandi continued to recount his experiences and I listened entranced and responded with such enthusiasm that his sorrow was changed to happiness.

Selma sat by the window, looking on with sorrowful eyes and not speaking, although beauty has its own heavenly language, loftier than he voices of tongues and lips. It is a timeless language, common to all humanity, a calm lake that attracts the singing rivulets to its depth and makes them silent.

Only our spirits can understand beauty, or live and grow with it. It puzzles our minds; we are unable to describe it in words; it is a sensation that our eyes cannot see, derived from both the one who observes and the one who is looked upon. Real beauty is a ray which emanates from the holy of holies of the spirit, and illuminates the body, as life comes from the depths of the earth and gives colour and scent to a flower.

Real beauty lies in the spiritual accord that is called love which can exist between a man and a woman.

Did my spirit and Selma's reach out to each other that day when we met, and did that yearning make me see her as the most beautiful woman under the sun? Or was I intoxicated with the wine of youth which made me fancy that which never existed.?

Did my youth blind my natural eyes and make me imagine the brightness of her eyes, the sweetness of her mouth, and the grace of her figure? Or was it that her brightness, sweetness, and grace opened my eyes and showed me the happiness and sorrow of love?

It is hard to answer these questions, but I say truly that in that hour I felt an emotion that I had never felt before, a new affection resting calmly in my heart, like the spirit hovering over the waters at the creation of the world, and from that affection was born my happiness and my sorrow. Thus ended the hour of my first meeting with Selma, and thus the will of Heaven freed me from the bondage of youth and solitude and let me walk in the procession of love

Love is the only freedom in the world because it so elevates the spirit that the laws of humanity and the phenomena of nature do not alter its course.

As I rose from my seat to depart, Farris Effandi came close to me and said soberly, "Now my son, since you know your way to this house, you should come often and feel that you are coming to your father's house. Consider me as a father and Selma as a sister." Saying this, he turned to Selma as if to ask confirmation of his statement. She nodded her head positively and then looked at me as one who has found an old acquaintance.

Those words uttered by Farris Effandi Karamy placed me side by side with his daughter at the altar of love. Those words were a heavenly song which started with exaltation and ended with sorrow; they raised our spirits to the realm of light and searing flame; they were the cup from which we drank happiness and bitterness.

I left the house. The old man accompanied me to the edge of the garden, while my heart throbbed like the trembling lips of a thirsty man.

The White Torch

The month of Nisan had nearly passed. I continued to visit the home of Farris Effendi and to meet Selma in that beautiful garden, gazing upon her beauty, marvelling at her intelligence, and hearing the stillness of sorrow. I felt an invisible hand drawing me to her.

Every visit gave me a new meaning to her beauty and a new insight into her sweet spirit, Until she became a book whose pages I could understand and whose praises I could sing, but which I could never finish reading. A woman whom Providence has provided with beauty of spirit and body is a truth, at the same time both open and secret, which we can understand only by love, and touch only by virtue; and when we attempt to describe such a woman she disappears like vapour.

Selma Karamy had bodily and spiritual beauty, but how can I describe her to one who never knew her? Can a dead man remember the singing of a nightingale and the fragrance of a rose and the sigh of a brook? Can a prisoner who is heavily loaded with shackles follow the breeze of the dawn? Is not silence more painful than death? Does pride prevent me from describing Selma in plain words since I cannot draw her truthfully with luminous colours? A hungry man in a desert will not refuse to eat dry bread if Heaven does not shower him with manna and quails.

In her white silk dress, Selma was slender as a ray of moonlight coming through the window. She walked gracefully and rhythmically. Her voice was low and sweet; words fell from her lips like drops of dew falling from the petals of flowers when they are disturbed by the wind.

But Selma's face! No words can describe its expression, reflecting first great internal suffering, then heavenly exaltation.

The beauty of Selma's face was not classic; it was like a dream of revelation which cannot be measured or bound or copied by the brush of a painter or the chisel of a sculptor. Selma's beauty was not in her golden hair, but in the virtue of purity which surrounded it; not in her large eyes, but in the light which emanated from them; not in her red lips, but in the sweetness of her words; not in her ivory neck, but in its slight bow to the front. Nor was it in her perfect figure, but in the nobility of her spirit, burning like a white torch between earth and sky. her beauty was like a gift of poetry. But poets care unhappy people, for, no matter how high their spirits reach, they will still be enclosed in an envelope of tears.

Selma was deeply thoughtful rather than talkative, and her silence was a kind of music that carried one to a world of dreams and made him listen to the throbbing of his heart, and see the ghosts of his thoughts and feelings standing before him, looking him in the eyes.

She wore a cloak of deep sorrow through her life, which increased her strange beauty and dignity, as a tree in blossom is more lovely when seen through the mist of dawn.

Sorrow linked her spirit and mine, as if each saw in the other's face what the heart was feeling and heard the echo of a hidden voice. God had made two bodies in one, and separation could be nothing but agony.

The sorrowful spirit finds rest when united with a similar one. They join affectionately, as a stranger is cheered when he sees another stranger in a strange land. Hearts that are united through the medium of sorrow will not be separated by the glory of happiness. Love that is cleansed by tears will remain externally pure and beautiful.

The Tempest

One day Farris Effandi invited me to dinner at his home. I accepted, my spirit hungry for the divine bread which Heaven placed in the hands of Selma, the spiritual bread which makes our hearts hungrier the more we eat of it. It was this bread which Kais, the Arabian poet, Dante, and Sappho tasted and which set their hearts afar; the bread which the Goddess prepares with the sweetness of kisses and the bitterness of tears.

As I reached the home of Farris Effandi, I saw Selma sitting on a bench in the garden resting her head against a tree and looking like a bride in her white silk dress, or like a sentinel guarding that place.

Silently and reverently I approached and sat by her. I could not talk; so I resorted to silence, the only language of the heart, but I felt that Selma was listening to my wordless call and watching the ghost of my soul in my eyes.

In a few minutes the old man came out and greeted me as usual. When he stretched his hand toward me, I felt as if he were blessing the secrets that united me and his daughter. Then he said, "Dinner is ready, my children; let us eat." We rose and followed him, and Selma's eyes brightened; for a new sentiment had been added to her love by her father's calling us his children.

We sat at the table enjoying the food and sipping the old wine, but our souls were living in a world far away. We were dreaming of the future and its hardships.

Three persons were separated in thoughts, but united in love; three innocent people with much feeling but little knowledge; a drama was being performed by an old man who loved his daughter and cared for her happiness, a young woman of twenty looking into the future with anxiety, and a young man, dreaming and worrying, who had tasted neither the wine of life nor its vinegar, and trying to reach the height of love and knowledge but unable to life himself up. We three sitting in twilight were eating and drinking in that solitary home, guarded by Heaven's eyes, but at the bottoms of our glasses were hidden bitterness and anguish.

As we finished eating, one of the maids announced the presence of a man at the door who wished to see Farris Effandi. "Who is he?" asked the old man. "The Bishop's messenger," said the maid. There was a moment of silence during which Farris Effandi stared at his daughter like a prophet who gazes at Heaven to divine its secret. Then he said to the maid, "Let the man in."

As the maid left, a man, dressed in oriental uniform and with big moustache curled at the ends, entered and greeted the old man, saying "His Grace, the Bishop, has sent me for you with his private carriage; he wishes to discuss important business with you." The old man's face clouded and his smile disappeared. After a moment of deep thought he came close to me and said in a friendly voice, "I hope to find you here when I come back, for Selma will enjoy your company in this solitary place."

Saying this, he turned to Selma and, smiling, asked if she agreed. She nodded her head, but her cheeks became red, and with a voice sweeter than the music of the lyre she said, "I will do my best, Father, to make our guest happy."

Selma watched the carriage that had taken her father and the Bishop's messenger until it disappeared. Then she came and sat opposite me on a divan covered with green silk. She looked like a lily bent to the carpet of green grass by the breeze of dawn. It was the will of Heaven that I should be with Selma alone, at night, in her beautiful home surrounded by trees, where silence, love, beauty and virtue dwelt together.

We were both silent, each waiting for the other to speak, but speech is not the only means of understanding between two souls. It is not the syllables that come from the lips and tongues that bring hearts together.

There is something greater and purer than what the mouth utters. Silence illuminates our souls, whispers to our hearts, and brings them together. Silence separates us from ourselves, makes us sail the firmament of spirit, and brings us closer to Heaven; it makes us feel that bodies are no more than prisons and that this world is only a place of exile.

Selma looked at me and her eyes revealed the secret of her heart. Then she quietly said, "Let us go to the garden and sit under the trees and watch the moon come up behind the mountains." Obediently I rose from my seat, but I hesitated.

"Don't you think we had better stay here until the moon has risen and illuminates the garden?" And I continued, "The darkness hides the trees and flowers. We can see nothing."

Then she said, "If darkness hides the trees and flowers from our eyes, it will not hide love from our hearts."

Uttering these words in a strange tone, she turned her eyes and looked through the window. I remained silent, pondering her words, weighing the true meaning of each syllable. Then she looked at me as if she regretted what she had said and tried to take away those words from my ears by the magic of her eyes. But those eyes, instead of making me forget what she had said, repeated through the depths of my heart more clearly and effectively the sweet words which had already become graven in my memory for eternity.

Every beauty and greatness in this world is created by a single thought or emotion inside a man. Every thing we see today, made by past generation, was, before its appearance, a thought in the mind of a man or an impulse in the heart of a woman. The revolutions that shed so much blood and turned men's minds toward liberty were the idea of one man who lived in the midst of thousands of men. The devastating wars which destroyed empires were a thought that existed in the mind of an individual. The supreme teachings that changed the course of humanity were the ideas of a man whose genius separated him from his environment. A single thought build the Pyramids, founded the glory of Islam, and caused the burning of the library at Alexandria.

One thought will come to you at night which will elevate you to glory or lead you to asylum. One look from a woman's eye makes you the happiest man in the world. One word from a man's lips will make you rich or poor.

That word which Selma uttered that night arrested me between my past and future, as a boat which is anchored in the midst of the ocean. That word awakened me from the slumber of youth and solitude and set me on the stage where life and death play their parts.

The scent of flowers mingled with the breeze as we came into the garden and sat silently on a bench near a jasmine tree, listening to the breathing of sleeping nature, while in the blue sky the eyes of heaven witnessed our drama.

The moon came out from behind Mount Sunnin and shone over the coast, hills, and mountains; and we could see the villages fringing the valley like apparitions which have suddenly been conjured from nothing. We could see the beauty of Lebanon under the silver rays of the moon.

Poets of the West think of Lebanon as a legendary place, forgotten since the passing of David and Solomon and the Prophets, as the Garden of Eden became lost after the fall of Adam and Eve. To those Western poets, the word "Lebanon" is a poetical expression associated with a mountain whose sides are drenched with the incense of the Holy Cedars. It reminds them of the temples of copper and marble standing stern and impregnable and of a herd of deer feeding in the valleys. That night I saw Lebanon dream-like with the eyes of a poet.

Thus, the appearance of things changes according to the emotions, and thus we see magic and beauty in them, while the magic and beauty are really in ourselves.

As the rays of the moon shone on the face, neck, and arms of Selma, she looked like a statue of ivory sculptured by the fingers of some worshiper of Ishtar, goddess of beauty and love. As she looked at me, she said, "Why are you silent? Why do you not tell me something about your past?" As I gazed at her, my muteness vanished, and I opened my lips and said, "Did you not hear what I said when we came to this orchard? The spirit that hears the whispering of flowers and the singing of silence can also hear the shrieking of my soul and the clamour of my heart."

She covered her face with her hands and said in a trembling voice, "Yes, I heard you—I heard a voice coming from the bosom of night and a clamour raging in the heart of the day."

Forgetting my past, my very existence—everything but Selma—I answered her, saying, "And I heard you, too, Selma. I heard exhilarating music pulsing in the air and causing the whole universe to tremble."

Upon hearing these words, she closed her eyes and her lips I saw a smile of pleasure mingled with sadness. She whispered softly, "Now I know that there is something higher than heaven and deeper than the ocean and stranger than life and death and time. I know now what I did not know before."

At that moment Selma became dearer than a friend and closer than a sister and more beloved than a sweetheart. She became a supreme thought, a beautiful, an overpowering emotion living in my spirit.

It is wrong to think that love comes from long companionship and persevering courtship. Love is the offspring of spiritual affinity and unless that affinity is created in a moment, it will not be created in years or even generations.

Then Selma raised her head and gazed at the horizon where Mount Sunnin meets the sky, and said, "Yesterday you were like a brother to me, with whom I lived and by whom I sat calmly under my father's care. Now, I feel the presence of something stranger and sweeter than brotherly affection, an unfamiliar commingling of love and fear that fills my heart with sorrow and happiness."

I responded, "This emotion which we fear and which shakes us when it passes through our hearts is the law of nature that guides the moon around the earth and the sun around the God."

She put her hand on my head and wove her fingers through my hair. Her face brightened and tears came out of her eyes like drops of dew on the leaves of a lily, and she said, "Who would believe our story—who would believe that in this hour we have surmounted the obstacles of doubt? Who would believe that the month of Nisan which brought us together for the first time, is the month that halted us in the Holy of Holies of life?"

Her hand was still on my head as she spoke, and I would not have preferred a royal crown or a wreath of glory to that beautiful smooth hand whose fingers were twined in my hair.

Then I answered her: "People will not believe our story because they do not know what love is the only flower that grows and blossoms without the aid of seasons, but was it Nisan that brought us together for the first time, and is it this hour that has arrested us in the Holy of Holies of life? Is it not the hand of God that brought our souls close together before birth and made us prisoners of each other for all the days and nights? Man's life does not commence in the womb and never ends in the grave; and this firmament, full of moonlight and stars, is not deserted by loving souls and intuitive spirits."

As she drew her hand away from my head, I felt a kind of electrical vibration at the roots of my hair mingled with the night breeze. Like a devoted worshiper who receives his blessing by kissing the altar in a shrine, I took Selma's hand, placed my burning lips on it, and gave it a long kiss, the memory of which melts my heart and awakens by its sweetness all the virtue of my spirit.

An hour passed, every minute of which was a year of love. The silence of the night, moonlight, flowers, and trees made us forget all reality except love, when suddenly we heard the galloping of horses and rattling of carriage wheels. Awakened from our pleasant swoon and plunged from the world of dreams into the world of perplexity and misery, we found that the old man had returned from his mission. We rose and walked through the orchard to meet him.

Then the carriage reached the entrance of the garden, Farris Effandi dismounted and slowly walked towards us, bending forward slightly as if he were carrying a heavy load. He approached Selma and placed both of his hands on her shoulders and stared at her. Tears coursed down his wrinkled cheeks and his lips trembled with sorrowful smile. In a choking voice, he said, "My beloved Selma, very soon you will be taken away from the arms of your father to the arms of another man. Very soon fate will carry you from this lonely home to the world's spacious court, and this garden will miss the pressure of your footsteps, and your father will become a stranger to you. All is done; may God bless you."

Hearing these words, Selma's face clouded and her eyes froze as if she felt a premonition of death. Then she screamed, like a bird shot down, suffering, and trembling, and in a choked voice said, "What do you say? What do you mean? Where are you sending me?"

Then she looked at him searchingly, trying to discover his secret. In a moment she said, "I understand. I understand everything. The Bishop has demanded me from you and has prepared a cage for this bird with broken wings. Is this your will, Father?"

His answer was a deep sigh. Tenderly he led Selma into the house while I remained standing in the garden, waves of perplexity beating upon me like a tempest upon autumn leaves. Then I followed them into the living room, and to avoid embarrassment, shook the old man's hand, looked at Selma, my beautiful star, and left the house.

As I reached the end of the garden I heard the old man calling me and turned to meet him. Apologetically he took my hand and said, "Forgive me, my son. I have ruined your evening with the shedding of tears, but please come to see me when my house is deserted and I am lonely and desperate. Youth, my dear son, does not combine with senility, as morning does not have meet the night; but you will come to me and call to my memory the youthful days which I spent with your father, and you will tell me the news of life which does not count me as among its sons any longer. Will you not visit me when Selma leaves and I am left here in loneliness?"

While he said these sorrowful words and I silently shook his hand, I felt the warm tears falling from his eyes upon my hand. Trembling with sorrow and filial affection. I felt as if my heart were choked with grief. When I raised my head and he saw the tears in my eyes, he bent toward me and touched my forehead with his lips. "Good-bye, son, Good-bye."

In old man's tear is more potent than that of a young man because it is the residuum of life in his weakening body. A young man's tear is like a drop of dew on the leaf of a rose, while that of an old man is like a yellow leaf which falls with the wind at the approach of winter.

As I left the house of Farris Effandi Karamy, Selma's voice still rang in my ears, her beauty followed me like a wraith, and her father's tears dried slowly on my hand.

My departure was like Adam's exodus from Paradise, but the Eve of my heart was not with me to make the whole world an Eden. That night, in which I had been born again, I felt that I saw death's face for the first time.

Thus the sun enlivens and kills the fields with its heat.

Lake of Fire

Everything that a man does secretly in the darkness of night will be clearly revealed in the daylight. Words uttered in privacy will become unexpectedly common conversation. Deed which we hide today in the corners of our lodgings will be shouted on every street tomorrow.

Thus the ghosts of darkness revealed the purpose of Bishop Bulos Galib's meeting with Farris Effandi Karamy, and his conversation was repeated all over the neighbourhood until it reached my ears.

The discussion that took place between Bishop Bulos Galib and Farris Effandi that night was not over the problems of the poor or the widows and orphans. The main purpose for sending after Farris Effandi and bringing him in the Bishops' private carriage was the betrothal of Selma to the Bishop's nephew, Mansour Bey Galib.

Selma was the only child of the wealthy Farris Effandi, and the Bishop's choice fell on Selma, not on account of her beauty and noble spirit, but on account of her father's money which would guarantee Mansour Bey a good and prosperous fortune and make him an important man.

The heads of religion in the East are not satisfied with their own munificence, but they must strive to make all members of their families superiors and oppressors. The glory of a prince goes to his eldest son by inheritance, but the exaltation of a religious head is contagious among his brothers and nephews. Thus the Christian bishop and the Moslem imam and the Brahman priest become like sea reptiles who clutch their prey with many tentacles and suck their blood with numerous mouths.

Then the Bishop demanded Selma's hand for his nephew, the only answer that he received from her father was a deep silence and falling tears, for he hated to lose his only child. Any man's soul trembles when he is separated from his only daughter whom he has reared to young womanhood.

The sorrow of parents at the marriage of a daughter is equal to their happiness at the marriage of a son, because a son brings to the family a new member, while a daughter, upon her marriage, is lost to them.

Farris Effandi perforce granted the Bishop's request, obeying his will unwillingly, because Farris Effandi knew the Bishop's nephew very well, knew that he was dangerous, full of hate, wickedness, and corruption.

In Lebanon, no Christian could oppose his bishop and remain in good standing. No man could disobey his religious head and keep his reputation. The eye could not resist a spear without being pierced, and the hand could not grasp a sword without being cut off.

Suppose that Farris Effandi had resisted the Bishop and refused his wish; then Selma's reputation would have been ruined and her name would have been blemished by the dirt of lips and tongues. In the opinion of the fox, high bunches of grapes that can't be reached are sour.

Thus destiny seized Selma and led her like a humiliated slave in the procession of miserable oriental woman, and thus fell that noble spirit into the trap after having flown freely on the white wings of love in a sky full of moonlight scented with the odour of flowers.

In some countries, the parent's wealth is a source of misery for the children. The wide strong box which the father and mother together have used for the safety of their wealth becomes a narrow, dark prison for the souls of their heirs. The Almighty Dinar which the people worship becomes a demon which punished the spirit and deadens the heart. Selma Karamy was one of those who were the victims of their parents' wealth and bridegrooms' cupidity. Had it not been for her father's wealth, Selma would still be living happily.

A week had passed. The love of Selma was my sole entertainer, singing songs of happiness for me at night and waking me at dawn to reveal the meaning of life and the secrets of nature. It is a heavenly love that is free from jealousy, rich and never harmful to the spirit. It is deep affinity that bathes the soul in contentment; a deep hunger for affection which, when satisfied, fills the soul with bounty; a tenderness that creates hope without agitating the soul, changing earth to paradise and life to a sweet and a beautiful dream. In the morning, when I walked in the fields, I saw the token of Eternity in the awakening of nature, and when I sat by the seashore I heard the waves singing the song of Eternity. And when I walked in the streets I saw the beauty of life and the splendour of humanity in the appearance of passers-by and movements of workers.

Those days passed like ghosts and disappeared like clouds, and soon nothing was left for me but sorrowful memories. The eye with which I used to look at the beauty of spring and the awakening of nature, could see nothing but the fury of the tempest and the misery of winter. The ears with which I formerly heard with delight the song of the waves, could hear only the howling of the wind and the wrath of the sea against the precipice. The soul which had observed happily the tireless vigour of mankind and the glory of the universe, was tortured by the knowledge of disappointment and failure. Nothing was more beautiful than those days of love, and nothing was more bitter than those horrible nights of sorrow.

When I could no longer resist the impulse, I went, on the weekend, once more to Selma's home—the shrine which Beauty had erected and which Love had blessed, in which the spirit could worship and the heart kneel humbly and pray. When I entered the garden I felt a power pulling me away from this world and placing me in a sphere supernaturally free from struggle and hardship. Like a mystic who receives a revelation of Heaven, I saw myself amid the trees and flowers, and as I approached the entrance of the house I beheld Selma sitting on the bench in the shadow of a jasmine tree where we both had sat the week before, on that night which Providence had chosen for the beginning of my happiness and sorrow.

She neither moved nor spoke as I approached her. She seemed to have known intuitively that I was coming, and when I sat by her she gazed at me for a moment and sighed deeply, then turned her head and looked at the sky. And, after a moment full of magic silence, she turned back toward me and tremblingly took my hand and said in a faint voice, "Look at me, my friend; study my face and I read in it that which you want to know and which I can not recite. Look at me, my beloved... look at me, my brother."

I gazed at her intently and saw that those eyes, which a few days ago were smiling like lips and moving like the wings of a nightingales, were already sunken and glazed with sorrow and pain. Her face, that had resembled the unfolding, sun kissed leaves of a lily, had faded and become colourless. Her sweet lips were like two withering roses that autumn has left on their stems. Her neck, that had been a column of ivory, was bent forward as if it no longer could support the burden of grief in her head.

All these changes I saw in Selma's face, but to me they were like a passing cloud that covered the face of the moon and makes it more beautiful. A look which reveals inward stress adds more beauty to the face, no matter how much tragedy and pain it bespeaks; but the face which, in silence, does not announce hidden mysteries is not beautiful, regardless of the symmetry of its features. The cup does not entice our lips unless the wine's colour is seen through the transparent crystal.

Selma, on that evening, was like a cup full of heavenly wine concocted of the bitterness and sweetness of life. Unaware, she symbolised the oriental woman who never leaves her parents' home until she puts upon her neck the heavy yoke of her husband, who never leaves her loving mother's arms until she must live as a slave, enduring the harshness of her husband's mother.

I continued to look at Selma and listen to her depressed spirit and suffer with her until I felt that time has ceased and the universe had faded from existence. I could see only her two large eyes staring fixedly at me and could feel only her cold, trembling hand holding mine.

I woke from my swoon hearing Selma saying quietly, "Come by beloved, let us discuss the horrible future before it comes, My father has just left the house to see the man who is going to be my companion until death. My father, whom God chose for the purpose of my existence, will meet the man whom the world has selected to be my master for the rest of my life. In the heart of this city, the old man who accompanied me during my youth will meet the young man who will be my companion for the coming years. Tonight the two families will set the marriage date. What a strange and impressive hour! Last week at this time, under this jasmine tree, Love embraced my soul for the first time, okay. While Destiny was writing the first word of my life's story at the Bishop's mansion. Now, while my father and my suitor are planning the day of marriage, I see your spirit quivering around me as a thirsty bird flickers above a spring of water guarded by a hungry serpent. Oh, how great this night is! And how deep is its mystery!"

Learning these words, I felt that dark ghost of complete despondency was seizing our love to choke it in its infancy, and I answered her, "That bird will remain flickering over that spring until thirst destroys him or falls into the grasp of a serpent and becomes its prey."

She responded, "No, my beloved, this nightingale should remain alive and sing until dark comes, until spring passes, until the end of the world, and keep on singing eternally. His voice should not be silenced, because he brings life to my heart, his wings should not be broken, because their motion removes the cloud from my heart.

When I whispered, "Selma, my beloved, thirst will exhaust him, and fear will kill him."

She replied immediately with trembling lips, "The thirst of soul is sweeter than the wine of material things, and the fear of spirit is dearer than the security of the body. But listen, my beloved, listen carefully, I am standing today at the door of a new life which I know nothing about. I am like a blind man who feels his way so that he will not fall. My father's wealth has placed me in the slave market, and this man has bought me. I neither know nor love him, but I shall learn to love him, and I shall obey him, serve him, and make him happy. I shall give him all that a weak woman can give a strong man. But you, my beloved, are still in the prime of life. You can walk freely upon life's spacious path, carpeted with flowers. You are free to traverse the world, making of your heart a torch to light your way. You can think, talk, and act freely; you can write your name on the face of life because you are a man; you can live as a master because your father's wealth will not place you in the slave market to be bought and sold; you can marry the woman of your choice and, before she lives in your home, you can let her reside in your heart and can exchange confidences without hindrances."

Silence prevailed for a moment, and Selma continued, "But, is it now that Life will tear us apart so that you may attain the glory of a man and I the duty of a woman? Is it for this that the valley swallows the song of the nightingale in its depths, and the wind scatters the petals of the rose, and the feet tread upon the wind cup? Were all those nights we spent in the moonlight by the jasmine tree, where our souls united, in vain? Did we fly swiftly toward the stars until our wings tired, and are we descending now into the abyss? Or was Love asleep when he came to us, and did he, when he woke, become angry and decide to punish us? Or did our spirits turn the nights' breeze into a wind that tore us to pieces and blew us like dust to the depth of the valley? We disobeyed no commandment, nor did we taste of forbidden fruit, so what is making us leave this paradise? We never conspired or practiced mutiny, then why are we descending to hell? No, no, the moments which united us are greater than centuries, and the light that illuminated our spirits is stronger than the dark; and if the tempest separates us on this rough ocean, the waves will unite us on the calm shore; and if this life kills us, death will unite us. A woman's heart will change with time or season; even if it dies eternally, it will never perish. A woman's heart is like a field turned into a battleground; after the trees are uprooted and the grass is burned and the rocks are reddened with blood and the earth is planted with bones and skulls, it is calm and silent as if nothing has happened; for the spring and autumn come at their intervals and resume their work. And now, my beloved, what shall we do? How shall we part and when shall we meet? Shall we consider love a strange visitor who came in the evening and left us in the morning? Or shall we suppose this affection a dream that came in our sleep and departed when we awoke? Shall we consider this week an hour of intoxication to be replaced by soberness? Raise your head and let me look at you, my beloved; open your lips and let me hear your voice. Speak to me! Will you remember me after this tempest has sunk the ship of our love? Will you hear the whispering of my wings in the silence of the night? Will you hear my spirit fluttering over you? Will you listen to my sighs? Will you see my shadow approach with the shadows of dusk and disappear with the flush of dawn? Tell me, my beloved, what will you be after having been magic ray to my eyes, sweet song to my ears, and wings to my soul? What will you be?"

Learning these words, my heart melted, and I answered her, "I will be as you want me to be, my beloved."

Then she said, "I want you to love me as a poet loves his sorrowful thoughts. I want you to remember me as a traveller remembers a calm pool in which his image was reflected as he drank its water. I want you to remember me as a mother remember her child that died before it saw the light, and I want you to remember me as a merciful king remembers a prisoner who died before his pardon reached him. I want you to be my companion, and I want you to visit my father and console him in his solitude because I shall be leaving him soon and shall be a stranger to him."

I answered her, saying, "I will do all you have said and will make my soul an envelope for your soul, and my heart a residence for your beauty and my breast a grave for your sorrows. I shall love you, Selma, as the prairies love the spring, and I shall live in you in the life of a flower under the sun's rays. I shall sing your name as the valley sings the echo of the bells of the village churches; I shall listen to the language of your soul as the shore listens to the story of the waves. I shall remember you as a stranger remembers his beloved country, and as a hungry man remembers a banquet, and as a dethroned king remembers the days of his glory, and as a prisoner remembers the hours of ease and freedom. I shall remember you as a sower remembers the bundles of wheat on his threshing flour, and as a shepherd remembers the green prairies the sweet brooks."

Selma listened to my words with palpitating heart, and said "tomorrow the truth will become ghostly and the awakening will be like a dream. Will a lover be satisfied embracing a ghost, or will a thirsty man quench his thirst from the spring or a dream?"

I answered her, "tomorrow, destiny will put you in the midst of a peaceful family, but it will send me into the world of struggle and warfare. You will be in the home of a person whom chance has made most fortunate through your beauty and virtue, while I shall be living a life of suffering and fear. You will enter the gate of life, while I shall enter the gate of death. You will be received hospitably, while I shall exist in solitude, but I shall erect a statue of love and worship it in the valley of death. Love will be my sole comforter, and I shall drink love like wine and wear it like garment. At dawn, Love will wake me from slumber and take me to the distant field, and at noon will lead me to the shadows of trees, where I will find shelter with the birds from the heat of the sun. In the evening, it will cause me to pause before sunset to hear nature's farewell song to the light of day and will show me ghostly clouds sailing in the sky. At night, Love will embrace me, and I shall sleep, dreaming of the heavenly world where the spirits of lovers and poets abide. In the Spring I shall walk side by side with love among violets and jasmines and drink the remaining drops of winter in the lily cups. In Summer we shall make the bundles of hay our pillows and the grass our bed, and the blue sky will cover us as we gaze at the stars and the moon. In Autumn, Love and I will go to the vineyard and sit by the wine press and watch the grapevines being denuded of their golden ornaments, and the migrating flocks of birds will wing over us. In Winter, we shall sit by the fireside reciting stories of long ago and chronicles of far countries. During my youth, Love will be my teacher; in middle age, my help; and in old age, my delight. Love, my beloved Selma, will stay with me to the end of my life, and after death the hand of God will unite us again."

All these words came from the depths of my heart like flames of fire which leap raging from the hearth and then disappear in the ashes. Selma was weeping as if her eyes were lips answering me with tears.

Those whom love has not given wings cannot fly the cloud of appearances to see the magic world in which Selma's spirit and mine existed together in that sorrowfully happy hour. Those whom Love has not chosen as followers do not hear when Love calls. This story is not for them. Even if they should comprehend these pages, they would not be able to grasp the shadowy meanings which are not clothed in words and do not reside on paper, but what human being is he who has never sipped the wine from the cup of love, and what spirit is it that has never stood reverently before that lighted altar in the temple whose pavement is the hearts of men and women and whose ceiling is the secret canopy of dreams? What flower is that on whose leaves the dawn has never poured a drop of dew; what streamlet is that which lost its course without going to the sea?

Selma raised her face toward the sky and gazed at the heavenly stars which studded the firmament. She stretched out her hands; her eyes widened, and her lips trembled. On her pale face, I could see the signs of sorrow, oppression, hopelessness, and pain. Then she cried, "Oh, Lord, what has a woman done that hath offended Thee? What sin has she committed to deserve such a punishment? For what crime has she been awarded everlasting castigation? Oh, Lord, Thou art strong, and I am weak. Why hast Thou made me suffer pain? Thou art great and almighty, while I am nothing but a tiny creature crawling before Thy throne. Why hast Thou crushed me with Thy foot? Thou art a raging tempest, and I am like dust; why, my Lord, hast Thou flung me upon the cold earth? Thou art powerful, and I am helpless; why art Thou fighting me? Thou art considerate, and I am prudent; why art Thou destroying me? Thou hast created woman with love, and why, with love, dost Thou ruin her? With Thy right hand dost Thou lift her, and with Thy left hand dost Thou strike her into the abyss, and she knows not why. In her mouth Thou blowest the breath of Life, and in her heart Thou sowest the seeds of death. Thou dost show her the path of happiness, but Thou leadest her in the road of misery; in her mouth Thou dost place a song of happiness, but then Thou dost close her lips with sorrow and dost fetter her tongue with agony. With Thy mysterious fingers dost Thou dress her wounds, and with Thine hands Thou drawest the dread of pain round her pleasures. In her bed Thou hidest pleasure and peace, but beside it Thou dost erect obstacles and fear. Thou dost excite her affection through Thy will, and from her affection does shame emanate. By Thy will Thou showest her the beauty of creation, but her love for beauty becomes a terrible famine. Thou dost make her drink life in the cup of death, and death in the cup of life. Thou purifiest her with tears, and in tears her life streams away. Oh, Lord, Thou hast opened my eyes with love, and with love Thou hast blinded me. Thou hast kissed me with Thy lips and struck me with Thy strong hand. Thou has planted in my heart a white rose, but around the rose a barrier of thorns. Thou hast tied my present with the spirit of a young man whom I love, but my life with the body of an unknown man. So help me, my Lord, to be strong in this deadly struggle and assist me to be truthful and virtuous until death. Thy will be done. Oh, Lord God."

Silence continued. Selma looked down, pale and frail; her arms dropped, and her head bowed and it seemed to me as if a tempest had broken a branch from a tree and cast it down to dry and perish.

I took her cold hand and kissed it, but when I attempted to console her it was I who needed consolation more than she did. I kept silent, thinking of our plight and listening to my heartbeats. Neither of us said more.

Extreme torture is mute, and so we sat silent, petrified, like columns of marble buried under the sand of an earthquake. Neither wished to listen to the other because our heart-threads had become weak and even breathing would have broken them.

It was midnight, and we could see the crescent moon rising from behind Mount Sunnin, and it looked in the midst of the stars, like the face of a corpse, in a coffin surrounded by the dim lights of candles. And Lebanon looked like an old man whose back was bent with age and whose eyes were a haven for insomnia, watching the dark and waiting for dawn, like asking sitting on the ashes of his throne in the debris of his palace.

The mountains, trees, and rivers change their appearance with the vicissitudes of times and seasons, as a man changes with his experiences and emotions. The lofty poplar that resembles a bride in the daytime, will look like a column of smoke in the evening; the huge rock that stands impregnable at noon, will appear to be a miserable pauper at night, with earth for his bed and the sky for his cover; and the rivulet that we see glittering in the morning and hear singing the hymn of Eternity, will, in the evening, turn to a stream of tears wailing like a mother bereft of her child, and Lebanon, that had looked dignified a week before, when the moon was full and our spirits were happy, looked sorrowful and lonesome that night.

We stood up and bade each other farewell, but love and despair stood between us like two ghosts, one stretching his wings with his fingers over our throats, one weeping and the other laughing hideously.

As I took Selma's hand and put it to my lips, she came close to me and placed a kiss on my forehead, then dropped on the wooden bench. She shut her eyes and whispered softly, "Oh, Lord God, have mercy on me and mend my broken wings!"

As I left Selma in the garden, I felt as if my senses were covered with a thick veil, like a lake whose surface is concealed by fog.

The beauty of trees, the moonlight, the deep silence, everything about me looked ugly and horrible. The true light that had showed me the beauty and wonder of the universe was converted to a great flame of fire that seared my heart; and the Eternal music I used to hear became a clamour, more frightening than the roar of a lion.

I reached my room, and like a wounded bird shot down by a hunter, I fell on my bed, repeating the words of Selma: "Oh, Lord God, have mercy on me and mend my broken wings!"

Before the Throne of Death

Marriage in these days is a mockery whose management is in the hands of young men and parents. In most countries the young men win while the parents lose. The woman is looked upon as a commodity, purchased and delivered from one house to another. In time her beauty fades and she becomes like an old piece of furniture left in a dark corner.

Modern civilisation has made woman a little wiser, but it has increased her suffering because of man's covetousness. The woman of yesterday was a happy wife, but the woman of today is a miserable mistress. In the past she walked blindly in the light, but now she walks open-eyed in the dark. She was beautiful in her ignorance, virtuous in her simplicity, and strong in her weakness. Today she has become ugly in her ingenuity, superficial and heartless in her knowledge. Will the day ever come when beauty and knowledge, ingenuity and virtue, and weakness of body and strength of spirit will be united in a woman?

I am one of those who believe that spiritual progress is a rule of human life, but the approach to perfection is slow and painful. If a woman elevates herself in one respect and is retarded in another, it is because the rough trail that leads to the mountain peak is not free of ambushes of thieves and lairs of wolves.

This strange generation exists between sleeping and waking. It holds in its hands the soil of the past and the seeds of the future. However, we find in every city a woman who symbolises the future.

In the city of Beirut, Selma Karamy was the symbol of the future Oriental woman, but, like many who lie ahead of their time, she became the victim of the present; and like a flower snatched from its stem and carried away by the current of a river, she walked in the miserable procession of the defeated.

Mansour Bey Galib and Selma were married, and lived together in a beautiful house at Ras Beyrouth, where all the wealthy dignitaries resided. Farris Effandi Karamy was left in his solitary home in the midst of his garden and orchards like a lonely shepherd amid his flock.

The days and merry nights of the wedding passed, but the honeymoon left memories of times of bitter sorrow, as wars leave skulls and dead bones on the battlefield. The dignity of an Oriental wedding inspires the hearts of young men and women, but its termination may drop them like millstones to the bottom of the sea. Their exhilaration is like footprints on sand which remain only till they are washed away by the waves.

Spring departed, and so did summer and autumn, but my love for Selma increased day by day until it became a kind of mute worship, the feeling that an orphan has toward the soul of his mother in Heaven. My yearning was converted to blind sorrow that could see nothing but itself, and the passion that drew tears from my eyes was replaced by perplexity that sucked the blood from my heart, and my sighs of affection became a constant prayer for the happiness of Selma and her husband and peace for her father.

My hopes and prayers were in vain, because Selma's misery was an internal malady that nothing but death could cure.

Mansour Bey was a man to whom all the luxuries of life came easily; but, in spite of that, he was dissatisfied and rapacious. After marrying Selma, he neglected her father in his loneliness and prayed for his death so that he could inherit what was left of the old man's wealth.

Mansour Bey's character was similar to his uncle's; the only difference between the two was that the Bishop got everything he wanted secretly, under the protection of his ecclesiastical robe and the golden cross which he wore on his chest, while his nephew did everything publicly. The Bishop went to church in the morning and spent the rest of the day pilfering from the widows, orphans, and simple-minded people. But Mansour Bey spent his days in pursuit of sexual satisfaction. On Sunday, Bishop Bulos Galib preached his Gospel; but during weekdays he never practiced what he preached, occupying himself with political intrigues of the locality. And, by means of his uncle's prestige and influence, Mansour Bey made it his business to secure political plums for those who could offer a sufficient bribe.

Bishop Bulos was a thief who hid himself under the cover of night, while his nephew, Mansour Bey, was a swindler who walked proudly in daylight. However, the people of Oriental nations place trust in such as they—wolves and butchers who ruin their country through covetousness and crush their neighbours with an iron hand.

Why do I occupy these pages with words about the betrayers of poor nations instead of reserving all the space for the story of a miserable woman with a broken heart? Why do I shed tears for oppressed peoples rather than keep all my tears for the memory of a weak woman whose life was snatched by the teeth of death?

But my dear readers, don't you think that such a woman is like a nation that is oppressed by priests and rulers? Don't you believe that thwarted love which leads a woman to the grave is like the despair which pervades the people of the earth? A woman is to a nation as light is to a lamp. Will not the light be dim if the oil in the lamp is low?

Autumn passed, and the wind blew the yellow leaves form the trees, making way for winter, which came howling and crying. I was still in the City of Beirut without a companion save my dreams, which would lift my spirit to the sky and then bury it deep in the bosom of the earth.

The sorrowful spirit finds relaxation in solitude. It abhors people, as a wounded deer deserts the herd and lives in a cave until it is healed or dead.

One day I heard Farris Effandi was ill. I left my solitary abode and walked to his home, taking a new route, a lonely path between olive trees, avoiding the main road with its rattling carriage wheels.

Arriving at the old man's house, I entered and found Farris Effandi lying on his bed, weak and pale. His eyes were sunken and looked like two deep, dark valleys haunted by the ghosts of pain. The smile which had always enlivened his face was choked with pain and agony; and the bones of his gentle hands looked like naked branches trembling before the tempest. As I approached him and inquired as to his health, he turned his pale face toward me, and on his trembling lips appeared a smile, and he said in a weak voice, "Go—go, my son, to the other room and comfort Selma and bring her to sit by the side of my bed."

I entered the adjacent room and found Selma lying on a divan, covering her head with her arms and burying her face in a pillow so that her father would not hear her weeping. Approaching slowly, I pronounced her name in a voice that seemed more like sighing than whispering. She moved fearfully, as if she had been interrupted in a terrible dream, and sat up, looking at me with glazed eyes, doubting whether I was a ghost or a living being. After a deep silence which took us back on the wings of memory to that hour when we were intoxicated with wine of love, Selma wiped away her tears and said, "See how time has changed us! See how time has changed the course of our lives and left us in these ruins. In this place spring united us in a bond of love, and in this place has brought us together before the throne of death. How beautiful was spring, and how terrible is this winter!"

Speaking thus, she covered her face again with her hands as if she were shielding her eyes from the spectre of the past standing before her. I put my hand on her head and said, "Come, Selma, come and let us be as strong towers before the tempest. Let us stand like brave soldiers before the enemy and face his weapons. If we are killed, we shall die as martyrs; and if we win, we shall live as heroes. Braving obstacles and hardships is nobler than retreat to tranquillity. The butterfly that hovers around the lamp until it dies is more admirable than the mole that lives in a dark tunnel. Come, Selma, let us walk this rough path firmly, with our eyes toward the sun so that we may not see the skulls and serpents among the rocks and thorns. if fear should stop us in middle of the road, we would hear only ridicule from the voices of the night, but if we reach the mountain peak bravely we shall join the heavenly spirits in songs of triumph and joy. Cheer up, Selma, wipe away your tears and remove the sorrow from your face. Rise, and let us sit by the bed of your father, because his life depends on your life, and your smile is his only cure."

Kindly and affectionately she looked at me and said, "Are you asking me to have patience, while you are in need of it yourself? Will a hungry man give his bread to another hungry man? Or will sick man give medicine to another which he himself needs badly?"

She rose, her head bent slightly forward and we walked to the old man's room and sat by the side of his bed. Selma forced a smile and pretended to be patient, and her father tried to make her believe that he was feeling better and getting stronger; but both father and daughter were aware of each other's sorrow and heard the unvoiced sighs. They were like two equal forces, wearing each other away silently. The father's heart was melting because of his daughter's plight. They were two pure souls, one departing and the other agonised with grief, embracing in love and death; and I was between the two with my own troubled heart. We were three people, gathered and crushed by the hands of destiny; an old man like a dwelling ruined by flood, a young woman whose symbol was a lily beheaded by the sharp edge of a sickle, and a young man who was a weak sapling, bent by a snowfall; and all of us were toys in the hands of fate.

Farris Effandi moved slowly and stretched his weak hand toward Selma, and in a loving and tender voice said, "Hold my hand, my beloved." Selma held his hand; then he said, "I have lived long enough, and I have enjoyed the fruits of life's seasons. I have experienced all its phases with equanimity. I lost your mother when you were three years of age, and she left you as a precious treasure in my lap. I watched you grow, and your face reproduced your mother's features as stars reflected in a calm pool of water. Your character, intelligence, and beauty are your mother's, even your manner of speaking and gestures. You have been my only consolation in this life because you were the image of your mother in every deed and word. Now, I grow old, and my only resting place is between the soft wings of death. Be comforted, my beloved daughter, because I have lived long enough to see you as a woman. Be happy because I shall live in you after my death. My departure today would be no different from my going tomorrow or the day after, for our days are perishing like the leaves of autumn. The hour of my days are perishing like the leaves of autumn. The hour of my death approaches rapidly, and my soul is desirous of being united with your mother's."

As he uttered these words sweetly and lovingly, his face was radiant. Then he put his hand under his pillow and pulled out a small picture in a gold frame. With his eyes on the little photograph, he said, "Come, Selma, come and see your mother in this picture."

Selma wiped away her tears, and after gazing long at the picture, she kissed it repeatedly and cried, "Oh, my beloved mother! Oh, mother!" Then she placed her trembling lips on the picture as if she wished to pour her soul into that image.

The most beautiful word on the lips of mankind is the word "Mother," and the most beautiful call is the call of "My mother." it is a word full of hope and love, a sweet and kind word coming from the depths of the heart. The mother is every thing—she is our consolation in sorrow, our hope in misery, and our strength in weakness. She is the source of love, mercy, sympathy, and forgiveness. He who loses his mother loses a pure soul who blesses and guards him constantly.

Every thing in nature bespeaks the mother. The sun is the mother of earth and gives it its nourishment of hear; it never leaves the universe at night until it has put the earth to sleep to the song of the sea and the hymn of birds and brooks. And this earth is the mother of trees and flowers. It produces them, nurses them, and weans them. The trees and flowers become kind mothers of their great fruits and seeds. And the mother, the prototype of all existence, is the eternal spirit, full of beauty and love.

Selma Karamy never knew her mother because she had died when Selma was an infant, but Selma wept when she saw the picture and cried, "Oh, mother!" The word mother is hidden in our hearts, and it comes upon our lips in hours of sorrow and happiness as the perfume comes from the heart of the rose and mingles with clear and cloudy air.

Selma stared at her mother's picture, kissing it repeatedly, until she collapsed by her father's bed.

The old man placed both hands on her head and said, "I have shown you, my dear child, a picture of your mother on paper. Now listen to me and I shall let you hear her words."

She lifted her head like a little bird in the nest that hears its mother's wing, and looked at him attentively.

Farris Effandi opened his mouth and said, "Your mother was nursing you when she lost her father; she cried and wept at his going, but she was wise and patient. She sat by me in this room as soon as the funeral was over and held my hand and said, 'Farris, my father is dead now and you are my only consolation in this world. The heart's affections are divided like the branches of the cedar tree; if the tree loses one strong branch, it will suffer but it does not die. It will pour all its vitality into the next branch so that it will grow and fill the empty place.' This is what your mother told me when her father died, and you should say the same thing when death takes my body to its resting place and my soul to God's care."

Selma answered him with falling tears and broken heart, "When Mother lost her father, you took his place; but who is going to take yours when you are gone? She was left in the care of a loving and truthful husband; she found consolation in her little daughter, and who will be my consolation when you pass away? You have been my father and mother and the companion of my youth."

Saying these words, she turned and looked at me, and, holding the side of my garment, said, "This is the only friend I shall have after you are gone, but how can he console me when he is suffering also? How can a broken heart find consolation in a disappointed soul? A sorrowful woman cannot be comforted by her neighbour's sorrow, nor can a bird fly with broken wings. He is the friend of my soul, but I have already placed a heavy burden of sorrow upon him and dimmed his eyes with my tears till he can see nothing but darkness. he is a brother whom I dearly love, but he is like all brothers who share my sorrow and help me shed tears which increase my bitterness and burn my heart."

Selma's words stabbed my heart, and I felt that I could bear no more. The old man listened to her with depressed spirit. The old man listened to her with depressed spirit, trembling like the light of a lamp before the wind. Then he stretched out his hand and said, "Let me go peacefully, my child. I have broken the bars of this cage; let me fly and do not stop me, for your mother is calling me. The sky is clear and the sea is calm and the boat is ready to sail; do not delay its voyage. Let my body rest with those who are resting; let my dream end and my soul awaken with the dawn; let your soul embrace mine and give me the kiss of hope; let no drops of sorrow or bitterness fall upon my body lest the flowers and grass refuse their nourishment. Do not shed tears of misery upon my hand, for they may grow thorns upon my grave. Do not draw lines of agony upon my forehead, for the wind may pass and read them and refuse to carry the dust of my bones to the green prairies... I love you, my child, while I lived, and I shall love you when I am dead, and my soul shall always watch over you and protect you."

When Farris Effandi looked at me with his eyes half closed and said, "My son, be a real brother to Selma as your father was to me. Be her help and friend in need, and do not let her mourn, because mourning for the dead is a mistake. Repeat to her pleasant tales and sing for her the songs of life so that she may forget her sorrows. Remember me to your father; ask him to tell you the stories of your youth and tell him that I loved him in the person of his son in the last hour of my life."

Silence prevailed, and I could see the pallor of death on the old man's face. Then he rolled his eyes and looked at us and whispered, "Don't call the physician, for he might extend my sentence in this prison by his medicine. The days of slavery are gone, and my soul seeks the freedom of the skies. And do not call the priest to my bedside, because his incantations would not save me if I were a sinner, nor would it rush me to Heaven if I were innocent. The will of humanity cannot change the will of God, as an astrologer cannot change the course of the stars. But after my death let the doctors and priest do what they please, for my ship will continue sailing until it reaches its destination."

At midnight Farris Effandi opened his tired eyes for the last time and focused them on Selma, who was kneeling by his bedside. He tried to speak, but could not, for death had already choked his voice; but he finally managed to say, "The night has passed... Oh, Selma...Oh...Oh, Selma..." Then he bent his head, his face turned white, and I could see a smile on his lips as he breathed his last.

Selma felt her father's hand. It was cold. Then she raised her head and looked at his face. It was covered with the veil of death. Selma was so choked that she could not shed tears, nor sigh, nor even move. For a moment she stared at him with fixed eyes like those of a statue; then she bent down until her forehead touched the floor, and said, "Oh, Lord, have mercy and mend our broken wings."

Farris Effandi Karamy died; his soul was embraced by Eternity, and his body was returned to the earth. Mansour Bey Galib got possession of his wealth, and Selma became a prisoner of life—a life of grief and misery.

I was lost in sorrow and reverie. Days and nights preyed upon me as the eagle ravages its victim. Many a time I tried to forget my misfortune by occupying myself with books and scriptures of past generation, but it was like extinguishing fire with oil, for I could see nothing in the procession of the past but tragedy and could hear nothing but weeping and wailing. The Book of Job was more fascinating to me than the Psalms and I preferred the Elegies of Jeremiah to the Song of Solomon. Hamlet was closer to my heart than all other dramas of western writers. Thus despair weakens our sight and closes our ears. We can see nothing but spectres of doom and can hear only the beating of our agitated hearts.

Between Christ and Ishtar

In the midst of the gardens and hills which connect the city of Beirut with Lebanon there is a small temple, very ancient, dug out of white rock, surrounded by olive, almond, and willow trees. Although this temple is a half mile from the main highway, at the time of my story very few people interested in relics and ancient ruins had visited it. It was one of many interesting places hidden and forgotten in Lebanon. Due to its seclusion, it had become a haven for worshippers and a shrine for lonely lovers.

As one enters this temple he sees on the wall at the east side an old Phoenician picture, carved in the rock depicting Ishtar, goddess of love and beauty, sitting on her throne, surrounded by seven nude virgins standing in different posses. The first one carries a torch; the second, a guitar; the third, a censer; the fourth a jug of wine; the fifth, a branch of roses; the sixth, a wreath of laurel; the seventh, a bow and arrow; and all of them look at Ishtar reverently.

In the second wall there is another picture, more modern than the first one, symbolising Christ nailed to the cross, and at His side stand His sorrowful mother and Mary Magdalene and two other women weeping. This Byzantine picture shows that it was carved in the fifteenth or sixteenth century.

In the west side wall there are two round transits through which the sun's rays enter the temple and strike the pictures and make them look as if they were painted with gold water colour. In the middle of the temple there is a square marble with old paintings on its sides, some of which can hardly be seen under the petrified lumps of blood which show that the ancient people offered sacrifices on this rock and poured perfume, wine, and oil upon it.

There is nothing else in that little temple except deep silence, revealing to the living the secrets of the goddess and speaking wordlessly of past generations and the evolution of religions.

Such a sight carries the poet to a world far away from the one in which he dwells and convinces the philosopher that men were born religious; they felt a need for that which they could not see and drew symbols, the meaning of which divulged their hidden secrets and their desires in life and death.

In that unknown temple, I met Selma once every month and spent the hours with her, looking at those strange pictures, thinking of the crucified Christ and pondering upon the young Phoenician men and women who lived, loved and worshipped beauty in the person of Ishtar by burning incense before her statue and pouring perfume on her shrine, people for whom nothing is left to speak except the name, repeated by the march of time before the face of Eternity.

It is hard to write down in words the memories of those hours when I met Selma—those heavenly hours, filled with pain, happiness, sorrow, hope, and misery.

We met secretly in the old temple, remembering the old days, discussing our present, fearing our future, and gradually bringing out the hidden secrets in the depths of our hearts and complaining to each other of our misery and suffering, trying to console ourselves with imaginary hopes and sorrowful dreams. Every now and then we would become calm and wipe our tears and start smiling, forgetting everything except Love; we embraced each other until our hearts melted; then Selma would print a pure kiss on my forehead and fill my heart with ecstasy; I would return the kiss as she bent her ivory neck while her cheeks became gently red like the first ray of dawn on the forehead of hills. We silently looked at the distant horizon where the clouds were coloured with the orange ray of sunset.

Our conversation was not limited to love; every now and then we drifted on to current topics and exchanged ideas. During the course of conversation Selma spoke of woman's place in society, the imprint that the past generation had left on her character, the relationship between husband and wife, and the spiritual diseases and corruption which threatened married life. I remember her saying: "The poets and writers are trying to understand the reality of woman, but up to this day they have not understood the hidden secrets of her heart, because they look upon her from behind the sexual veil and see nothing but externals; they look upon her through the magnifying glass of hatefulness and find nothing except weakness and submission.

In another occasion she said, pointing to the carved pictures on the walls of the temple, "In the heart of this rock there are two symbols depicting the essence of a woman's desires and revealing the hidden secrets of her soul, moving between love and sorrow—between affection and sacrifice, between Ishtar sitting on the throne and Mary standing by the cross. The man buys glory and reputation, but the woman pays the price."

No one knew about our secret meetings except God and the flock of birds which flew over the temple. Selma used to come in her carriage to a place named Pasha park and from there she walked to the temple, where she found me anxiously waiting for her.

We feared not the observer's eyes, neither did our consciences bother us; the spirit which is purified by fire and washed by tears is higher than what the people call shame and disgrace; it is free from the laws of slavery and old customs against the affections of the human heart. That spirit can proudly stand unashamed before the throne of God.

Human society has yielded for seventy centuries to corrupted laws until it cannot understand the meaning of the superior and eternal laws. A man's eyes have become accustomed to the dim light of candles and cannot see the sunlight. Spiritual disease is inherited from one generation to another until it has become a part of people, who look upon it, not as a disease, but as a natural gift, showered by God upon Adam. If those people found someone free from the germs of this disease, they would think of him with shame and disgrace.

Those who think evil of Selma Karamy because she left her husband's home and met me in the temple are the diseased and weak-minded kind who look upon the healthy and sound as rebels. They are like insects crawling in the dark for fear of being stepped upon by the passer-by.

The oppressed prisoners, who can break away from his jail and does not do so, is a coward. Selma, an innocent and oppressed prisoner, was unable to free herself from slavery. Was she to blame because she looked through the jail window upon the green fields and spacious sky? Will the people count her as being untruthful to her husband because she came from his home to sit by me between Christ and Ishtar? Let the people say what they please; Selma had passed the marshes which submerge other spirits and had landed in a world that could not be reached by the howling of wolves and rattling of snakes. People may say what they want about me, for the spirit who has seen the spectre of death cannot be scared by the faces of thieves; the soldier who has seen the swords glittering over his head and streams of blood under his feet does not care about rocks thrown at him by the children on the streets.

Sacrifice

One day in the late part of June, as the people left the city for the mountain to avoid the heat of summer, I went as usual to the temple to meet Selma, carrying with me a little book of Andalusian poems. As I reached the temple I sat there waiting for Selma, glancing at intervals at the pages of my book, reciting those verses which filled my heart with ecstasy and brought to my soul the memory of the kings, poets, and knights who bade farewell to Granada, and left, with tears in their eyes and sorrow in their hearts, their palaces, institutions and hopes behind. In an hour I saw Selma walking in the midst of the gardens and I approaching the temple, leaning on her parasol as if she were carrying all the worries of the world upon her shoulders. As she entered the temple and sat by me, I noticed some sort of change in her eyes and I was anxious to inquire about it.

Selma felt what was going on in my mind, and she put her hand on my head and said, "Come close to me, come my beloved, come and let me quench my thirst, for the hour of separation has come."

I asked her, "Did your husband find out about our meeting her?" She responded, "My husband does not care about me, neither does he know how I spend my time, for he is busy with those poor girls whom poverty has driven into the houses of ill fame; those girls who sell their bodies for bread, kneaded with blood and tears."

I inquired, "What prevents you from coming to this temple and sitting by me reverently before God? Is your soul requesting our separation?"

She answered with tears in her eyes, "No, my beloved, my spirit did not ask for separation, for you are a part of me. My eyes never get tired of looking at you, for you are their light; but if destiny ruled that I should walk the rough path of life loaded with shackles, would I be satisfied if your fate should be like mine?" Then she added, "I cannot say everything, because the tongue is mute with pain and cannot talk; the lips are sealed with misery and cannot move; all I can say to you is that I am afraid you may fall in the same trap I fell in."

When I asked, "What do you mean, Selma, and of whom are you afraid?" She covered her face with her hands and said, "The Bishop has already found out that once a month I have been leaving the grave which he buried me in."

I inquired, "Did the Bishop find out about our meetings here?" She answered, "If he did, you would not see me here sitting by you, but he is getting suspicious and he informed all his servants and guards to watch me closely. I am feeling that the house I live in and the path I walk on are all eyes watching me, and fingers pointing at me, and ears listening to the whisper of my thoughts."

She was silent for a while, and then she added, with tears pouring down her cheeks, "I am not afraid of the Bishop, for wetness does not scare the drowned, but I am afraid you might fall into the trap and become his prey; you are still young and free as the sunlight. I am not frightened of fate which has shot all its arrows in my breast, but I am afraid the serpent might bite your feet and detain you from climbing the mountain peak where the future awaits you with its pleasure and glory."

I said, "He who has not been bitten by the serpents of light and snapped at by the wolves of darkness will always be deceived by the days and nights. But listen, Selma, listen carefully; is separation the only means of avoiding people's evils and meanness? Has the path of love and freedom been closed and is nothing left except submission to the will of the slaves of death?"

She responded, "Nothing is left save separation and bidding each other farewell."

With rebellious spirit I took her hand and said excitedly, "We have yielded to the people's will for a long time; since the time we met until this hour we have been led by the blind and have worshipped with them before their idols. Since the time I met you we have been in the hands of the Bishop like two balls which he has thrown around as he pleased. Are we going to submit to his will until death takes us away? Did God give us the breath of life to place it under death's feet? Did He give us liberty to make it a shadow of slavery? He who extinguishes his spirit's fire with his own hands is an infidel in the eyes of Heaven, for Heaven set the fire that burns in our spirits. He who does not rebel against oppression is doing himself injustice. I love you, Selma, and you love me, too; and Love is a precious treasure, it is God's gift to sensitive and great spirits. Shall we throw this treasure away and let the pigs scatter it and trample on it? This world is full of wonder and beauty. Why are we living in this narrow tunnel which the Bishop and his assistants have dug out for us? Life is full of happiness and freedom; why don't we take this heavy yoke off our shoulders and break the chains tied to our feet, and walk freely toward peace? Get up and let us leave this small temple for God's great temple. Let us leave this country and all its slavery and ignorance for another country far away and unreached by the hands of the thieves. Let us go to the coast under the cover of night and catch a boat that will take us across the oceans, where we can find a new life full of happiness and understanding. Do not hesitate, Selma for these minutes are more precious to us than the crowns of kings and more sublime than the thrones of angels. Let us follow the column of light that leads us from this arid desert into the green fields where flowers and aromatic plants grow."

She shook her head and gazed at something invisible on the ceiling of the temple; a sorrowful smile appeared on her lips; then she said, "No, no my beloved. Heaven placed in my hand a cup, full of vinegar and gall; I forced myself to drink it in order to know the full bitterness at the bottom until nothing was left save a few drops, which I shall drink patiently. I am not worthy of a new life of love and peace; I am not strong enough for life's pleasure and sweetness, because a bird with broken wings cannot fly in the spacious sky. The eyes that are accustomed to the dim light of a candle are not strong enough to stare at the sun. Do not talk to me of happiness; its memory makes me suffer. Mention not peace to me; its shadow frightens me; but look at me and I will show you the holy torch which Heaven has lighted in the ashes of my heart—you know that I love you as a mother loves her only child, and Love only taught me to protect you even from myself. It is Love, purified with fire, that stops me from following you to the farthest land. Love kills my desires so that you may live freely and virtuously. Limited love asks for possession of the beloved, but the unlimited asks only for itself. Love that comes between the naiveté and awakening of youth satisfies itself with possessing, and grows with embraces. But Love which is born in the firmament's lap and has descended with the night's secrets is not contended with anything but Eternity and immortality; it does not stand reverently before anything except deity. When I knew that the Bishop wanted to stop me from leaving his nephew's house and to take my only pleasure away from me, I stood before the window of my room and looked toward the sea, thinking of the vast countries beyond it and the real freedom and personal independence which can be found there. I felt that I was living close to you, surrounded by the shadow of your spirit, submerged in the ocean of your affection. But all these thoughts which illuminate a woman's heart and make her rebel against old customs and live in the shadow of freedom and justice, made me believe that I am weak and that our love is limited and feeble, unable to stand before the sun's face. I cried like a king whose kingdom and treasure have been usurped, but immediately I saw your face through my tears and your eyes gazing at me and I remembered what you said to me once (Come, Selma, come and let us be strong towers before the tempest. Let us stand like brave soldiers before the enemy and face his weapons. If we are killed, we shall die as martyrs; and if we win, we shall live as heroes. Braving obstacles and hardships is nobler than retreat to tranquillity.) These words, my beloved, you uttered when the wings of death were hovering around my father's bed; I remembered them yesterday when the wings of despair were hovering above my head. I strengthened myself and felt, while in the darkness of my prison, some sort of precious freedom easing our difficulties and diminishing our sorrows. I found out that our love was as deep as the ocean and as high as the stars and as spacious as the sky. I came here to see you, and in my weak spirit there is a new strength, and this strength is the ability to sacrifice a great thing in order to obtain a greater one; it is the sacrifice of my happiness so that you may remain virtuous and honourable in the eyes of the people and be far away from their treachery and persecution. In the past, when I came to this place I felt as if heavy chains were pulling down on me, but today I came here with a new determination that laughs at the shackles and shortens the way. I used to come to this temple like a scared phantom, but today I came like a brave woman who feels the urgency of sacrifice and knows the value of suffering, a woman who likes to protect the one she loves from the ignorant people and from her hungry spirit. I used to sit by you like a trembling shadow, but today I came here to show you my true self before Ishtar and Christ. I am a tree, grown in the shade, and today I stretched my branches to tremble for a while in the daylight. I came here to tell you good-bye, my beloved, and it is my hope that our farewell will be great and awful like our love. Let our farewell be like fire that bends the gold and makes it more resplendent."

Selma did not allow me to speak or protest, but she looked at me, her eyes glittering, her face retaining its dignity, seeming like an angel worthy of silence and respect. Then she flung herself upon me, something which she had never done before, and put her smooth arms around me and printed a long, deep, fiery kiss on my lips.

As the sun went down, withdrawing its rays from those gardens and orchards, Selma moved to the middle of the temple and gazed along at its walls and corners as if she wanted to pour the light of her eyes on its pictures and symbols. Then she walked forward and reverently knelt before the picture of Christ and kissed His feet, and she whispered, "Oh, Christ, I have chosen Thy Cross and deserted Ishtar's world of pleasure and happiness; I have worn the wreath of thorns and discarded the wreath of laurel and washed myself with blood and tears instead of perfume and scent; I have drunk vinegar and gall from a cup which was meant for wine and nectar; accept me, my Lord, among Thy followers and lead me toward Galilee with those who have chosen Thee, contended with their sufferings and delighted with their sorrows."

When she rose and looked at me and said, "Now I shall return happily to my dark cave, where horrible ghosts reside, Do not sympathise with me, my beloved, and do not feel sorry for me, because the soul that sees the shadow of God once will never be frightened, thereafter, of the ghosts of devils. And the eye that looks on heaven once will not be closed by the pains of the world."

Uttering these words, Selma left the place of worship; and I remained there lost in a deep sea of thoughts, absorbed in the world of revelation where God sits on the throne and the angels write down the acts of human beings, and the souls recite the tragedy of life, and the brides of Heaven sing the hymns of love, sorrow and immortality.

Night had already come when I awakened from my swoon and found myself bewildered in the midst of the gardens, repeating the echo of every word uttered by Selma and remembering her silence, her actions, her movements, her expression and the touch of her hands, until I realised the meaning of farewell and the pain of lonesomeness. I was depressed and heart-broken. It was my first discovery of the fact that men, even if they are born free, will remain slaves of strict laws enacted by their forefathers; and that the firmament, which we imagine as unchanging, is the yielding of today to the will of tomorrow and submission of yesterday to the will of today—Many a time, since the night, I have thought of the spiritual law which made Selma prefer death to life, and many a time I have made a comparison between nobility of sacrifice and happiness of rebellion to find out which one is nobler and more beautiful; but until now I have distilled only one truth out of the whole matter, and this truth is sincerity, which makes all our deeds beautiful and honourable. And this sincerity was in Selma Karamy.

The Rescuer

Five years of Selma's marriage passed without bringing children to strengthen the ties of spiritual relation between her and her husband and bind their repugnant souls together.

A barren woman is looked upon with disdain everywhere because of most men's desire to perpetuate themselves through posterity.

The substantial man considers his childless wife as an enemy; he detests her and deserts her and wishes her death. Mansour Bey Galib was that kind of man; materially, he was like earth, and hard like steel and greedy like a grave. His desire of having a child to carry on his name and reputation made him hate Selma in spite of her beauty and sweetness.

A tree grown in a cave does not bear fruit; and Selma, who lived in the shade of life, did not bear children.

The nightingale does not make his nest in a cage lest slavery be the lot of its chicks. Selma was a prisoner of misery and it was Heaven's will that she would not have another prisoner to share her life. The flowers of the field are the children of sun's affection and nature's love; and the children of men are the flowers of love and compassion.

The spirit of love and compassion never dominated Selma's beautiful home at Ras Beyrouth; nevertheless, she knelt down on her knees every night before Heaven and asked God for a child in whom she would find comfort and consolation. She prayed successively until Heaven answered her prayers.

The tree of the cave blossomed to bear fruit at last. The nightingale in the cage commenced making its nest with the feathers of its wings.

Selma stretched her chained arms toward Heaven to receive God's precious gift and nothing in the world could have made her happier than becoming a potential mother.

She waited anxiously, counting the days and looking forward to the time when Heaven's sweetest melody, the voice of her child, should ring in her ears.

She commenced to see the dawn of a brighter future through her tears.

It was the month of Nisan when Selma was stretched on the bed of pain and labour, where life and death were wrestling. The doctor and the midwife were ready to deliver to the world a new guest. Late at night Selma started her successive cry, a cry of life's partition from life, a cry of continuance in the firmament of nothingness, a cry of a weak force before the stillness of great forces, the cry of poor Selma who was lying down in despair under the feet of life and death.

At dawn Selma gave birth to a baby boy. When she opened her eyes she saw smiling faces all over the room, then she looked again and saw life and death still wrestling by her bed. She closed her eyes and cried, saying for the first time, "Oh, my son." The midwife wrapped the infant with silk swaddles and placed him by his mother, but the doctor kept looking at Selma and sorrowfully shaking his head.

The voices of joy woke the neighbours, who rushed into the house to felicitate the father upon the birth of his heir, but the doctor still gazed at Selma and her infant and shook his head.

The servants hurried to spread the good news to Mansour Bey, but the doctor stared at Selma and her child with a disappointed look on his face.

As the sun came out, Selma took the infant to her breast; he opened his eyes for the first time and looked at his mother; then he quivered and close them for the last time. The doctor took the child from Selma's arms and on his cheeks fell tears; then he whispered to himself, "He is a departing guest."

The child passed away while the neighbours were celebrating with the father in the big hall at the house and drinking to the health of their heir; and Selma looked at the doctor, and pleaded, "Give me my child and let me embrace him."

Though the child was dead, the sounds of the drinking cups increased in the hall.

He was born at dawn and died at sunrise.

He was born like a thought and died like a sigh and disappeared like a shadow.

He did not live to console and comfort his mother.

His life began at the end of the night and ended at the beginning of the day, like a drop of few poured by the eyes of the dark and dried by the touch of the light.

A pearl brought by the tide to the coast and returned by the ebb into the depth of the sea.

A lily that has just blossomed from the bud of life and is mashed under the feet of death.

A dear guest whose appearance illuminated Selma's heart and whose departure killed her soul.

This is the life of men, the life of nations, the life of suns, moons and stars.

And Selma focused her eyes upon the doctor and cried, "Give me my child and let me embrace him; give me my child and let me nurse him."

Then the doctor bent his head. His voice choked and he said, "Your child is dead, Madame, be patient.

Upon hearing her doctor's announcement, Selma uttered a terrible cry. Then she was quiet for a moment and smiled happily. Her face brightened as if she had discovered something, and quietly she said, "Give me my child; bring him close to me and let me see him dead."

The doctor carried the dead child to Selma and placed him between her arms. She embraced him, then turned her face toward the wall and addressed the dead infant saying, "You have come to take me away my child; you have come to show me the way that leads to the coast. Here I am my child; lead me and let us leave this dark cave.

And in a minute the sun's ray penetrated the window curtains and fell upon two calm bodies lying on a bed, guarded by the profound dignity of silence and shaded by the wings of death. The doctor left the room with tears in his eyes, and as he reached the big hall the celebrations was converted into a funeral, but Mansour Bey Galib never uttered a word or shed a tear. He remained standing motionless like a statue, holding a drinking cup with his right hand.

The second day Selma was shrouded with her white wedding dress and laid in a coffin; the child's shroud was his swaddle; his coffin was his mother's arms; his grave was her calm breast. Two corpses were carried in one coffin, and I walked reverently with the crowd accompanying Selma and her infant to their resting place.

Arriving at the cemetery, Bishop Galib commenced chanting while the other priests prayed, and on their gloomy faces appeared a veil of ignorance and emptiness.

As the coffin went down, one of the bystanders whispered, "This is the first time in my life I have seen two corpses in one coffin." Another one said, "It seems as if the child had come to rescue his mother from her pitiless husband."

A third one said, "Look at Mansour Bey: he is gazing at the sky as if his eyes were made of glass. He does not look like he has lost his wife and child in one day." A fourth one added, "His uncle, the Bishop, will marry him again tomorrow to a wealthier and stronger woman.

The Bishop and the priests kept on singing and chanting until the grave digger was through filing the ditch. Then, the people, individually, approached the Bishop and his nephew and offered their respects to them with sweet words of sympathy, but I stood lonely aside without a soul to console me, as if Selma and her child meant nothing to me.

The farewell-bidders left the cemetery; the grave digger stood by the new grave holding a shovel with his hand.

As I approached him, I inquired, "Do you remember where Farris Effandi Karamy was buried?"

He looked at me for a moment, then pointed at Selma's grave and said, "Right here; I placed his daughter upon him and upon his daughter's breast rests her child, and upon all I put the earth back with this shovel."

Then I said, "In this ditch you have also buried my heart."

As the grave digger disappeared behind the poplar trees, I could not resist anymore; I dropped down on Selma's grave and wept.

A Tear and a Smile

The Creation

The God separated a spirit from Himself and fashioned it into Beauty. He showered upon her all the blessings of gracefulness and kindness. He gave her the cup of happiness and said, "Drink not from this cup unless you forget the past and the future, for happiness is naught but the moment." And He also gave her a cup of sorrow and said, "Drink from this cup and you will understand the meaning of the fleeting instants of the joy of life, for sorrow ever abounds."

And the God bestowed upon her a love that would desert he forever upon her first sigh of earthly satisfaction, and a sweetness that would vanish with her first awareness of flattery.

And He gave her wisdom from heaven to lead to the all-righteous path, and placed in the depth of her heart and eye that sees the unseen, and created in he an affection and goodness toward all things. He dressed her with raiment of hopes spun by the angels of heaven from the sinews of the rainbow. And He cloaked her in the shadow of confusion, which is the dawn of life and light.

Then the God took consuming fire from the furnace of anger, and searing wind from the desert of ignorance, and sharp-cutting sands from the shore of selfishness, and coarse earth from under the feet of ages, and combined them all and fashioned Man. He gave to Man a blind power that rages and drives him into a madness which extinguishes only before gratification of desire, and placed life in him which is the spectre of death.

And the god laughed and cried. He felt an overwhelming love and pity for Man, and sheltered him beneath His guidance.

Two Infants

A prince stood on the balcony of his palace addressing a great multitude summoned for the occasion and said, "Let me offer you and this whole fortunate country my congratulations upon the birth of a new prince who will carry the name of my noble family, and of whom you will be justly proud. He is the new bearer of a great and illustrious ancestry, and upon him depends the brilliant future of this realm. Sing and be merry!" The voices of the throngs, full of joy and thankfulness, flooded the sky with exhilarating song, welcoming the new tyrant who would affix the yoke of oppression to their necks by ruling the weak with bitter authority, and exploiting their bodies and killing their souls. For that destiny, the people were singing and drinking ecstatically to the heady of the new Emir.

Another child entered life and that kingdom at the same time. While the crowds were glorifying the strong and belittling themselves by singing praise to a potential despot, and while the angels of heaven were weeping over the people's weakness and servitude, a sick woman was thinking. She lived in an old, deserted hovel and, lying in her hard bed beside her newly born infant wrapped with ragged swaddles, was starving to death. She was a penurious and miserable young wife neglected by humanity; her husband had fallen into the trap of death set by the prince's oppression, leaving a solitary woman to whom God had sent, that night, a tiny companion to prevent her from working and sustaining life.

As the mass dispersed and silence was restored to the vicinity, the wretched woman placed the infant on her lap and looked into his face and wept as if she were to baptise him with tears. And with a hunger weakened voice she spoke to the child saying, "Why have you left the spiritual world and come to share with me the bitterness of earthly life? Why have you deserted the angels and the spacious firmament and come to this miserable land of humans, filled with agony, oppression, and heartlessness? I have nothing to give you except tears; will you be nourished on tears instead of milk? I have no silk clothes to put on you; will my naked, shivering arms give you warmth? The little animals graze in the pasture and return safely to their shed; and the small birds pick the seeds and sleep placidly between the branches. But you, my beloved, have naught save a loving but destitute mother."

Then she took the infant to her withered breast and clasped her arms around him as if wanting to join the two bodies in one, as before. She lifted her burning eyes slowly toward heaven and cried, "God! Have mercy on my unfortunate countrymen!"

At that moment the clouds floated from the face of the moon, whose beams penetrated the transom of that poor home and fell upon two corpses.

The House of Fortune

My wearied heart bade me farewell and left for the House of Fortune. As he reached that holy city which the soul had blessed and worshipped, he commenced wondering, for he could not find what he had always imagined would be there. The city was empty of power, money, and authority.

And my heart spoke to the daughter of Love saying, "Oh Love, where can I find Contentment? I heard that she had come here to join you."

And the daughter of Love responded, "Contentment has already gone to preach her gospel in the city, where greed and corruption are paramount; we are not in need of her."

Fortune craves not Contentment, for it is an earthly hope, and its desires are embraced by union with objects, while Contentment is naught but heartfelt.

The eternal soul is never contented; it ever seeks exaltation. Then my heart looked upon Life of Beauty and said: "Thou art all knowledge; enlighten me as to the mystery of Woman." And he answered, "Oh human heart, woman is your own reflection, and whatever you are, she is; wherever you live, she lives; she is like religion if not interpreted by the ignorant, and like a moon, if not veiled with clouds, and like a breeze, if not poisoned with impurities."

And my heart walked toward Knowledge, the daughter of Love and Beauty, and said, "Bestow upon me wisdom, that I might share it with the people." And she responded, "Say not wisdom, but rather fortune, for real fortune comes not from outside, but begins in the Holy of Holies of life. Share of thyself with the people."

A Poet's Death is His Life

The dark wings of night enfolded the city upon which Nature had spread a pure white garment of snow; and men deserted the streets for their houses in search of warmth, while the north wind probed in contemplation of laying waste the gardens. There in the suburb stood an old hut heavily laden with snow and on the verge of falling. In a dark recess of that hovel was a poor bed in which a dying youth was lying, staring at the dim light of his oil lamp, made to flicker by the entering winds. He a man in the spring of life who foresaw fully that the peaceful hour of freeing himself from the clutches of life was fast nearing. He was awaiting Death's visit gratefully, and upon his pale face appeared the dawn of hope; and on his lops a sorrowful smile; and in his eyes forgiveness.

He was poet perishing from hunger in the city of living rich. He was placed in the earthly world to enliven the heart of man with his beautiful and profound sayings. He as noble soul, sent by the Goddess of Understanding to soothe and make gentle the human spirit. But alas! He gladly bade the cold earth farewell without receiving a smile from its strange occupants.

He was breathing his last and had no one at his bedside save the oil lamp, his only companion, and some parchments upon which he had inscribed his heart's feeling. As he salvaged the remnants of his withering strength he lifted his hands heavenward; he moved his eyes hopelessly, as if wanting to penetrate the ceiling in order to see the stars from behind the veil clouds.

And he said, "Come, oh beautiful Death; my soul is longing for you. Come close to me and unfasten the irons life, for I am weary of dragging them. Come, oh sweet Death, and deliver me from my neighbours who looked upon me as a stranger because I interpret to them the language of the angels. Hurry, oh peaceful Death, and carry me from these multitudes who left me in the dark corner of oblivion because I do not bleed the weak as they do. Come, oh gentle Death, and enfold me under your white wings, for my fellowmen are not in want of me. Embrace me, oh Death, full of love and mercy; let your lips touch my lips which never tasted a mother's kiss, not touched a sister's cheeks, not caresses a sweetheart's fingertips. Come and take me, by beloved Death."

Then, at the bedside of the dying poet appeared an angel who possessed a supernatural and divine beauty, holding in her hand a wreath of lilies. She embraced him and closed his eyes so he could see no more, except with the eye of his spirit. She impressed a deep and long and gently withdrawn kiss that left and eternal smile of fulfilment upon his lips. Then the hovel became empty and nothing was lest save parchments and papers which the poet had strewn with bitter futility.

Hundreds of years later, when the people of the city arose from the diseases slumber of ignorance and saw the dawn of knowledge, they erected a monument in the most beautiful garden of the city and celebrated a feast every year in honour of that poet, whose writings had freed them. Oh, how cruel is man's ignorance!

The Criminal

A young man of strong body, weakened by hunger, sat on the walker's portion of the street stretching his hand toward all who passed, begging and repeating his hand toward all who passed, begging and repeating the sad song of his defeat in life, while suffering from hunger and from humiliation.

When night came, his lips and tongue were parched, while his hand was still as empty as his stomach.

He gathered himself and went out from the city, where he sat under a tree and wept bitterly. Then he lifted his puzzled eyes to heaven while hunger was eating his inside, and he said, "Oh Lord, I went to the rich man and asked for employment, but he turned me away because of my shabbiness; I knocked at the school door, but was forbidden solace because I was empty-handed; I sought any occupation that would give me bread, but all to no avail. In desperation I asked alms, but They worshippers saw me and said "He is strong and lazy, and he should not beg."

"Oh Lord, it is Thy will that my mother gave birth unto me, and now the earth offers me back to You before the Ending."

His expression then changed. He arose and his eyes now glittered in determination. He fashioned a thick and heavy stick from the branch of the tree, and pointed it toward the city, shouting, "I asked for bread with all the strength of my voice, and was refused. Not I shall obtain it by the strength of my muscles! I asked for bread in the name of mercy and love, but humanity did not heed. I shall take it now in the name of evil!"

The passing years rendered the youth a robber, killer and destroyer of souls; he crushed all who opposed him; he amassed fabulous wealth with which he won himself over to those in power. He was admired by colleagues, envied by other thieves, and feared by the multitudes.

His riches and false position prevailed upon the Emir to appoint him deputy in that city—the sad process pursued by unwise governors. Thefts were then legalised; oppression was supported by authority; crushing of the weak became commonplace; the throngs curried and praised.

Thus does the first touch of humanity's selfishness make criminals of the humble, and make killers of the sons of peace; thus does the early greed of humanity grow and strike back at humanity a thousand fold!

Song Of Fortune

Man and I are sweethearts
He craves me and I long for him,
But alas!
Between us has appeared a rival who brings us misery.
She is cruel and demanding,
Possessing empty lure.
Her name is Substance.
She follows wherever we go
And watches like a sentinel,
Bringing restlessness to my lover.

I ask for my beloved in the forest,
Under the trees, by the lakes.
I cannot find him,
For Substance has spirited him to the clamourous city
And placed him on the throne
Of quaking, metal riches.

I call for him with the voice of knowledge
And the song of Wisdom.
He does not hearken,
For Substance has enticed him into the dungeon
Of selfishness, where avarice dwells.

I seek him in the field of Contentment,
But I am alone,
For my rival has imprisoned him ,
I the cave of gluttony and greed,
And locked him there
With painful chains of gold.

I call to him at dawn, when Nature smiles,
But he does not hear,
For excess has laden his drugged eyes with sick slumber.

I beguile him at eventide, when Silence rules
And the flowers sleep.
But he responds not,
For his fear over what the morrow will bring shadows his
thoughts.

He yearns to love me;
He asks for me in this own acts.
But he will find me not except in God's acts.
He seeks me in the edifices of his glory
Which he has built upon the bones of others;
He whispers to me from among his heaps of gold and silver;
But he will find me only by coming to the house of Simplicity
Which God has built at the brink of the stream of affection.

He desires to kiss me before his coffers,
But his lips will never touch mine,
Except in the richness of the pure breeze.

He asks me to share with him his fabulous wealth,
But I will not forsake God's fortune;
I will not cast off my cloak of beauty.

He seeks deceit for medium;
I seek only the medium of his heart.
He bruises his heart in his narrow cell;
I would enrich his heart with all my love.

My beloved has learned how to shriek and cry for my enemy,
Substance;
I would teach him how to shed tears of affection
And mercy from the eyes of his soul
For all things,
And utter sighs of contentment through those tears.

Man is my sweetheart;
I want to belong to him.

Song of the Rain

I am dotted silver threads dropped from heaven by the gods.
Nature then takes me, to adorn her fields and valleys.

I am beautiful pearls,
Plucked from the crown of Ishtar by the daughter of Dawn to embellish the gardens.

When I cry the hills laugh;
When I humble myself the flowers rejoice;
When I bow, all things are elated.

The field and the cloud are lovers
And between them I am a messenger of mercy.
I quench the thirst of one;
I cure the ailment of the other.

The voice of thunder declares my arrival;
The rainbow announces my departure.
I am like earthly life,
Which begins at the feet of the mad elements
And ends under the upraised wings of death.

I emerge from the heard of the sea
Soar with the breeze.
When I see a field in need,
I descend and embrace the flowers and the trees in a million little ways.

I touch gently at the windows with my soft fingers,

And my announcement is a welcome song all can hear
But only the sensitive can understand.

The heat in the air gives birth to me,
But in turn I kill it,
As woman overcomes man with the strength she takes from him.

I am the sigh of the sea;
The laughter of the field;
The tears of heaven.

So with love—
Sighs from the deep sea of affection;
Laughter from the colourful field of the spirit;
Tears from the endless heaven of memories.

The Poet

He is a link between this and the coming world.
He is a pure spring from which all thirsty souls may drink.

He is a tree watered by the River of Beauty,
Bearing fruit which the hungry heart craves;

He is a nightingale,
Soothing the depressed spirit with his beautiful melodies;
He is a white cloud appearing over the horizon,
Ascending and growing until it fills the face of the sky.
Then it falls on the flows in the field of Life,
Opening their petals to admit the light.

He is an angel,
Sent by the goddess to preach the Deity's gospel;
He is a brilliant lamp,
Unconquered by darkness
And inextinguishable by the wind.
It is filled with oil by Ihstar of Love,
And lighted by Apollon of Music.

He is a solitary figure,
Robed in simplicity and kindness;
He sits upon the lap of Nature to draw his inspiration,
And stays up in the silence of the night,
Awaiting the descending of the spirit.

He is a sower
Who sows the seeds of his heart in the prairies of affection,
And humanity reaps the harvest for her nourishment.

This is the poet—whom the people ignore in this life,
And who is recognised only when he bids the earthly world farewell
And returns to his arbour in heaven.

This is the poet—who asks naught of humanity but a smile.
This is the poet—whose spirit ascends and fills the firmament with beautiful sayings;
Yet the people deny themselves his radiance.

Until when shall the people remain asleep?
Until when shall they continue to glorify those who attain greatness by moments of advantage?
How long shall they ignore those who enable them to see the beauty of their spirit,
Symbol of peace and love?
Until when shall human beings honour the dead and forget the living,
Who spend their lives encircled in misery,
And who consume themselves,
Like burning candles to illuminate the way
For the ignorant and lead them into the path of light?

Poet, you are the life of this life,
And you have triumphed over the ages of despite their severity.

Poet, you will one day rule the hearts,
And therefore, your kingdom has no ending.

Poet, examine your crown of thorns;
You will find concealed in it a budding wreath of laurel.

Laughter and Tears

As the Sun withdrew his rays from the garden, and the moon threw cushioned beams upon the flowers, I sat under the trees pondering upon the phenomena of the atmosphere, looking through the branches at the strewn stars which glittered like chips of silver upon a blue carpet; and I could hear from a distance the agitated murmur of the rivulet singing its way briskly into the valley.

When the birds took shelter among the boughs, and the flowers folded their petals, and tremendous silence descended, I heard a rustle of feet though the grass. I took heed and saw a young couple approaching my arbour. The say under a tree where I could see them without being seen.

After he looked about in every direction, I heard the young man saying, "Sit by me, my beloved, and listen to my heart; smile, for your happiness is a symbol of our future; be merry, for the sparkling days rejoice with us.

"My soul is warning me of the doubt in your heart, for doubt in love is a sin.

"Soon you will be the owner of this vast land, lighted by this beautiful moon; soon you will be the mistress of my palace, and all the servants and maids will obey your commands.

"Smile, my beloved, like the gold smiles from my father's coffers.

"My heart refuses to deny you its secret. Twelve months of comfort and travel await us; for a year we will spend my father's gold at the blue lakes of Switzerland, and viewing the edifices of Italy and Egypt, and resting under the Holy Cedars of Lebanon; you will meet the princesses who will envy you for your jewels and clothes.

"All these things I will do for you; will you be satisfied?"

In a little while I saw them walking and stepping on flowers as the rich step upon the hearts of the poor. As they disappeared from my sight, I commenced to make comparison between love and money, and to analyse their position in the heart.

Money! The source of insincere love; the spring of false light and fortune; the well of poisoned water; the desperation of old age!

I was still wandering in the vast desert of contemplation when a forlorn and spectre-like couple passed by me and sat on the grass; a young man and a young woman who had left their farming shacks in the nearby fields for this cool and solitary place.

After a few moments of complete silence, I heard the following words uttered with sighs from weather-bitten lips, "Shed not tears, my beloved; love that opens our eyes and enslaves our hearts can give us the blessing of patience. Be consoled in our delay our delay, for we have taken an oath and entered Love's shrine; for our love will ever grow in adversity; for it is in Love's name that we are suffering the obstacles of poverty and the sharpness of misery and the emptiness of separation. I shall attack these hardships until I triumph and place in your hands a strength that will help over all things to complete the journey of life.

"Love—which is God—will consider our sighs and tears as incense burned at His altar and He will reward us with fortitude. Good-bye, my beloved; I must leave before the heartening moon vanishes."

A pure voice, combined of the consuming flame of love, and the hopeless bitterness of longing and the resolved sweetness of patience, said, "Good-bye, my beloved."

They separated, and the elegy to their union was smothered by the wails of my crying heart.

I looked upon slumbering Nature, and with deep reflection discovered the reality of a vast and infinite thing—something no power could demand, influence acquire, nor riches purchase. Nor could it be effaced by the tears of time or deadened by sorrow; a thing which cannot be discovered by the blue lakes of Switzerland or the beautiful edifices of Italy.

It is something that gathers strength with patience, grows despite obstacles, warms in winter, flourishes in spring, casts a breeze in summer, and bears fruit in autumn—I found Love.

Vision

There in the middle of the field, by the side of a crystalline stream, I saw a bird-cage whose rods and hinges were fashioned by an expert's hands. In one corner lay a dead bird, and in another were two basins—one empty of water and the other of seeds. I stood there reverently, as if the lifeless bird and the murmur of the water were worthy of deep silence and respect—something worth of examination and meditation by the heard and conscience.

As I engrossed myself in view and thought, I found that the poor creature had died of thirst beside a stream of water, and of hunger in the midst of a rich field, cradle of life; like a rich man locked inside his iron safe, perishing from hunger amid heaps of gold.

Before my eyes I saw the cage turned suddenly into a human skeleton, and the dead bird into a man's heart which was bleeding from a deep wound that looked like the lips of a sorrowing woman. A voice came from that wound saying, "I am the human heart, prisoner of substance and victim of earthly laws.

"In God's field of Beauty, at the edge of the stream of life, I was imprisoned in the cage of laws made by man.

"In the centre of beautiful Creation I died neglected because I was kept from enjoying the freedom of God's bounty.

"Everything of beauty that awakens my love and desire is a disgrace, according to man's conceptions; everything of goodness that I crave is but naught, according to his judgment.

"I am the lost human heart, imprisoned in the foul dungeon of man's dictates, tied with chains of earthly authority, dead and forgotten by laughing humanity whose tongue is tied and whose eyes are empty of visible tears."

All these words I heard, and I saw them emerging with a stream of ever thinning blood from that wounded heart.

More was said, but my misted eyes and crying should prevented further sight or hearing.

Two Wishes

In the silence of the night Death descended from God toward the earth. He hovered above a city and pierced the dwellings with his eyes. He say the spirits floating on wings of dreams, and the people who were surrendered to the Slumber.

When the moon fell below the horizon and the city became black, Death walked silently among the houses—careful to touch nothing—until he reached a palace. He entered through the bolted gates undisturbed, and stood by the rich man's bed; and as Death touched his forehead, the sleeper's eyes opened, showing great fright.

When he saw the spectre, he summoned a voice mingled with fear and anger, and said, "God away, oh horrible dream; leave me, you dreadful ghost. Who are you? How did you enter this place? What do you want? Leave this place at once, for I am the lord of the house and will call my slaves and guards, and order them to kill you!"

Then Death spoke, softly but with smouldering thunder, "I am Death. Stand and bow!"

The man responded, "What do you want? What have you come here when I have not yet finished my affairs? What see you from strength such as mine? Go to the weak man, and take him away!

"I loathe the sight of your bloody paws and hollow face, and my eyes take sick at your horrible ribbed winds and cadaverous body."

After a moment of fearful realisation he added, "No, No, oh merciful Death! Mind not talk, for even fear reveals what the heart forbids.

"Take a bushelful of my gold, or a handful of my slave's souls, but leave me. I have accounts with Life requiring settling; I have due from people much gold; my ships have not reached the harbour; my demand, but spare my life. Death, I own harems of supernatural beauty; your choice is my gift to you. Give heed, Death—I have but one child, and I love him dearly for he is my only joy in this life. I offer supreme sacrifice—take him, but spare me!"

Death murmured, "You are not rich, but pitifully poor." Then Death took the hand of that earthly slave, removed his reality, and gave to the angels the heavy task of correction.

And Death walked slowly amidst the dwellings of the poor until he reached the most miserable he could find. He entered and approached a bed upon which a youth slept fitfully. Death touched his eyes; the lad sprang up as he saw Death standing by, and, with a voice full of love and hope he said, "Here I am, my beautiful Death. Accept my soul, for you are the hope of my dreams. Be their accomplishment! Embrace me, oh beloved Death! You are merciful; do not leave me. You are God's messenger; deliver me to Him. You are the right hand of Truth and the heart of Kindness; do not neglect me.

"I have begged for you many times, but you did not come; I have sought you, but you avoided me; I called out to you, but you listened not. You hear me now—embrace my soul, beloved Death!"

Death placed his softened hand upon the trembling lips, removed all reality, and enfolded it beneath his wings for secure conduct. And returning to the sky, Death looked back and whispered his warning:

"Only those return to Eternity. Who on earth seek out Eternity."

Yesterday and Today

The gold-hoarder walked in his palace park and with him walked his troubles. And over his head hovered worries as a vulture hovers over a carcass, until he reached a beautiful lake surrounded by magnificent marble statuary.

He sat there pondering the water which poured from the mouths of the statues like thoughts flowing freely from a lover's imagination, and contemplating heavily his palace which stood upon a knoll like a birth-mark upon the cheek of a maiden. His fancy revealed to him the pages of his life's drama which he read with falling tears that veiled his eyes and prevented him from viewing man's feeble additions to Nature.

He looked back with piercing regret to the images of his early life, woven into pattern by the gods, until he could no longer control his anguish. He said aloud, "Yesterday I was grazing my sheep in the green valley, enjoying my existence, sounding my flute, and holding my head high. Today I am a prisoner of greed. Gold leads into gold, then into restlessness and finally into crushing misery.

"Yesterday I was like a singing bird, soaring freely here and there in the fields. Today I am a slave to fickle wealth, society's rules, and city's customs, and purchased friends, pleasing the people by conforming to the strange and narrow laws of man. I was born to be free and enjoy the bounty of life, but I find myself like a beast of burden so heavily laden with gold that his back is breaking.

"Where are the spacious plains, the singing brooks, the pure breeze, the closeness of Nature? Where is my deity? I have lost all! Naught remains save loneliness that saddens me, gold that ridicules me, slaves who curse to my back, and a palace that I have erected as a tomb for my happiness, and in whose greatness I have lost my heart.

"Yesterday I roamed the prairies and the hills together with the Bedouin's daughter; Virtue was our companion, Love our delight, and the moon our guardian. Today I am among women with shallow beauty who sell themselves for gold and diamonds.

"Yesterday I was carefree, sharing with the shepherds all the joy of life; eating, playing, working, singing, and dancing together to the music of the heart's truth. Today I find myself among the people like a frightened lamb among the wolves. As I walk in the roads, they gaze at me with hateful eyes and point at me with scorn and jealousy, and as I steal through the park I see frowning faces all about me.

"Yesterday I was rich in happiness and today I am poor in gold.

"Yesterday I was a happy shepherd looking upon his head as a merciful king looks with pleasure upon his contented subjects. Today I am a slave standing before my wealth, my wealth which robbed me of the beauty of life I once knew.

"Forgive me, my Judge! I did not know that riches would put my life in fragments and lead me into the dungeons of harshness and stupidity. What I thought was glory is naught but an eternal inferno."

He gathered himself wearily and walked slowly toward the palace, sighing and repeating, "Is this what people call wealth? Is this the god I am serving and worshipping? Is this what I seek of the earth? Why can I not trade it for one particle of contentment? Who would sell me one beautiful thought for a ton of gold? Who would give me one moment of love for a handful of gems? Who would grant me an eye that can see others' hearts, and take all my coffers in barter?"

As he reached the palace gates he turned and looked toward the city as Jeremiah gazed toward Jerusalem. He raised his arms in woeful lament and shouted, "Oh people of the noisome city, who are living in darkness, hastening toward misery, preaching falsehood, and speaking with stupidity...until when shall you remain ignorant? Unit when shall you abide in the filth of life and continue to desert its gardens? Why wear you tattered robes of narrowness while the silk raiment of Nature's beauty is fashioned for you? The lamp of wisdom is dimming; it is time to furnish it with oil. The house of true fortune is being destroyed; it is time to rebuild it and guard it. The thieves of ignorance have stolen the treasure of your peace; it is time to retake it!"

At that moment a poor man stood before him and stretched forth his hand for alms. As he looked at the beggar, his lips parted, his eyes brightened with a softness, and his face radiated kindness. It was as if the yesterday he had lamented by the lake had come to greet him. He embraced the pauper with affection and filled his hands with gold, and with a voice sincere with the sweetness of love he said, "Come back tomorrow and bring with you your fellow sufferers. All your possessions will be restored."

He entered his palace saying, "Everything in life is good; even gold, for it teaches a lesson. Money is like a stringed instrument; he who does not know how to use it properly will hear only discordant music. Money is like love; it kills slowly and painfully the one who withholds it, and it enlivens the other who turns it upon his fellow man."

Leave Me, My Blamer

Leave me, my blamer,
For the sake of the love which unites your soul with that of your beloved one;
For the sake of that which joins spirit with mothers affection,
And ties your heart with filial love.
Go, and leave me to my own weeping heart.

Let me sail in the ocean of my dreams;
Wait until tomorrow comes,
For tomorrow is free to do with me as he wishes.
Your laying is naught but shadow
That walks with the spirit to the tomb of abashment,
And shows heard the cold, solid earth.

I have a little heart within me
And I like to bring him out of his prison and carry him on the palm of my hand
To examine him In depth and extract his secret.
Aim not your arrows at him,
Lest he takes fright and vanish 'ere he pours the secret blood
As a sacrifice at the altar of his own faith,
Given him by Deity
When he fashioned him of love and beauty.

The sun is rising and the nightingale is singing,
And the myrtle is breathing its fragrance into space.
I want to free myself from the quilted slumber of wrong.
Do not detain me, my blamer!

Cavil me not by mention of the lions of the forest
Or the snakes of the valley,
For me soul knows no fear of earth
And accepts no warning of evil before evil comes.

Advise me not, my blamer,
For calamities have opened my heart
And tears have cleansed my eyes,
And errors have taught me the language of the hearts.

Talk not of banishment, for conscience is my judge
And he will justify me and protect me if I am innocent,
And will deny me of life if I am a criminal.

Love's procession is moving;
Beauty is waving her banner;
Youth is sounding the trumpet of joy;
Disturb not my contrition, my blamer.
Let me walk, for the path is rich with roses and mint,
And the air is scented with cleanliness.

Relate not the tales of wealth and greatness,
For my soul is rich with bounty and great with God's glory.

Speak not of peoples and laws and kingdoms,
For the whole earth is my birthplace
And all humans are my brothers.

Go from me, for you are taking away life—
Giving repentance and bringing needless words.

The Beauty Of Death

Part One — The Calling

Let me sleep, for my soul is intoxicated with love and
Let me rest, for my spirit has had its bounty of days and nights;
Light the candles and burn the incense around my bed, and
Scatter leaves of jasmine and roses over my body;
Embalm my hair with frankincense and sprinkle my feet with perfume,
And read what the hand of Death has written on my forehead.

Let me rest in the arms of Slumber, for my open eyes are tired;
Let the silver-stringed lyre quiver and soothe my spirit;
Weave from the harp and lute a veil around my withering heart.

Sing of the past as you behold the dawn of hope in my eyes, for
It's magic meaning is a soft bed upon which my heart rests.

Dry your tears, my friends, and raise your heads as the flowers
Raise their crowns to greet the dawn.
Look at the bride of Death standing like a column of light
Between my bed and the infinite;
Hold your breath and listen with me to the beckoning rustle of
her white wings.

Come close and bid me farewell;
Touch my eyes with smiling lips.
Let the children grasp my hands with soft and rosy fingers;
Let the ages place their veined hands upon my head and bless me;
Let the virgins come close and see the shadow of God in my eyes,
And hear the echo of His will racing with my breath.

Part Two — The Ascending

I have passed a mountain peak
And my soul is soaring in the firmament of complete and
unbound freedom;
I am far, far away, my companions,
And the clouds are hiding the hills from my eyes.
The valleys are becoming flooded with an ocean of silence,
And the hands of oblivion are engulfing the roads and
the houses;
The prairies and fields are disappearing behind a white spectre
That looks like the spring cloud, yellow as the candlelight
And red as the twilight.

The songs of the waves and the hymns of the streams
are scattered,
And the voices of the throngs reduced to silence;
And I can hear naught but the music of Eternity
In exact harmony with the spirit's desires.
I am cloaked in full whiteness;
I am in comfort; I am in peace.

Part Three — The Remains

Unwrap me from this white linen shroud
And clothe me with leaves of jasmine and lilies;
Take my body from the ivory casket and let it rest
Upon pillows of orange blossoms.
Lament me not, but sing songs of youth and joy;
Shed not tears upon me, but sing of harvest and the winepress;
Utter no sigh of agony,
But draw upon my face with your finger the symbol of Love
and Joy.
Disturb not the air's tranquillity with chanting and requiems,
But let your hearts sing with me the song of Eternal Life;
Mourn me not with apparel of black,
But dress in colour and rejoice with me;

Talk not of my departure with sighs in your hearts;
Close your eyes and you will see me with you forevermore.

Place me upon clusters of leaves
And carry my upon your friendly shoulders
And walk slowly to the deserted forest.
Take me not to the crowded burying ground
Lest my slumber be disrupted by the rattling of bones and skulls.
Carry me to the cypress woods
And dig my grave where violets and poppies grow not in the
other's shadow;
Let my grave be deep
So that the flood will not carry my bones to the open valley;
Let my grace be wide,
So that the twilight shadows will come and sit by me.

Take from me all earthly raiment
And place me deep in my Mother Earth;
And place me with care upon my mother's breast.
Cover me with soft earth,
And let each handful be mixed with seeds of jasmine, lilies
and myrtle;
And when they grow above me,
And thrive on my body's element they will breathe the
fragrance of my heart into space;
And reveal even to the sun the secret of my peace;
And sail with the breeze and comfort the wayfarer.

Leave me then, friends—leave me and depart on mute feet,
As the silence walks in the deserted valley;
Leave me to God and disperse yourselves slowly,
As the almond and apple blossoms disperse under the vibration
of Nisan's breeze.
Go back to the joy of your dwellings
And you will find there that which Death cannot remove from
you and me.
Leave with place, for what you see here is far away in meaning
From the earthly world. Leave me.

A Poet's Voice

Part One

The power of charity sows deep in my heart, and I reap and gather the wheat in bundles and give them to the hungry.

My soul gives life to the grapevine and I press its bunches and give the juice to the thirsty.

Heaven fills my lamp with oil and I place it at my window to direct the stranger through the dark.

I do all these things because I live in them; and if destiny should tie my hands and prevent me from so doing, then death would be my only desire. For I am a poet, and if I cannot give, I shall refuse to receive.

Humanity rages like a tempest, but I sigh in silence for I know the storm must pass away while a sigh goes to God.

Human kinds cling to earthly things, but I seek ever to embrace the torch of love so it will purify me by its fire and sear inhumanity from my heart.
Substantial things deaden a man without suffering; love awakens him with enlivening pains.

Humans are divided into different clans and tribes, and belong to countries and towns. But I find myself a stranger to all communities and belong to no settlement. The universe is my country and the human family is my tribe.

Men are weak, and it is sad that they divide amongst themselves. The world is narrow and it is unwise to cleave it into kingdoms, empires, and provinces.

Human kinds unite themselves one to destroy the temples of the soul, and they join hands to build edifices for earthly bodies. I stand alone listening to the voice of hope in my deep self saying, "As love enlivens a man's heart with pain, so ignorance teaches him the way of knowledge." Pain and ignorance lead to great joy and knowledge because the Supreme Being has created nothing vain under the sun.

Part Two

I have a yearning for my beautiful country, and I love its people because of their misery. But if my people rose, stimulated by plunder and motivated by what they call "patriotic spirit" to murder, and invaded my neighbour's country, then upon the committing of any human atrocity I would hate my people and my country.

I sing the praise of my birthplace and long to see the home of my children; but if the people in that home refused to shelter and feed the needy wayfarer, I would convert my praise into anger and my longing to forgetfulness. My inner voice would say, "The house that does not comfort the need is worthy of naught by destruction."

I love my native village with some of my love for my country; and I love my country with part of my love for the earth, all of which is my country; and I love the earth will all of myself because it is the haven of humanity, the manifest spirit of God.

Humanity is the spirit of the Supreme Being on earth, and that humanity is standing amidst ruins, hiding its nakedness behind tattered rags, shedding tears upon hollow cheeks, and calling for its children with pitiful voice. But the children are busy singing their clan's anthem; they are busy sharpening the swords and cannot hear the cry of their mothers.

Humanity appeals to its people but they listen not. Were one to listen, and console a mother by wiping her tears, other would say, "He is weak, affected by sentiment."

Humanity is the spirit of the Supreme Being on earth, and that Supreme Being preaches love and good-will. But the people ridicule such teachings. The Nazarene Jesus listened, and crucifixion was his lot; Socrates heard the voice and followed it, and he too fell victim in body. The followers of The Nazarene and Socrates are the followers of Deity, and since people will not kill them, they deride them, saying, "Ridicule is more bitter than killing."

Jerusalem could not kill The Nazarene, nor Athens Socrates; they are living yet and shall live eternally. Ridicule cannot triumph over the followers of Deity. They live and grow forever.

Part Three

Thou art my brother because you are a human, and we both are sons of one Holy Spirit; we are equal and made of the same earth.

You are here as my companion along the path of life, and my aid in understanding the meaning of hidden Truth. You are a human, and, that fact sufficing, I love you as a brother. You may speak of me as you choose, for tomorrow shall take you away and will use your talk as evidence for his judgment, and you shall receive justice.

You may deprive me of whatever I possess, for my greed instigated the amassing of wealth and you are entitled to my lot if it will satisfy you.

You may do unto me whatever you wish, but you shall not be able to touch my Truth.

You may shed my blood and burn my body, but you cannot kill or hurt my spirit.

You may tie my hands with chains and my feet with shackles, and put me in the dark prison, but who shall not enslave my thinking, for it is free, like the breeze in the spacious sky.

You are my brother and I love you. I love you worshipping in your church, kneeling in your temple, and praying in your mosque. You and I and all are children of one religion, for the varied paths of religion are but the fingers of the loving hand of the Supreme Being, extended to all, offering completeness of spirit to all, anxious to receive all.

I love you for your Truth, derived from your knowledge; that Truth which I cannot see because of my ignorance. But I respect it as a divine thing, for it is the deed of the spirit. Your Truth shall meet my Truth in the coming world and blend together like the fragrance of flowers and becoming one whole and eternal Truth, perpetuating and living in the eternity of Love and Beauty.

I love you because you are weak before the strong oppressor, and poor before the greedy rich. For these reasons I shed tears and comfort you; and from behind my tears I see you embraced in the arms of Justice, smiling and forgiving your persecutors. You are my brother and I love you.

Part Four

You are my brother, but why are you quarrelling with me? Why do you invade my country and try to subjugate me for the sake of pleasing those who are seeking glory and authority?

Why do you leave your wife and children and follow Death to the distant land for the sake of those who buy glory with your blood, and high honour with your mother's tears?

Is it an honour for a man to kill his brother man? If you deem it an honour, let it be an act of worship, and erect a temple to Cain who slew his brother Abel.

Is self-preservation the first law of Nature? Why, then, does Greed urge you to self-sacrifice in order only to achieve his aim in hurting your brothers? Beware, my brother, of the leader who says, "Love of existence obliges us to deprive the people of their rights!" I say unto you but this: protecting others' rights is the noblest and most beautiful human act; if my existence requires that I kill others, then death is more honourable to me, and if I cannot find someone to kill me for the protection of my honour, I will not hesitate to take my life by my own hands for the sake of Eternity before Eternity comes.

Selfishness, my brother, is the cause of blind superiority, and superiority creates clanship, and clanship creates authority which leads to discord and subjugation.

The soul believes in the power of knowledge and justice over dark ignorance; it denies the authority that supplies the swords to defend and strengthen ignorance and oppression—that authority which destroyed Babylon and shook the foundation of Jerusalem and left Rome in ruins. It is that which made people call criminals great mean; made writers respect their names; made historians relate the stories of their inhumanity in manner of praise.

The only authority I obey is the knowledge of guarding and acquiescing in the Natural Law of Justice.

What justice does authority display when it kills the killer? When it imprisons the robber? When it descends on a neighbourhood country and slays its people? What does justice think of the authority under which a killer punishes the one who kills, and a thief sentences the one who steals?

You are my brother, and I love you; and Love is justice with its full intensity and dignity. If justice did not support my love for you, regardless of your tribe and community, I would be a deceiver concealing the ugliness of selfishness behind the outer garment of pure love.

Conclusion

My soul is my friend who consoles me in misery and distress of life. He who does not befriend his soul is an enemy of humanity, and he who does not find human guidance within himself will perish desperately. Life emerges from within, and derives not from environs.

I came to say a word and I shall say it now. But if death prevents its uttering, it will be said by tomorrow, for tomorrow never leaves a secret in the book of Eternity.

I came to live in the glory of Love and the light of Beauty, which are the reflections of God. I am here living, and the people are unable to exile me from the domain of life for they know I will live in death. If they pluck my eyes I will hearken to the murmurs of Love and the songs of Beauty.

If they close my ears I will enjoy the touch of the breeze mixed with the incense of Love and the fragrance of Beauty.

If they place me in a vacuum, I will live together with my soul, the child of Love and Beauty.

I came here to be for all and with all, and what I do today in my solitude will be echoed by tomorrow to the people.

What I say now with one heart will be said tomorrow by many hearts.

The Life of Love

Spring

Come, my beloved; let us walk amidst the knolls,
For the snow is water,
And life is alive from its slumber and is roaming the hills and valleys.
Let us follow the footprints of Spring into the distant fields,
And mount the hilltops to draw inspiration high above the cool green plains.

Dawn of Spring has unfolded her winter-kept garment
And placed it on the peach and citrus trees;
And they appear as brides in the ceremonial custom of the Night of Kedre.

The sprigs of grapevine embrace each other like sweethearts,
And the brooks burst out in dance between the rocks,
Repeating the song of joy;
And the flowers bud suddenly from the heart of nature,
Like foam from the rich heart of the sea.

Come, my beloved; let us drink the last of Winter's tears from the cupped lilies,

And soothe our spirits with the shower of notes from the birds,
And wander in exhilaration through the intoxicating breeze.

Let us sit by that rock, where violets hide;
Let us pursue their exchange of the sweetness of kisses.

Summer

Let us go into the fields, my beloved,
For the time of harvest approaches,
And the sun's eyes are ripening the grain.
Let us tend the fruit of the earth,
As the spirit nourishes the grains of joy from the seeds of Love, sowed deep in our hearts.
Let us fill our bins with the products of nature,
As life fills so abundantly the domain of our hearts with her endless bounty.
Let us make the flowers our bed,
And the sky our blanket,
And rest our heads together upon pillows of soft hay.
Let us relax after the day's toil, and listen to the provoking murmur of the brook.

Autumn

Let us go and gather grapes in the vineyard for the winepress,
And keep the wine in old vases,
As the spirit keeps Knowledge of the ages in eternal vessels.

Let us return to our dwelling,
For the wind has caused the yellow leaves to fall
And shroud the withering flowers that whisper elegy to Summer.

Come home, my eternal sweetheart,
For the birds have made pilgrimage to warmth
And lest the chilled prairies suffering pangs of solitude.
The jasmine and myrtle have no more tears.

Let us retreat, for the tired brook has ceased its song;
And the bubblesome springs are drained of their copious weeping;
And their cautious old hills have stored away their colourful garments.

Come, my beloved; Nature is justly weary
And is bidding her enthusiasm farewell
With quiet and contented melody.

Winter

Come close to me, oh companion of my full life;
Come close to me and let not Winter's touch enter between us.
Sit by me before the hearth,
For fire is the only fruit of Winter.

Speak to me of the glory of your heart,
For that is greater than the shrieking elements beyond our door.
Bind the door and seal the transoms,
For the angry countenance of the heaven depresses my spirit,
And the face of our snow-laden fields makes my soul cry.

Feed the lamp with oil and let it not dim,
And place it by you,
So I can read with tears what your life with me has written
upon your face.

Bring Autumn's wine.
Let us drink and sing the song of remembrance to Spring's
carefree sowing,
And Summer's watchful tending,
And Autumn's reward in harvest.

Come close to me, oh beloved of my soul;
The fire is cooling and fleeing under the ashes.
Embrace me, for I fear loneliness;
The lamp is dim, and the wine which we pressed is closing our eyes.

Let us look upon each other before they are shut.
Find me with your arms and embrace me;
Let slumber then embrace our souls as one.
Kiss me, my beloved, for Winter has stolen all but our moving lips.

You are close by me, my Forever.
How deep and wide will be the ocean of Slumber,
And how recent was the dawn!